BUTTERFLY MIRACLES AND MYSTERIES

BY THE SAME AUTHOR

NAVIES OF TO-DAY AND TO-MORROW
THE NAVY AND THE NEXT WAR
THE RESTORATION OF ENGLAND'S SEA POWER
BRITAIN IN DANGER
BACK TO THE COAL STANDARD
THIS PROGRESS
THIS BONDAGE
HOW THE WAR WILL BE WON
WHAT WE ARE FIGHTING FOR
THE CUCKOO AND OTHER BIRD MYSTERIES
SWIFT

Children's Books

THE NAVY'S HERE
LIFE IN A SUBMARINE

LIFE HISTORY OF FOUR REPRESENTATIVE SPECIES

1. Clouded Yellow (female butterfly) 3. Painted Lady (male butterfly)
2. Grayling (female butterfly) 4. Large Blue (female butterfly)

Eggs highly magnified; caterpillars and chrysalids life-size; butterflies two-thirds life-size

BUTTERFLY MIRACLES AND MYSTERIES

By

BERNARD ACWORTH

Illustrated by

A. D. A. RUSSWURM, F.R.E.S.

1947
EYRE & SPOTTISWOODE

THIS BOOK, FIRST PUBLISHED IN 1947, IS PRODUCED IN COMPLETE CONFORMITY WITH THE AUTHORISED ECONOMY STANDARDS AND HAS BEEN PRINTED IN GREAT BRITAIN FOR EYRE AND SPOTTISWOODE (PUBLISHERS) LIMITED, 15 BEDFORD STREET, STRAND, W.C.2., BY JARROLD AND SONS LTD. THE EMPIRE PRESS, NORWICH

CONTENTS

Then the Lord answered Job out of the whirlwind, and said,

Who is this that darkeneth counsel by words without knowledge?

Gird up now thy loins like a man; for I will demand of thee, and answer thou me.

Where wast thou when I laid the foundations of the earth? declare, if thou hast understanding.

Who hath laid the measures thereof, if thou knowest? or who hath stretched the line upon it?

Whereupon are the foundations thereof fastened? or who hath laid the corner stone thereof?

When the morning stars sang together, and all the sons of God shouted for joy?

JOB xxxviii

FOREWORD

THIS modest book on butterflies owes its inspiration to happy memories revived by a broadcast by Mr. Compton Mackenzie and Mr. Moray McLaren on December 29th, 1944, the title of which was *Butterflies* and *Brown Trout*. In both of these creatures the author has taken a profound interest since he was five years old. Though the first collection made by him in his own childhood, and the second when his younger children were growing up, have long since mouldered into dust, the fascination of watching and observing butterflies, and of catching trout, has never left him. This book is that of a layman, but the majority of the more obscure facts which it contains are derived from the works of high authorities, or from quotations from authorities by other authorities. A list of these will be found on page 254.

The author's thanks are due to Mr. A. D. A. Russwurm, F.R.E.S., for the coloured plate, and for the unique black and white drawings accompanying each butterfly's life-history: these were drawn exclusively from specimens in his magnificent collection. Also for providing the latest classification which is printed as an Appendix. The book was completed before Mr. Russwurm had most generously consented to illustrate it. These illustrations, it is thought, will compensate for deficiencies, as there must be, in the verbal descriptions of the perfect insect.

The author's thanks are also due to Mr. F. W. Frohawk, M.B.O.U., F.R.E.S., for his generosity in allowing him to borrow so liberally from his great work, *Natural History of British Butterflies*; to Mr. J. Lorne Campbell of Canna for his valuable information on Hebridean butterfly curiosities which, in some cases, have been incorporated; and to Mr. Eric Daniels for his constructive secretarial assistance, and particularly for the Index.

And last but not least to his son Richard, whose keen scrutiny of the text has led to the rewriting of certain passages in order to remove any possible obscurities.

BERNARD ACWORTH

June 1946

PREFACE

WHEN the world of man's contriving is in a state of acute crisis, it will seem to many that to write or to read about butterflies is bordering on frivolity. Is it not absurd, they may ask, to invite seriously minded men and women, boys and girls, to turn away for a while from the contemplation of man's self-ordained and disorderly affairs to consider the perfectly ordered life of an insect, which does as it must and not as it wills? Tens of thousands of men and women in the struggle for the survival of the strong, though not necessarily of the fittest, are dying daily at the hands of their own species, thereby proving that in this respect, as in others, man with his free-will is distinct from all other creatures on earth where civil war among the same species of animal, be it beast, bird, insect or fish, is almost unknown.

That the author has undertaken a study of butterflies at such a time is evidence that he does not share the view that when the world-system is out of joint a book such as this is out of place. On the contrary, he believes that when everything that man has so laboriously planned is out of order, the study of perfectly ordered life over which he has no control is a source of relief and comfort; comfort meaning strengthening, and not, as is supposed by some, ease or evasion.

Between natural history and human history there is a great gulf fixed. The history of a butterfly by a competent observer of 100 years ago, or 3,500, is found to be identical with its history to-day. Its story is one of sustained perfection. In this connection Holland, in his book on North American butterflies, remarks that the fossil butterflies found "show a very close affinity to genera existing at the present time. . . . This fixity of type is certainly remarkable in creatures so lowly in their organisation." The butterflies depicted in the Theban frescoes in the British Museum, though the outlines are blurred, are representations of an orange and black species which is to be seen flitting over Egypt to-day.

But what of the history of Man? No matter how we strive for perfection of health, of beauty, of contentment or of anything else, we lamentably fail where a Camberwell Beauty or a Red Admiral, shall we say, so marvellously succeeds in living at the pinnacle of its humble being. How can we account for this other than by admitting, that whereas fallen Man is a product of his own conceptions and imaginations, the creatures of the field are obedient to the perfect, and therefore fixed, laws of their being without any say by themselves in the matter. The truth is, *Man is an abnormality*. As Philip Mauro has truly said, "Man cannot fail to perceive, if he uses to any purpose his powers of observation and reflection, that Man is abnormal in that, among all the orders of living creatures, he alone lives far below the possibilities of his nature. All other species of living creatures (including butterflies) are in this respect manifestly *normal*. He alone has somehow missed his way; has suffered a permanent impairment of his capabilities. And this is true of *every member* of his species.

"This abnormality is the more remarkable and significant because Man is the only creature that is capable of forming a concept of perfection, and the only creature that has a standard of conduct. How comes it, then, that the only race of beings among the innumerable tribes of earth that has the capacity for moral distinctions is likewise the only race that habitually does what is injurious to himself and others of his kind? For men habitually abuse themselves and their powers, and do injury to their health, and jeopardise and shorten their lives by indulgences of one sort and another.

"What a contrast in this respect between men and the brutes! For among all the species and varieties of the latter, there is not the slightest observable tendency to depart from those habits and ways of life that are conducive to creature welfare." Man, in short, is a creature spoilt, though many still regard him as a god unfinished.

It is certainly hard to conceive how a Peacock, a Fritillary, a Swallow-tail, a Painted Lady, or indeed any butterfly, could improve its beauty, or advantageously change its ways, or improve upon its established manner of life.

How different is man who, alone endowed with a sense of beauty and with a craving for it, is not merely dissatisfied with his own appearance, but is even, and with good reason, ashamed of it. And because of this, men and women ransack all nature, rob other creatures of furs, wings and feathers, and exhaust the resources of art and industry in the vain endeavour to give themselves a tolerably pleasing appearance.

If "Go to the ant" is a wise proverb for a man, "Go to the Painted Lady" is no bad one for a woman.

Such reflections bring us to one of the most striking and significant of the differences between Man and other living creatures, and one which should humble some of our natural historians and philosophers who, it sometimes seems to the author, are over-apt to exalt themselves and their cleverness in the presence of the wonders of nature.

As Mauro has pointed out, with the sole exception of human beings, all creatures having life, whether in earth, sea or air, are supplied with a beautiful, comfortable, appropriate, adaptable and perfectly fitting suit of clothes. Their garments never become dingy or threadbare, never get out of fashion, and, in short, are so perfect in every way that it would be impossible to devise an improvement upon them. How comes it that Man, with the significant exception of the worm, is the only unclad creature in nature? This seems to the author, as it does to Philip Mauro, to be a fact worthy of the profoundest reflection of some of our modern philosophers and biologians. And of all creatures on this earth, which provide more shining examples of adornment, and of the triumphant survival of the weak, than frail and lovely butterflies which, from infancy to old age, arouse the wonder, delight and interest of those with eyes to see, minds to think, and lips to praise. But the physical and intellectual pleasure to be derived from the beauty and brightness of these creatures is immeasurably reinforced with astonishment, if not with awe, when we learn something of the inner history of these insects which the patient and brilliant studies of many specialists in this branch of natural history, armed with lenses, have made available to mankind.

It is upon the miracles and mysteries of their existence, rather than upon any attempt to write a general history or scientific treatise on butterflies, that the author has concentrated.

There are already in existence many volumes which will give collectors and future specialised students the details of all the British butterflies and moths, and of those of other lands. This is true whether we are considering the distribution of the various 'species,' 'genera,' 'families,' 'races,' 'varieties,' or their habits and anatomy. The immense value of these books, and the brilliant and patient labour of great investigators that has made their existence possible, are not in question. Indeed, the author's knowledge of the astonishing facts about butterflies and moths is, for the most part, gleaned from these classic works, to the authors of which he is so greatly indebted. All of them, however, have this in common. They are, in the main, textbooks of facts for specialised students and collectors rather than books for reading by that large number of men and women who are generally, rather than particularly, interested in natural history from the philosophic or observational points of view. This is especially true of the more modern treatises which are most easily available to the general public.

It is for these reasons that the author has devoted the first part of this book to what he thinks will be regarded as miracles and mysteries of the butterfly world by others besides himself. And here it may be well to emphasise the distinction he will draw between those phenomena that are merely mysterious, and capable of analysis, and those that are miraculous if words still have any meaning. As already pointed out in the Foreword, it is mainly to the work and observation of others that the author is indebted for his facts. He is at liberty, however, to draw his own conclusions from these facts, and these will be found, as in the case of birds, to be in some important respects at variance with those of specialised authorities who, though in general agreement on facts, differ strongly among themselves on the conclusions to be drawn from them. This is particularly marked in the scientific treatises written by acknowledged authorities before and since the appearance of Darwin's *Origin of Species*.

Most noticeably is this true when we come to the problem of butterfly 'migration' and distribution which, as in the case of birds, are so largely regulated, where they are not dominated, by wind. It is this aspect of butterfly life on which the author hopes, as in the case of bird migration, to be able especially to throw new light, and in a manner that may be interesting as well as convincing to any readers into whose hands this modest book may come. While endeavouring to solve some *mysteries*, the author hopes that he will be able to re-establish in the minds of some, who may have come to doubt it, that miracles, in the strict sense of that rather loosely used term, are still being manifested daily before our eyes, and during every moment of time in every corner of this planet.

It is also his hope that he may be able to stimulate the interest of some boys and girls to the point at which they may be inclined to start as a hobby the study and collection of butterflies early in life, thus furnishing themselves with a never-failing source of innocent pleasure and occupation in their leisure time. Artificial pleasures and excitements are not only costly, but are apt to lose their appeal as the years pass. Unlike man-contrived pleasures which fade, the book of nature discloses ever-increasing wonder and delight to those who open it when young. It is for this reason that the author has included in his book a brief guide to the appearance, life habits, and principal localities of all the British butterflies. The second part of the book may not, in those respects, appeal to experienced collectors, who will already have a library of reference on such matters, though it is hoped that the notes may interest even these. It has been included mainly for any, if there be any, whose interest the first part of the book has been able to stimulate to the point of joining the happy band of lay naturalists, of which the author himself has all his life been a modest member.

PART I

MIRACLES AND MYSTERIES

Chapter I

THE EGG

THERE can be few to whom bird's eggs are not, or at some time have not been, objects of interest and admiration, whether lying point to point in their nests or in an egg-collector's cabinet. There can certainly be few boys and girls who do not remember their childish excitement on finding some curious type of nest containing beautifully marked and coloured eggs new to their experience. Little wonder that from the earliest times egg-collecting has been an innocent and exciting pursuit for those who have the good fortune to live and play in the country and the fields, instead of on the pavements and in the alleys of great towns and cities. In the case of birds there is the added attraction of the nests, the architecture of which at once betrays to the initiated the nature of his prize. But what of butterflies' eggs of which, according to Frohawk,[1] the total number of distinct British species is sixty-eight? The majority even of country-folk have never so much as seen a butterfly's egg. Butterflies do not build tell-tale nests. To those who have, outside the ranks of expert entomologists, they must have seemed as trivial and uninteresting as small seeds in a seed-packet, which they closely resemble. But to the entomologist with his lens, these butterfly eggs are in many respects more remarkable, varied and beautiful, than are the eggs of birds. Indeed, if some ingenious mind could invent and contrive butterfly egg-cabinets that would magnify their contents to the size of the examples illustrated in this book, such collections would soon become common. And what a surprising sight would such a collection of eggs present! Some round, some oblong, some shaped like tiny champagne-bottles standing upright. Some pale green, some pale yellow, others pure ivory white. But whatever their size, shape or colour, all but a few possess what is lacking in birds' eggs—beautiful *carving*; and carving, to quote the great naturalist Newman,[2] "a thousand times more delicate and fine than any human hand could execute. Some are exquisitely fluted; others are ribbed; some are covered with a network of raised lines; others have rows of minute keels, forty or fifty in number, all of which converge to a point at the top of the egg; others are perfectly smooth; some few of them have a lid at the top which the young caterpillar gently lifts off when he makes his first appearance in the world."

One of the most remarkable facts is the extreme difference in the eggs of distinct species which, in the butterfly state, closely resemble one another. For example, the egg of the Large Tortoiseshell is pear-shaped and smooth,

[1] F. W. Frohawk, M.B.O.U., F.R.E.S., etc., author of *The Natural History of British Butterflies*.

[2] Edward Newman, F.L.S., F.Z.S., author of *Natural History of British Butterflies and Moths*.

whereas that of the Small Tortoiseshell is oblong with eight conspicuous ribs. Here is a reminder to those who are apt to dispute it, that all distinct species of creatures are 'after their kind,' with their seed in themselves. Reinforcing this scientific statement is the fact that the character of the eggs of every true species is so constant that a trained naturalist can foretell with certainty what kind of butterfly will develop from that particular egg. And this in objects no larger than small seeds.

The substance of the shell of all these eggs is very elastic, tough and pliable. Kirby and Spence[1] likened these egg-shells to the membrane that lines the egg-shell of a bird, though Haworth[2] considered them to be much less pliable and more elastic.

The content of the egg is a transparent colourless fluid, closely resembling in appearance the white of a bird's egg. Nothing corresponding to the yolk is found.

Turning from the eggs themselves to the laying, or 'sowing,' of them by the parent butterfly, the author cannot hope to better the description given by Newman in his *Natural History of British Butterflies and Moths*. He writes: "It is a most interesting occupation to watch the female depositing her eggs, and to observe the extraordinary sagacity she displays in selecting the leaf proper for the food of the future caterpillar. In a hedge or coppice, densely crowded with every kind of native shrub, the Emperor selects the sallow, the White Admiral the honeysuckle, and the Brimstone the buckthorn. Hardly ever, by any chance, is the egg of one species laid on the food plant of another. There are, however, occasional exceptions; and these very exceptions display an amount of botanical knowledge which, of course, we must regard as instinctive or intuitive knowledge, possessed by these *females*, that cannot fail to excite our admiration." Newman emphasises this extraordinary instinctive, or intuitive, faculty in the *female* butterfly which suggests in the lower orders of creatures a phenomenon that is disclosed in the crown of creation—Mankind. Women often astonish men by their faculty of arriving at obscure truths intuitively, or *instinctively*, where man employs his fallible reasoning power, often with less accurate results! But to continue: "Thus, when the usual food plant is not at hand, and the egg must be extruded, the most nearly allied species is selected and made to serve as a substitute. For instance, when the common species of buckthorn (*Rhamnus Catharticus*) cannot be found, the rarer species (*Rhamnus frangula*) is made to supply its place."

Here is an authenticated fact which should be borne in mind, because this point will constantly recur at a later stage when we come to the problem of 'varieties' or 'races' within the ring-fence, so to speak, of

[1] The Rev. William Kirby, F.R.S., F.L.S., etc., Hon. President of the Entomological Society, 1837, to which he bequeathed his collection of insects; William Spence, F.L.S., President, 1847, of the Entomological Society, which he helped to found; joint authors of the classic work, *Introduction to Entomology*.

[2] A. D. Haworth, F.L.S., author of *Synopsis Plantarum Succulentarum*, and founder of Aurelian and Entomological Societies, 1806.

species which Professor E. B. Poulton, F.R.S., as Chairman of the British Association in 1926, so aptly and decisively defined as "inter-breeding communities."

"When a female butterfly is about to lay her eggs her conduct is totally different from that ordinarily to be observed; she assumes a grave, important and business-like demeanour, with which the practical observer soon becomes familiar. She exhibits none of that volatility and causelessness which characterises a butterfly when engaged in the lighter labours of life, such as making love or sipping honey. Her eggs are generally covered with a liquid glue at the moment they are laid, and this glue fastens them to whatever substances the parent butterfly pleases, generally the surface of a leaf, but sometimes to a twig or the bark of a tree.

"There is, however, one striking exception to this rule, and others, of course, may be expected. The Marbled White drops her egg at random among the herbage, being perfectly well assured that the young caterpillar when hatched will find out, and will crawl up, some blade of grass suitable for it to feed on." (See Marbled White, Part II.)

Here again is a point which should be remembered when the question of *varieties* of the same species is being considered. Frohawk, in discussing the Marbled White, and in his beautiful illustrations, refers to the remarkable variation of the colour of the underside of the wings of this species of butterfly which lays its eggs at random on various types of herbage. Having laid her eggs in these exposed positions the parent butterfly ceases to have any further regard for them. In this she behaves unlike most birds, but notably like the cuckoo (of which the author has written elsewhere), and the ostrich, of which it was written many thousands of years ago, in the wonderful natural history portion of the Book of Job, believed to be the oldest book of the Bible: "Gavest thou the goodly wings unto the peacock, or wings and feathers unto the ostrich? which leaveth her eggs in the earth, and warmeth them in the dust, and forgetteth that the foot may crush them, or that the wild beast may break them. She is hardened against her young ones as though they were not hers: her labour is in vain without fear; because God has deprived her of wisdom, neither hath He imparted unto her understanding."

Eltringham,[1] in his book *Butterfly Lore*, confirms this similarity between the butterfly and the ostrich when he writes: "Probably the butterfly never sees its eggs, and would have little regard for them if she did."

Different species of butterflies lay varying numbers of eggs; some in clutches of hundreds on a single leaf, others singly on many leaves; the laying of their eggs, and thus the assured continuance of descendants, being the closing act in the creature's life cycle of approximately one year, and the end for which it has lived.

Some species hibernate in the egg state, some as caterpillars, and some

[1] The late H. Eltringham, M.A., D.Sc. (Oxon), F.R.E.S., F.Z.S., Joint Secretary and sometime Vice-President of the Entomological Society.

as chrysalids, and the remainder in the winged state. But all the individuals comprising a particular species of butterfly always hibernate in the *same* state: each adheres strictly to the habit of its kind.[1] Thus if one Hairstreak butterfly, for example, passes the winter in the egg state, so will its children, and its children's children, for countless generations. So with those that hibernate in the other three states of the caterpillar, the chrysalis and the winged butterfly.

Butterfly eggs may remain as such for days or weeks, the exact period varying, as in flower seeds, according to weather conditions, or for a whole winter; but be the time short or long the caterpillar is formed within, and the process of biting its way out, or lifting its little trap-hatch, begins.

That, very briefly, is the story of the butterfly's egg, no bigger than a small flower seed whose method of germination it so closely resembles. Here, in a moment of time, a spark of life has been kindled which in due course will bring into being a creeping earthbound reptile which, after 'death' and self-entombment, will rise again on painted wings to greet the sun. This, surely, is a miracle, rather than a mystery which man, by taking thought, may be able to solve. But as the solution of some butterfly mysteries is the purpose of this book, readers are invited to bear in mind for future reference the following authenticated facts which have been emphasised in this chapter.

(1) The easily recognisable differences between all the eggs of the various true species, and notably between those of species which closely resemble one another in the final winged state.

(2) The fact that the species of a future butterfly can be detected in the egg stage. Where doubt exists, as for example in the case of some of the British 'Blues,' doubt must also arise as to whether specimens treated as distinct species are not, in fact, geographical races of the same species.

(3) The selection of a closely related leaf for egg deposition, as in the case of the Brimstone, when the normal leaf is not available.

(4) The random egg-laying of some species, notably the Marbled White, and thus the variety of food-plants in such cases.

(5) The often widely varying periods required for the germination of the eggs according to weather conditions, of which temperature is the prime factor. Herein lies a sharp distinction separating butterflies and moths from birds, whose egg incubation periods and temperatures are fixed within narrow limits.

[1] Partial exceptions to this rule occur in the Speckled Wood, Wall, and Meadow Brown, but the curious variability of the species is constant *in* the species. See Speckled Wood, Wall, etc., and page 93.

Chapter II

THE CATERPILLAR

The helpless crawling caterpillar trace
From the first period of his reptile race.
Cloth'd in dishonour, on the leafy spray
Unseen he wears his silent hours away;
Till satiate grown of all that life supplies,
Self-taught, the voluntary martyr dies.
Deep under earth his darkening course he bends,
And to the tomb, a willing guest, descends.
There long secluded, in his lonely cell,
Forgets the sun, and bids the world farewell.
O'er the wide wastes the wintry tempests reign,
And driving snows usurp the frozen plain:
In vain the tempest beats, the whirlwind blows;
No storms can violate his grave's repose.
But when revolving months have won their way,
When smile the woods, and when the zephyrs play,
When laughs the vivid world in summer's bloom
He bursts; and flies triumphant from the tomb;
And while his new-born beauties he displays,
With conscious joy his altered form surveys.
Mark while he woos amid the sunny beam,
O'er his soft wings the varying lustres gleam.
Launched into air, on purple plumes he soars,
Gay nature's face with wanton glance explores;
Proud of his varying beauties wings his way,
And spoils the finest flowers, himself more fair than they.

HAWORTH

THE writer of the above lines, A. D. Haworth, F.L.S., was not only a founder of the Entomological Society in 1806 but, as readers will agree, a poet. And it is to his poetical requirements that we must attribute his departure from scientific accuracy when he writes of the butterfly:

With *conscious* joy his altered form surveys.

And again:

Proud of his varying beauties wings his way.

As an entomologist he was as definite as are all natural historians to-day that the butterfly in all its stages is totally devoid of any knowledge or understanding, and therefore of self-consciousness. But apart from this poetic licence, he traces in a few delightful lines the life-history of the butterfly, and of its caterpillar stage with which we are concerned in this chapter.

The caterpillar emerges from the egg at all seasons and, in the words of Newman—"as the young lawyer is said to eat his way to the bar, so does the young caterpillar prepare himself for public life by gnawing away a sufficient portion of the egg-shell in which he had been confined to allow of his escape, and by swallowing the chips he had made during the operation. Indeed, this gastronomic feat is often followed by a more extensive performance of the same kind; for I have often watched him devour the whole of his cradle, except a small shining circular patch where it had been glued to the object on which it was laid."

Having demolished his original appurtenances he then proceeds to feed on the leaves of the trees and herbage upon which he was laid as an egg—that is to say on the food agreeable to his particular species, thereby obeying the law of his being and thriving accordingly. And how he thrives! No indigestion; no rickets, no stomach-ache; and this in spite of the fact that, according to some naturalists, he eats several times his own weight in twenty-four hours. From its emergence from the egg to its time for transformation into a chrysalis the Swallow-tail, for example, increases its length over fifteen-fold, and its bulk proportionately. This rapid and almost fabulous growth is derived from its absorption of the leaves of its appropriate food-plant: the caterpillar may therefore almost literally be regarded as an animated or crawling leaf. Further reference will be made to this matter when we come to the phenomena of 'mimicry,' variety, and 'cannibalism.' Little wonder that he outgrows his clothes, as we should say of ourselves, or his successive skins in the case of a caterpillar. When faced with this frequently recurring emergency he shuffles them off, sometimes as many as six times in his short career as a caterpillar; short, that is to say, in all cases other than those where the caterpillar *hibernates* as such, in some cases for as long as nine or ten months.

It is generally supposed that the wearing of clothes is peculiar to mankind. But this is not so. We share the art of dressmaking with some caterpillars—notably those of the Psyche moth—when they first emerge from the egg. They make their first suit from the materials of the old one in which their mother lived, for she is hardly recognisable as a moth, and never leaves the covering she made as a caterpillar. This old garment is made of tiny sticks interwoven with silk. After biting out the pith from the tiny sticks of its dead mother's cast-off clothing, it makes it into small pellets, fastening them together with its own silk. Having made a band of this it passes it round its body and fastens the end with more silk. Gradually adding to the edge of this girdle the caterpillar moves forward within it, so that, in Fabre's words, "the garment is first a scarf, then a waistcoat, then a short jacket, and lastly a sack or conical hood." The materials which Fabre offered to the caterpillar for dressmaking were varied, and included blotting-paper, cork, the scales from a moth's wings and powdered iron-ore.

The means by which the caterpillar changes its old coats and underclothing, and literally hangs them neatly up, were wonderfully described by William Kirby and William Spence over a hundred years ago, and their facts remain, in all important respects, authentic. "When the process of moulting goes on favourably it may thus be described: the fore part of the body is turned vigorously from side to side, the skin of the second, third, and fourth segments opens down the back, and the head and interior part of the caterpillar protrudes through the opening; then immediately beneath the head may be seen the shell-like covering of the old head, split down the middle and often into three pieces; the caterpillar next, with a series of convulsive struggles, creeps out of his old skin, which is left attached to the carpet, and is frequently so perfect and apparently so plump that I have been completely deceived into supposing that he was still wearing his old clothes.

"The head, antennae, jaws, and legs, of the caterpillar are persistent, and their hairy covering only is shed at the period of moult. Swammerdam recorded that not only the hairy covering of these parts and the skin of the body come away at each moult, but also the throat and a part of the stomach, and even the inward surface of the great gut, change their skin at the same time. But this is not the whole of these wonders, for at the same time some hundreds of pulmonary pipes within the body cast also each its delicate and tender skin. These several skins are afterwards collected into eighteen thicker, and as it were compounded, ropes—nine on each side of the body—which, when the skin is cast, slip gently and by degrees from within the body through eighteen apertures or orifices of the pulmonary tubes, nine on each side. Two other branches of the pulmonary pipes, that are smaller and have no points of respiration, cast a skin likewise. If anyone separates the cast little ropes or congeries of the pulmonary pipes with a fine needle he will very distinctly see the branches and ramifications of these several pipes, and also their annular composition."

Allusion has been made to the perfect power of discrimination that caterpillars exhibit in the selection of their food. This, according to Newman and other naturalists, seems to be vested in twelve minute microscopic eyes, seated six on each cheek close to the mouth. These eyes are highly convex lenses, so arranged as to be useless unless they are brought into contact, or nearly so. A caterpillar, as anyone can confirm by watching it, seems to examine with its mouth the surface of each leaf before it nibbles, but whether these 'eyes' see as we see with ours is, in the author's view, open to doubt because we see, or at least *discriminate*, with our *minds*. The truth is that the most expert anatomist that has ever lived, or ever will live, is really guessing when he describes the senses and sensations of the insect world because it is only possible to speak in terms of senses that we human beings know. There can be little doubt that new worlds would be open to us if we could sense the physical world as butterflies sense it. But as entomologists, ancient and modern, seem to be agreed that a butterfly in its various stages is unconscious of itself, it seems to follow that a butterfly is as near to vegetable life as we are removed from it. Even plants show indications of *deliberate* activities, for some, we are given to understand, 'catch,' 'eat,' and nourish themselves upon, flies!

This modest book, as has already been said, does not profess to be a scientific treatise, though great care has been taken to check all facts quoted from high and acknowledged authorities. For this reason it is not proposed to set forth, or to consider in detail, the infinitely varied anatomical machinery of the thousands of caterpillar species which crawl about this planet on what appear to the layman to be eight pairs of legs. Of these sixteen 'legs,' only the front six are legs proper, and of these six, the anterior two are in certain species of insects more in the nature of 'arms.' It is these six legs, or four legs and two 'arms,' which undergo eventual resurrection with the winged body.[1] The remaining ten are 'claspers,' instruments used by the caterpillar for clasping firmly the food-plant on which it is standing. They are left behind when the creature ceases to be earthbound and rises triumphantly from its chrysalis 'tomb.'

The caterpillar is composed of thirteen rings, or segments. The first is the head furnished with two antennae, two feelers, two jaws and the twelve microscopic eyes.

The second has two spiracles or breathing holes, one on each side, and two jointed legs.

The third has two jointed legs only.

The fourth has two jointed legs only.

The fifth has two spiracles only.

The sixth has two spiracles only.

The seventh, eighth, ninth and tenth have each two claspers and two spiracles.

The eleventh and twelfth have each two spiracles only.

The thirteenth has two claspers only.

The drawing below shows the arrangement which is universal in all butterfly caterpillars.

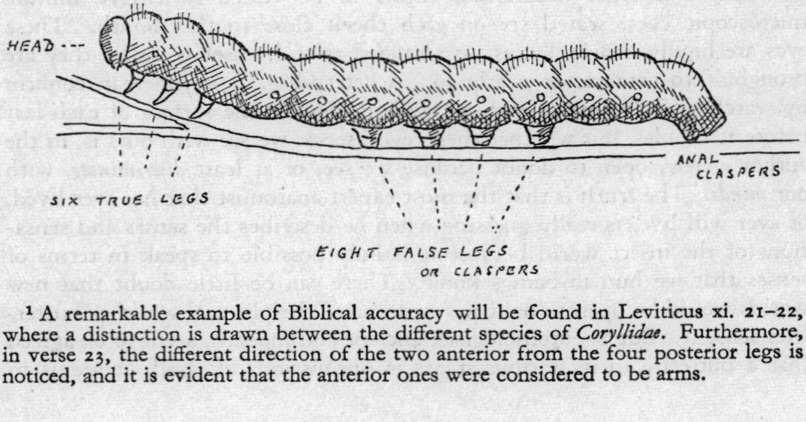

[1] A remarkable example of Biblical accuracy will be found in Leviticus xi. 21–22, where a distinction is drawn between the different species of *Coryllidae*. Furthermore, in verse 23, the different direction of the two anterior from the four posterior legs is noticed, and it is evident that the anterior ones were considered to be arms.

Some caterpillars, known to many as 'woolly bears,' are armed with hairs, which it is alleged are a means of defence against enemies in various ways. Others are said to have a scent that is nauseous to birds and other hostile competitors in the 'fight for survival.' It may be so, but here again such theories can only be speculative, because we have no means of knowing just what is, or is not, nauseous to another species of creature. It would be thought, by such a process of reasoning, that a rotting rat, or a piece of filthy dung, would be obnoxious both in scent and taste to that most beautiful of butterflies—the Purple Emperor. And yet such putrefaction is nectar to it, and is actually used as bait for snaring it.

So with the brilliant colours that adorn some caterpillars, and which grow in intensity, and change under observation as the caterpillar changes its coat or retires into its chrysalis. It is generally assumed that these are a means of *defence* against their enemies, a theory in direct opposition to the 'mimicry' which is said to provide protection by making the creature indistinguishable from its surroundings. But as this interesting subject will receive further attention in due course, no more will be said about it here.

There are, however, just a few anatomical features of the caterpillar to which a short reference should be made. Has it a heart? Not in the ordinary sense of the term. Instead, it is provided with a long pulsating tube running down its back and open at the ends, which keeps the life-blood, or sap, to give it a more analogous name, moving at pressure through all the spaces of the interior.

Has it lungs? No, like all other insects it breathes through little openings—the spiracles—in its body, which lead to a network of tubes carrying air to every part of its anatomy.

Has it a brain? Yes, it has what Eltringham calls "a very simple one." It consists of two little masses of nerve tissue from which two delicate nerve-cords pass through the whole length of the body, giving off many finer branches. To a layman such a brain, operating as it does every bit of the multitudinous machinery in the body, is marvellously complicated rather than simple, as we should quickly find if we set about modelling it in inanimate material which we can make and handle.

Another extraordinary anatomical or mechanical feature of the caterpillar must be mentioned. Its stomach, a regular chemical laboratory as well as a machine shop, is fitted with machinery for varying degrees of silk production and weaving, the silk being required for various functions of its life as well as for the manufacture of its own eventual 'death' shroud in the case of most moths and a few butterflies.

Before leaving the consideration of the caterpillar, there are two extraordinary characteristics which deserve to be recorded because, unlike the anatomical miracles of its construction which the mind of man cannot fathom, they may provide clues to other 'mysteries' of butterfly life which, on the contrary, may be found capable of analysis, if not of final solution.

The first of these are the remarkable habits of some, and notably of the Pine Processionary, caterpillars. The eggs of this moth are laid in batches, and the young caterpillars make a nest of silk in which they live, eating the enclosed pine needles. When these are consumed they move on and enclose fresh ones. They pass the winter in a similar but thicker nest, in which they do not eat the pine needles. This winter nest is built gradually, the caterpillar feeding by day outside it, and adding layer on layer of silk. But here is the point that deserves stressing. Fabre, by cutting a hole in the nest, found that the creatures made no effort to mend it, thereby proving to the satisfaction of Eltringham as well as of himself that "the construction of the nest is an unconscious and blind instinct," just as it is in the case of birds.

These Pine Processionaries are so called because on their expeditions abroad they walk in a procession, sometimes numbering three hundred, and measuring twelve yards in length. In doing so, they spin fine threads of silk, to which each adds its quota, ultimately forming a silk ribbon which serves as a highway back to the nest. If feeding *separately*, each continues to lay a single silk thread. For what purpose is this thread? According to Eltringham, for the purpose of finding its way back to the nest, a conclusion which deprives this particular creature of that strange unaccountable 'sense of direction' which, as it is hoped to show, is one of the governing elements in the migration of butterflies as it is in that of birds and fish. Surely it is plain that the fine silk thread is still a highway and a *bridge* across miniature precipices for the solitary insect, as the broad silk ribbon is for the creatures when they move in mass formation.

In conclusion, a reference must be made to yet one other strange phenomenon of these strange creatures. Fabre discovered that if he arranged these caterpillars in a circle round their food they would continue to walk in a circle, head to stern, without ever breaking it, until they died of starvation or exhaustion. This strange fact is quoted less on account of its inherent interest than for the purpose of demonstrating again the utter lack of any gleam of conscious intelligence or objectivity in a butterfly or moth in its caterpillar stage.

Volumes might be, and indeed have been, written on caterpillars, but enough has now been said for the author's purpose, which is mainly to demonstrate certain facts which will be of importance when we come to explore such mysteries as migration and instinct, just as in the last chapter he stressed facts which had a bearing on species and varieties. It is therefore hoped that readers will remember these points when we come to the subjects upon which they have an intimate bearing.

Chapter III

THE CHRYSALIS

WE now come to that marvel of nature—the transformation of a lively, ravenous, multi-legged creeping caterpillar into a seemingly dead coffined corpse. But before examining the characteristics of a few particular species of chrysalis, it may be well to give some general account of some of the varieties of chrysalis, and their methods of formation and maintenance. In the first place there is a general distinction between the chrysalids of butterflies and moths. The former rarely make a silken cocoon or bury themselves underground, whereas moths do both. An extraordinary example of the burial of a moth chrysalis will be recorded in due course.

Some species of butterflies and moths remain in the chrysalis stage for no more than a few weeks; but others pass the winter, and in a few cases as much as two or three years, in this state of suspended animation. The keenest frost holds no terrors for the chrysalis. Many of our loveliest summer butterflies must frequently be frozen as hard as a rock during part of their brief careers from the egg to the perfect imago.

Sir George Nares found five species of butterflies thriving in Lat. 83° North—7° short of the Pole.

Though butterfly chrysalids are sometimes found on the ground, they are usually suspended, either upright or horizontal, hooked at the posterior end by their rear claspers to a silken pad, and supported by a silken girdle round the waist to the twig or whatnot which any particular species selects for its period of inanition. Some, on the other hand, hang loose in an inverted position; and to guard them against damage if they swing to and fro in a wind they are provided with projections which act as shock-absorbers. Chrysalids not protected by thick silken cocoons or buried beneath the ground, that is to say most butterfly chrysalids, are generally very inconspicuous; though here, as in many other attributes of butterflies in the various stages of their life-history, there are startling exceptions which form awkward obstacles to the 'mimicry' theory of protection of frail creatures in their 'fight for survival.' This fact of startling exceptions to a general rule is of great importance because it will have a bearing on the mysteries of 'mimicry' and 'varieties' when we come to consider these interesting questions.

Chrysalids of insects are of three kinds: they are called *Amorphous* when they have no resemblance to the perfect insect; *Necromorphous* when they have a close resemblance and exhibit all their limbs swathed as it were in swaddling clothes; and *Isomorphous* when they resemble the perfect insect in everything but the possession of wings. The amorphous and necromorphous kinds can neither eat, fly nor run; the isomorphous, on the other hand, eat voraciously, leap and run, but cannot fly.

Butterflies belong to the *amorphous* division because their chrysalids, which are seemingly dead, show no resemblance to the butterfly that will eventually emerge.

Before the caterpillar sets about entombing itself, it ceases to eat; and not only so: it takes the utmost pains to remove every particle of food from the alimentary canal, and evacuates with its excrement the very lining of its intestines. Indeed, it rids itself of everything that would suffer corruption if retained in its death-like state.

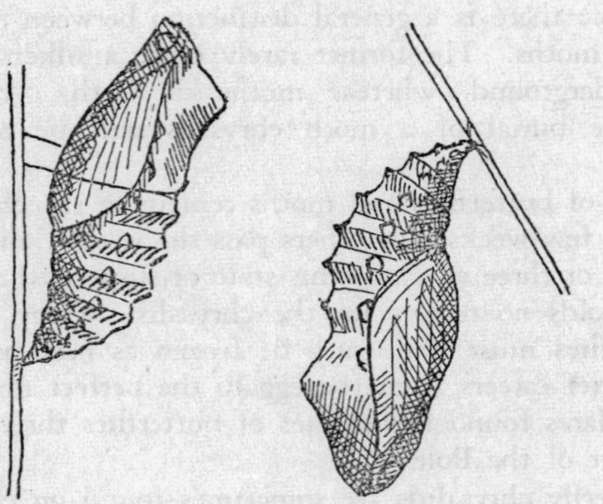

Many naturalists have told the story of the extraordinary means that the caterpillar employs to prepare itself for its chrysalis stage, which in the case of some may, as already mentioned, last as much as three years. Of all the accounts given, none exceeds in clarity that of Kirby and Spence in their *Introduction to Entomology*. This classic, though written 130 years ago, is still authoritative. It is therefore upon that source of knowledge that the author will draw.

Having emptied itself as described, the colours of the skin change, fade and entirely disappear. The creature then wanders 'witlessly' and, as we should say, unmeaningly from place to place. Whatever the object of this last earthly crawl, it ends invariably in the finding of some suitable cemetery. Having found it, the caterpillar spins a little pad of silken threads crossing and criss-crossing each other in every direction. Almost every caterpillar has the power of making silk, and of emitting it through its mouth in the form of thread.[1]

When the silken pad is complete, the caterpillar grasps it with his last pair of 'claspers,' and then, hanging down, waits for the transformation

[1] Of the silkworm it is not necessary to speak, beyond comparing the 'genius' of this lowly worm with the relatively insignificant intelligence of Man in his efforts to manufacture a sorry substitute for the reality, that is to say for the truth.

going on inside it. After one or two days of stillness there is a renewal of those contortions which precede or accompany each of the moultings, or suit-changings, in the growing state, and which have already been described. Now the caterpillar's skin is seen to open behind the head, and by alternate contractions and dilations the chrysalis, now perfectly formed, is seen to force itself through the opening, the upper part of the back coming first, and acting as a wedge to open the slit wider until all the chrysalis has passed through the opening. The caterpillar's skin, wrinkled and shrivelled, is pushed down to the lower end of the chrysalis; and there remains, much like a stocking rolled down to the ankle, before being withdrawn from the foot. The remainder of the almost incredible story had best be told in the exact words of Kirby and Spence.

"The chrysalis being much shorter than the caterpillar is as yet at some distance from the silken pad on which it is to be fastened; it is supported mainly by the upright terminal portion of the latter's skin. How shall it disengage itself from the remnant of its case and be suspended in the air while it climbs up to take its place? Without arms and legs to support itself, the anxious spectator expects it to fall to the earth. His fears, however, are vain; the supple segments of the body of the chrysalis serve in the place of arms. Between two of them, as with a pair of pincers, it seizes on a portion of the skin, and bending its body once more, entirely extricates its tail from it. It is now wholly out of the skin, against one side of which it is supported, but yet at some distance from the leaf.

"The next step it must take is to climb up to the required height. For this purpose it repeats the same ingenious manœuvre. Making its cast-off skin serve as a sort of ladder, it successively with different segments seizes a higher and higher portion, until in the end it reaches the summit: with its tail it feels for the silken threads that are to support it. But how can the tail be fastened to them, you may ask. This difficulty has been provided against by Creative Wisdom. The tail of the chrysalis is furnished with numerous little hooks pointing in several directions, as well adapted to the end in view as the crochets on the caterpillar's claspers, and some of these hooks are sure to fasten themselves upon the silk the moment the tail is thrust amongst it.

"Our chrysalis has now nearly performed its labours; it has withdrawn its tail from the slough, climbed up it, and suspended itself from the silken pad, manœuvres so delicate and perilous that we cannot but admire that an insect which executes them but once in its life should execute them so well. Nor could it, as Reamur has well and piously observed, 'had it not been instructed by a Great Master.'

"One more operation remains: it seems to have as great an antipathy to its cast-off skin as one of us should, when newly clothed after a long imprisonment, to the filthy garments we had put off. It will not suffer the memento of its former state to remain near it, and is no sooner suspended in security than it endeavours to make it fall. For this end it seizes, as it were, with its tail, the threads to which the skin is fastened, and then very rapidly whirls itself round, often not fewer than twenty times. By this means it generally succeeds in breaking them, and the skin falls down. Sometimes, however, the first attempt fails: in that case, after a moment's rest, it makes a second, twirling itself in an opposite direction, and this is rarely unsuccessful. After these exertions it hangs the remainder of its existence in this state until the butterfly is disclosed."

Now let us turn to the very different method of entombment employed by some moths.

The making of the cocoon of the Puss moth, generally sited on the bark of a tree, is a truly marvellous engineering feat, the details of which are most graphically described by Eltringham. From him we learn that in captivity it will choose cardboard, cork, or even a hard wooden board. Slowly it weaves its silk covering which resembles a fine net with a multitude of minute openings. Having reached this stage, it begins to fill up each opening with a particle of wood, if the cocoon is located on wood, and the tiny but powerful jaws can actually be heard rasping off the wooden particles. These particles are retained in place by the adhesive property of the silk, and by the additional application of a fluid solvent with which the creature licks it. The whole cocoon thus becomes a mass of silk and wood, of glue and sawdust. At first it is comparatively soft, but it rapidly stiffens and darkens till it becomes so hard that it is difficult to pierce it with a penknife.

Inside this hard coffin, which a man can hardly open with a steel knife, what was once a caterpillar lies not unlike a mummy through the long winter. But on some fine morning in spring a beautiful moth will be found sitting beside its empty tomb. "How has it performed this apparent miracle?" asks Eltringham—or, as some would put it more bluntly, this *plain* miracle? It has used its chemical laboratory, because, as Latter discovered, at the moment of emergence the moth ejects a drop of caustic potash on to the end of its tomb, which thus becomes softened. The moth's own head is guarded from damage by the fluid by what appears to be a blackhead, but which turns out to be the top of the chrysalis skin worn for resurrection purposes as a helmet. This 'helmet of salvation,' as we might almost say, is also used as a tool for cutting through the cocoon already softened by the fluid. This helmet, or shield, is held in place by special hooks, and is removed by the creature's legs when no longer needed.

Here, indeed, is an example of the undertaker's business and the excavator's craft which must excite our wonder.

The Puss moth, having emerged from its cocoon as described, is now free and ready for the process of drying its wings.

But what of caterpillars which bury themselves in the ground? Here is a different and seemingly greater obstacle to be overcome—that of the earth beneath which the chrysalis lies buried. Some species make their way in the chrysalis state to the surface before emerging winged for flight. Others emerge from the chrysalis while still underground and afterwards make their way upwards; though, to quote Eltringham, "it is not clear how so delicate a creature as a moth is able to perform, without injury, so laborious a resurrection." He tells us, however, that the late Dr. Chapman discovered that some species eject a softening fluid at the moment of emergence, but he adds that the quantity of this fluid, a solution of potassium chloride, is so small that it is difficult to account for its doing more than moisten the surface of the cell in which the chrysalis lies.

But the Pine Processionary, of whose antics and peculiarities as a caterpillar some account has already been given, has come under the scrutiny of that observer without a peer—Henri Fabre. This moth, after emerging underground from its chrysalis as a winged creature, digs its way up from a depth of as much as ten inches. On emerging as a moth from what, to such a creature, are almost the bowels of the earth, it occupies little space, as its wings and antennae fit closely to the body, the legs only being free. On its head it carries hard projections which act as a boring tool. With these it breaks away the particles of earth above it and thrusts them down with its feet. These extraordinary feats of excavation by a creature with infinitely delicate wings were carefully observed in a long glass tube and recorded by Fabre.

Much more might be written on the many and varying means by which caterpillars, whether of butterflies or moths, entomb themselves as creeping reptiles and resurrect themselves with wings. But enough has been said to prove conclusively that there is not a craft or an art of the engineer, the chemist, the sculptor, the weaver, or of that final servant of every man born of woman—the undertaker—that is not known to the butterfly or moth at this astounding stage of its brief existence. And yet, like the ostrich, it is deprived of wisdom, neither has it had understanding imparted unto it. This fact of perfect craftsmanship and purpose performed by a creature bereft of any gleam of understanding or self-consciousness will come under consideration when we explore that mystery which we call *instinct*.

Chapter IV

THE BUTTERFLY

When bursting forth to life and light,
The offspring of enraptured May,
The butterfly on pinions bright
Launched in full splendour on the day.

Unconscious of a mother's care,
No infant wretchedness she knew;
But as she felt the vernal air,
At once to full perfection grew.

Her slender form, ethereal light,
Her velvet-textured wings unfold;
With all the rainbow's colours bright,
And dropt with spots of burnished gold.

Trembling with joy awhile she stood,
And felt the sun's enlivening ray;
Drank from the skies the vital flood,
And wondered at her plumage gay!

And balanced oft her broidered wings,
Through fields of air prepared to sail;
Then on her vent'rous journey springs,
And floats along the rising gale.

Go, child of pleasure, range the fields,
Taste all the joys that spring can give;
Partake what bounteous summer yields,
And live while yet 'tis thine to live.

Go sip the rose's fragrant dew,
The lily's honey'd cup explore;
From flower to flower the search renew,
And rifle all the woodbine's store.

And let me trace thy vagrant flight,
Thy moments too of short repose,
And mark thee then with fresh delight
Thy golden pinions ope and close.

But hark! while thus I musing stand
Pours on the gale an airy note,
And breathing from a viewless hand
Soft silvery tones around me float.

They cease,—but still a voice I hear,
  A whispered voice of hope and joy,
"Thy hour of rest approaches near,
  Prepare thee mortal—thou must die!

"Yet start not! on thy closing eyes
  Another day shall still unfold,
A sun of milder radiance rise,
  A happier age of joys untold.

"Shall the poor worm that shocks thy sight,
  The humblest form in nature's train
Thus rise in new-born lustre bright,
  And yet the emblem teach in vain?

"Ah! where were once her golden eyes,
  Her glittering wings of purple pride?
Concealed beneath a rude disguise,
  A shapeless mass to earth allied.

"Like thee the hapless reptile lived,
  Like thee he toiled, like thee he spun;
Like thine, his closing hour arrived,
  His labour ceased, his web was done.

"And shalt thou, numbered with the dead,
  No happier state of being know?
And shall no future morrow shed
  On thee a beam of brighter glow?

"Is this the bound of power divine,
  To animate an insect frame?
Or shall not He who moulded thine
  Wake at His will the vital flame?

"Go mortal, in thy reptile state,
  Enough to know to thee is given;
Go, and the joyful truth relate;
  Frail child of earth! high heir of heaven."

ANON

THESE anonymous lines, taken from a newspaper and quoted by Kirby and Spence, reveal very clearly the spirit of reverence and awe in which these two great scientists approached their classic studies of nature. Both of them, as Presidents of the Entomological Society which they helped to found, and to which it is still an honour and a hall-mark of scientific competence to belong, had no difficulty in deciding where miracles ended and mysteries capable of analysis began. And who that has studied or may study their *Introduction to Entomology*, still revered by the Zoological

Society as a classic, will doubt that a spirit of reverent humility is an aid rather than a barrier to scientific observation of the wonderful and perfect works of nature? These two great men shared the fervent faith of Leonardo Da Vinci: "Learning the Laws of nature, we magnify the First Inventor, the Designer of the World."

Having given some account of the remarkable stages in the making of a butterfly, from the ignition of the vital spark in the tiny egg to its emergence from the chrysalis, we may now consider the finishing touches, so to speak, that have to be applied before the erstwhile reptile takes to its multi-coloured wings, painted as the greatest human artist could never paint. When the dramatic moment has arrived for the chrysalis to yield its treasure, the colours and markings of the perfect insect begin to gleam through the horny shell which envelops it. As shown in the last chapter, the horny shell is split and the perfect butterfly emerges. Perfect in fact, yes, but not even yet perfect in appearance. The wings, instead of being the delicate and yet strong and rigid organs upon which the butterfly will be borne, are small shapeless abortions, folded over its chest much as our hands will in due course be folded over ours when we are entering, instead of emerging from, the chrysalis stage. They are limp, pliable bags, filled with colourless blood which has yet to be diffused throughout the body. This final process is again so perfectly described by Kirby and Spence that it would be impertinence for the author to substitute words of his own for the sake of avoiding inverted commas and thus full acknowledgment of the source from which his knowledge is drawn. Quotation honours him who is quoted, whereas by slightly modifying the wording of other men's records without acknowledgment an author usurps credit. This thought was ever present in Newman's mind when he wrote his great work on British Butterflies. The same is true of Eltringham in *Butterfly Lore* in his generous references to Henri Fabre; and indeed of all great naturalists.

Having made this acknowledgment, let us follow the beautifully told tale of the final perfecting of the newly risen Swallow-tail—one of the loveliest of British butterflies.

"At first it was unable to elevate, or even move, its wings, but in proportion as the aerial or other fluid was forced by the motion of its trunk into the nervures (veins, nerves, or rays as other entomologists call them for lack of any counterpart in any other creature), their numerous corrugations and folds gradually yielded to the action, till they had gathered their greatest extent, and the film between all the nervures became tense. The ocelli and spots and bars, which appeared at first as but germs or rudiments of what they were to be, grew with the growing wings, and shone forth upon its complete expansion in full magnitude and beauty. To understand more clearly the cause of this rapid expansion and development of the wings, I have before explained that these organs, though often exceedingly thin, are always composed of two membranes, having most commonly a number of hollow vessels, miscalled nerves, running between them. These tubes contribute as well to the development of the wings as to their subsequent tension.

"In the chrysalis, and commonly afterwards, the two membranes composing the organs in question do not touch each other's inner surface as they afterwards do: there is consequently a space between them; and being moist and corrugated into a vast number of folds, like those of a fan, but transverse as well as longitudinal, and so minute as to be imperceptible to the naked eye, the wing appears much thicker than in the end.

"Now, as soon as the insect is disclosed, a fluid enters the tubes, and being impelled into their minutest ramifications, necessarily expands their folds; for the nervures themselves are folded, and as they gradually extend in length with them, the moist membranes attached to them are also unfolded and extended. In proportion as this takes place the expanding membranes approach each other, and at last, being dried by the action of the atmosphere, become one. To promote this motion of the fluid seems the object of the agitations which the creature gives from time to time to its unexpanded wings."

Readers are invited to bear this expert account of the construction of a butterfly's wing in mind, because experts on colour may possibly find that it has a bearing on the colours and markings of the wings.

That brings us to the end of the extraordinary tale of the general construction of a butterfly, from the moment of its conception inside its mother to the moment when it is about to soar on its own wings for its brief life as a winged insect of two or three days to a maximum of nearly a year. Problems with regard to the *senses* of butterflies—sight, hearing, scent, feeling—will be considered in a separate chapter.

But what of the infinite variety of colour in the wings of the British species, not to mention the more gorgeous and startling colours of the multitudinous species of foreign butterflies? Whence are these colours derived? What is the nature of colour? There can be few in these days who are not aware that colour is not a *substance*; that, in fact, it has no material existence at all. Colour is a sensation—it might almost be said an illusion—and is produced by the *filtering* of direct and reflected rays of light between the object observed and the observing eye. Butterflies' wings would record no colour in darkness of a degree just sufficient to allow its form to be discerned because there are no light rays for them to absorb and reflect. A pure red object observed through a piece of pure green glass appears to be perfectly black because the red object only reflects the kind of light which gives us the sensation we call 'red.' And pure green glass cannot pass that sort of light, stopping it as a filter would stop sand.

Readers will not want a long dissertation on the phenomena of light and colour, but it is relevant to remind ourselves of the great variety of matter which must go into the construction of a butterfly's wing in order to give the sensation of infinite variety of colour and shading in the appearance it presents to our eyes. Each species of butterfly has its own specialised chemical and physical factory in its frail body—whether in the creeping or flying state. On this question of colouring, the constant association of a purple sheen, and of heavy 'dusting,' or 'powdering,' on the upper membranes, with brown lower membranes; and of the fading of purple to brown when the 'powder' is removed, will be shown when we come to the life-histories of the Purple Emperor, Purple Hairstreak, Holly Blue, Long-tailed Blue, Mazarine Blue, and Camberwell Beauty, in Part II.

The transformations through which a butterfly passes in its career from the egg to the perfect imago are wonderful indeed; but to the author's way of thinking the most arresting aspect of the whole phenomenon is the preservation of the creature's *identity*. The gulf that separates the creeping reptile in appearance and mode of life from the aerial creature on painted wings is as wide as the imagination can compass. And yet both are manifestations of the same *entity*. Indeed, had not experience revealed this miracle of transformation to man, neither his speculation nor his finite reason could have conceived such a possibility. Is it not reasonable to believe analogously that there are other and greater miracles of transformation, outside our experience, which are undreamed of by philosophy unaided by revelation. We know that in all its states the butterfly is without understanding or self-consciousness, and therefore without regret for, or remembrance of, the past, and without hope or anticipation for the future. It lives its little life and is gone as a tale that is told, unless the survival of its identical self in one of its numerous offspring is to be regarded as immortality. But what if, in imagination, we endow this creature in all its stages with personality or soul, that is to say with understanding, hope, memory, and affections of the same kind as those with which we ourselves are endowed? It was reflections of this nature which inspired the writer of the lines with which this chapter opened, as it was inspiration of a higher order that gave us the consolation and certain hope of 1 Corinthians xv.

Chapter V

BUTTERFLY SENSES

UP to now the life story of the butterfly has been comparatively straightforward and simple in the sense that its various transformations from the egg to the perfect imago have become commonplaces to expert observers. Furthermore, the anatomical marvels, and extraordinary changes, in the three stages of the creature's development are sufficiently distinct under the expert anatomist's powerful lens to enable the function of each piece of machinery to be accurately assessed, and actually *observed* in its operation. What has so far been described is the method of construction of a small and delicate natural flying machine. Most reflecting folk will agree that its infinite delicacy and complication are not made any the less miraculous by man's ability to observe and record the main details of it. He can make rough diagrams of the design and working parts, but the complete 'blue-print' is not in his hands, neither could he read such a blue-print perfectly if it were. The utmost limit of his microscopically-aided vision does no more than bring him to the threshold of further anatomical and mechanical mysteries which may, for all he knows, contain 'senses' undreamed of in his philosophy.

The pulsating life of the insect; the intangible and invisible spirit which drives it, much as physical motor spirit drives the flying machines of man, is manifestly and admittedly an Essence beyond our comprehension or analysis—and explicable only by assuming a Source of Life which must Itself *be* Life. Reason, reinforced by decisive experiments by Pasteur and others, assures us that life cannot emanate from non-life. Indeed, this significant truism is admitted by all but a few materialistic philosophers, a notable exception being the late Sir J. Arthur Thomson, F.R.S., who in his book *Evolution*, which ran into ten or more editions, suggested to his thousands of medical and biological students that "although the doctrine of the origin of the living from the non-living cannot be held at present with a clear or easy mind, yet we must admit that as a hypothesis it is in harmony with the general trend of evolutionary theory."

So far, therefore, we have got a perfectly efficient pulsating machine. But what of the pilot of it? Who or what directs its activities in the maintenance of its existence and subsequent reproduction? Is the 'pilot' in the driving-seat of the machine an automatic pilot or a sentient one? That is the next question to be investigated, because man-made flying machines, as the war has so vividly demonstrated, can be operated by either.

Here we are passing from the realm of miracle to that of mystery—the mystery surrounding what we call *sense*. Has a butterfly got senses such as our own? Can it see, taste, smell, hear and feel, as man does? Is it by such senses, modified to its requirements, that a butterfly steers itself through its brief existence? In other words, do the 'senses' of butterflies differ in degree only, or in kind, from those of Man? Are they automatic senses, or are they senses which act, as in Man, as a summons to take thoughtful and calculated action? As a preliminary to the inquiry it may be well to give some short account of what little is known of what are assumed to be the sense-organs of a butterfly.

The creature, in addition to its four wings, is divided into three main and distinct parts. The *head*, containing the great compound eyes; the coiled proboscis, not unlike that of what some believe to be its cousin, the elephant; and the long antennae. The *thorax*, bearing the legs and wings; and the *abdomen* or body, containing the digestive and other organs. For the purposes of this study of butterfly *senses* we will consider, mainly, the anatomy of the head, because it is in this part of the creature that the 'senses' are generally assumed to be located.

The head, unlike that of the caterpillar, has no jaws: instead it has this proboscis or sucking-organ which, when not in use, lies coiled up like the hair-spring of a watch. On either side of the proboscis are two small jointed projections, called palpi, which *seem* to form a kind of case for the proboscis but which *undoubtedly*, according to Eltringham, and many other biologians, have other and more important functions, ***but the nature of which is unknown***.

The two great compound eyes are formed of thousands of lenses and their attendant nervous mechanisms. These eyes are fixed and immovable. They cannot therefore be turned towards an object, nor can they be opened or closed. It follows, therefore, that only the movement of the whole insect can alter the position of the eye in relation to its surroundings. This limitation should be borne in mind for future consideration. Conveying air to these multitudinous lenses there are said to be at least forty thousand air-tubes in the eye of the Tortoiseshell butterfly. If these have, in fact, been counted, the tribute due to the power of modern lenses, and to the patience and observant skill of anatomists, falls short only of what is due to the knowledge and wisdom which went to the design and creation of such an instrument.

From the general optical construction of these strange organs, quite different from that of the human eye, Eltringham and other authorities *assume* that, whereas the caterpillar can do little more than distinguish light from darkness (an admitted assumption in itself), "the butterfly can see, and *perhaps* appreciate, the flowers, its mate, and the other attractions of its little world."

In a few butterflies, and many moths, there are also said to be *simple* 'eyes' on the top of the head, but as they are usually covered by the adjoining scales Eltringham guesses that "they can be of *little* use and are *probably* vestiges of some former condition, though they *may* still help the insect to the extent of distinguishing between light and shadow."

Can a butterfly distinguish and differentiate between variously coloured flowers? Many ingenious tests have been made to resolve this interesting question, even to the point of fitting an insect with the equivalent of red spectacles. This was done by painting a transparent red dye on to the surface of a butterfly's eye. The butterfly was then liberated, and *seemed* to be unaffected as it was still able to alight on flowers. From which it was deduced that at all events it was *not* red-blind. A similarly fitted Large Cabbage butterfly, on the other hand, was said to fly about 'aimlessly,' and to be 'confused,' the deduction being that this species *is* red-blind. To most lay observers the flight of butterflies generally appears aimless, and they would hesitate to describe a butterfly as 'confused.' But however this may be, some experts still regard butterflies as colour-blind, while others believe the reverse. The truth is that nobody *knows*. All we do know is that its eyes are *fixed*, so that they cannot turn about selectively, so to speak. Their arc of vision is not known.

It is hoped that readers will excuse the generally irritating use of italics, but they are employed here for the sake of brevity and in order to demonstrate, without lengthy argument and circumlocution, that the greatest experts in the world are only guessing when they come to consider the nature of the simplest and apparently most evident sense possessed by a butterfly—sight.

The *proboscis*, the instrument through which the creature feeds, is assumed to be the organ in which is located the sense of taste, though some place this sense in the antennae. Writing on this matter in *Butterfly Lore*, Eltringham says: "As to the sense of taste, we may *at least assume* that even butterflies can distinguish different kinds of food. Even in ourselves taste is a very limited sense. It is supplemented in many ways by the sense of smell, and all the delicate shades of difference which we call flavours are really distinguished by smell. At the end of the butterfly's long coiled proboscis are tiny projections or papillae, and these are *considered* to be organs of taste. Minnich has, however, shown that some butterflies *appear* to have taste-organs in their feet."

Here, again, it will be admitted that the most painstaking, anatomical analysis has produced no *knowledge* of such an inorganic thing as taste. Strange and minute machinery has been observed, but its purpose remains guesswork, with different guesses by different biological experts. Some of these place this sense-organ in the proboscis, some in the antennae, and some in the feet. The intelligent layman is left to choose between the experts.

In this connection a reference will not be out of place to the mystery of how a female butterfly unerringly selects its appropriate food-plant for the deposition of her eggs—or the sowing of her seed! It cannot be by taste or scent, or even sight, because in innumerable cases these senses could not be operative in a butterfly flying at some distance from a rare food-plant. Its eyes are fixed, and cannot therefore 'look around.' Scent will not travel to windward if, as Eltringham says, scent consists of particles. Newman, it will be remembered, spoke of the marvellous 'intuition' of female butterflies which enables them to discover the truth without reasoning. But this is only another name for 'instinct,' and gets us no further. Furthermore, this 'intuition' or 'instinct' is only cited as the means by which the butterfly differentiates between the different kinds of plants in the immediate vicinity of the appropriate food-plant. It does not account for the discovery of the existence at any given spot of the necessary food-plant. This latter mystery, in the author's view, is to be accounted for by the creature's authenticated 'sense of direction,' and its inveterate habit of clinging to, or making for, its own place of origin, or nativity—that identical food-plant. That some other sense works in conjunction with this 'homing' sense is possible, but this return to the spot on which the butterfly itself was born seems to be the more generalised aspect of the phenomenon. Much more has yet to be said on this 'homing' sense and 'urge' which, if they exist, provide the solution of many, if not most, butterfly phenomena.

So much, in a few words, for the senses of sight and taste as they are assumed to exist in a butterfly. Let us now turn to the third strange feature of the head—the antennae, which are assumed to hold "the great complex sense organs of the insect." "These," writes Eltringham, "are *certainly* the seat of its often acute sense of smell, *possibly* also of hearing, in some cases, and there is *little doubt* that they govern its sense of equilibrium, since *many* butterflies, when deprived of them, are unable to control their direction of flight." In passing it must be said that to most observers the direction of flight of most butterflies, with their antennae intact, seems to change every moment, and that it must therefore be difficult to determine the cause of flight vagaries, with or without antennae. In any case, the sense of equilibrium is not always upset, and Kirby and Spence record that butterflies have been known to fly when deprived not only of their antennae but of their heads! Furthermore, the anatomy of the antennae of different species of butterfly and moth differ, a fact which must render a correct interpretation of the various parts impossible beyond guesswork.

With regard to the sense of hearing, it is admitted that "evidence that butterflies and moths have a sense of hearing is extremely difficult to obtain. That an insect 'takes no notice' of sound is no evidence that it is deaf." In the case of *moths* an organ is described, not in the *antennae* but in the *thorax*, which it is suggested *may* be a *sort* of ear, though to the author, from the description and drawing of it, it sounds and looks more like nothing on earth. But however this may be, this particular moth-organ is not found in butterflies, and it is therefore assumed that the butterfly's 'ears' are located in the antennae, which are thus most accommodating fitments.

But it is the sense of smell upon which the greatest emphasis is laid because it is assumed that upon this sense depends the ability of the male to locate its female mate, thus assuring the survival of the species. Fabre totally disbelieved that scent had anything to do with mating, or that the scent of the female could be perceived at great distances. "As well might one expect to tint a lake with a drop of carmine as suppose the scent of the female to affect the atmosphere to such great distances." In this connection, Fabre's remarkable experiment with a female Great Peacock moth is of interest. On emerging from its cocoon, it was placed indoors in a wire cage, and on successive nights scores of males visited the room. When he put the female into an hermetically sealed vessel, no males arrived. He repeated his experiments with other species, even including the introduction of pungent smells, but with the same results. When, however, he moved the female in the wire cage to a new spot in the room, the males continued to visit the vacated spot where the cage had stood, but they totally disregarded the female moth herself. Here, indeed, is a mysterious example of the compelling attraction for a winged creature of some spot in space connected in some way with reproduction; a matter to which further reference has yet to be made. This experiment did not shake Fabre's conviction that scent, *as we understand the term*, plays no part in mating, on the ground, among others, that "scent" cannot travel to windward, and in this particular experiment a strong wind was blowing: he seems to admit, however, that a moth or a butterfly has some other form of attraction for the opposite sex of its species which is a substitute for what we mean by "scent," but which is beyond man's power of analysis, as is the proved exact "sense of direction" in all winged creatures.

The argument of the opposing school is, briefly, this: "*Given* that the moth does produce *particles* capable of being carried by the air, and of affecting certain sense-organs which happen to lie in their *path*, our remaining difficulty would seem to be that of supposing these *particles* to be sufficiently numerous to taint so large a bulk of air as may lie between the moth and its mate.

"But is the difficulty so great after all? Our own senses are susceptible to the odour of musk. An extremely small quantity of this substance will scent a room for long periods of time, without suffering any appreciable loss in *weight*. If so small a quantity of *material* can make the presence of its *particles* felt in the circulating air of a room for months and years, there seems no great difficulty in supposing that the moth's sense, *probably infinitely* more volatile, can, for a short time, fill the air for hundreds of yards, or even for miles, AROUND. The error seems to lie in the idea that because we cannot perceive the scent it must of necessity be very weak, whereas it *may* be, and *undoubtedly* is, extremely strong. What strength of colour has a scarlet begonia to a person who is red-blind?"

Readers' attention is drawn to the words italicised in this quotation from *Butterfly Lore*. First they will note the progression from admitted assumption to dogmatic and almost triumphant assertion; a characteristic weakness of many learned biologians on imponderable matters. But what is even more important is the assertion that scent consists of airborne *particles* and *material*, and that it has *weight*. If scent is in fact material, and consists of particles, it is subject to the laws that govern other airborne material, and cannot therefore travel to windward. How then can scent, as so defined, travel for miles *around*?

More will be said in due course of the scent discharged by butterflies, but for the argument of this chapter the foregoing will suffice.

Much more might be written on the 'senses' of butterflies as expounded by the majority of modern life-scientists; but to avoid repetition of details about the varying organs of various species, only the salient features of the arguments employed by the modern school of entomologists have been considered. Eltringham's thesis on 'senses' concludes with this sentence: "Our butterflies have their senses similar to our own. Hearing is probably present in most moths; taste, touch, sight and smell, especially smell, are well developed." This conclusion is a necessary one to those who have become convinced that all creatures, including Man, spring from a common original stock.

Illuminating facts on the sense of feeling of insects are given by Kirby and Spence in Letter XXXVII of *Introduction to Entomology*, which seem to be at variance with the theory that the antennae are the main seat of the senses, or that butterflies have a brain, as have animals, through which sensations are conveyed. Animals if they are beheaded become paralytic, thereby proving that the organ by which they feel is the brain. In the case of butterflies and other insects, if the head be cut off the remainder of the body will continue to give proof of life and sensation longer than the head: both portions will live after the separation for a considerable period; but the largest will survive the longest, and will *move*, *walk* and even *fly*, at first almost as actively without the head as with it. A caterpillar has been known to walk for some days after being beheaded; and, when *touched*, the headless creature made the same movements as when entire. A honey-bee will eat greedily though deprived of its abdomen. The head of a wasp will attempt to bite after it is separated from the rest of its body, and the abdomen under similar circumstances, if the finger be moved to it, will attempt to sting. The headless trunk of a male mantis has been known to unite itself to the other sex. All insects, *including butterflies*, show these and other extraordinary physical powers of functioning in spite of what, in man or mammals, would mean instant death or paralysis. Fabre discovered that butterflies do not appear to notice the removal of their antennae. Eltringham confirms this when he writes: "A butterfly's antennae may be snipped off without its betraying, even by a movement, any consciousness of the injury."

From the earliest times of microscopical observation of butterflies their antennae have been a matter of keen speculation; but it is noticeable that the conclusions on this question, as on most others, of the older school of entomologists are in sharp conflict with those of the more modern school. Thus Newman, writing on the antennae, says: "It is almost useless to say anything about the use or objects of the antennae, after all that has been written; but it is the fault of all scientific men who have written on the subject to assume that they must be the seat of one of those senses the use of which we seem to understand so well in ourselves. Now, it is most illogical to assume that the antennae serve for purposes of sight, taste, smell, hearing or touch, because we possess these senses seated in certain organs in our own bodies. We cannot refer the wings of insects to any organs we ourselves possess, and we only learn their use by seeing them employed. Why may not the antennae be the site of some other function not performed by any of our own organs. Why seek to invest them with the powers of our own eyes or ears? The subject may well be left as one above our comprehension."

Edward Newman, F.L.S., F.Z.S., was as great an authority in his day as was the late H. Eltringham, F.R.E.S., F.Z.S., in his.

Well, there are two opinions of admitted authorities on this matter of butterfly senses. The former, not knowing, frankly acknowledged his agnosticism on this vitally important matter from the philosophical and scientific standpoints. The latter, equally not knowing, is gnostic.

Volumes have been written, and no doubt will yet be written, on this mystery of insect sense, and we may be sure that the contrariety of view will be sustained among biological and entomological specialists.

The author has already disclaimed any pretence of being a scientist, or expert, or a specialist on any matter under heaven, unless it be in the handling of a submarine with all its unusual and ingenious equipment for performing functions conceived only three years before he joined his first one. But lay readers will, it is believed, agree that a layman equipped with all the relevant facts of any problem is quite as capable of forming sound, and sometimes sounder, conclusions on facts as is a specialist who tackles his subject from a special angle. If this were not so, few men would accept the awful responsibility of a judge who may have to sentence a man to death on circumstantial evidence derived, perhaps, from medical or anatomical technicalities of which he had no self-acquired knowledge of his own. Not only so, but a judge's decision is seldom, if ever, questioned on such a ground.

Such considerations, therefore, seem to justify an examination of this 'sense' problem by a totally different form of approach to that adopted by specialised entomologists. In reaching and setting out his own judgment in a manner unorthodox in natural history study, the author hopes he may be able to steer a straight course between the Scylla of dullness and the Charybdis of fantasy.

It has already been said that the finished butterfly is a natural flying machine, the building of which has been briefly recorded. Just how like an aeroplane it can be is shown in the drawing on page 29 by Mr. Russwurm of a specimen of a moth in his collection.

Let us now start with this little flying machine grounded outside its recent tomb, with its wings finally expanded and dry, fuelled up with the motive spirit of Life, and ready for the first 'take-off.' The question we have to examine is this: is this tiny machine a robot, without consciousness of its own existence, or is it a machine with a sentient pilot aboard who will direct its comings and goings, and operations generally? In other words, is a butterfly self-conscious and capable of making for itself the vital decisions upon which depend its life as surely as do the decisions of a bomber pilot?

Let us first consider the operating of a piloted *aeroplane*. We know that every motion of the 'plane, the fulfilment of every purpose for which it was constructed, is under the direction of the reasoning and therefore objective mind of the pilot. Calculation of distance run, height, course, fuel remaining, and many other factors, and the handling of emergencies, are dependent upon thought, the train of which is set in motion mainly by the physical 'sense' of sight. Certainly the pilot must be extremely conscious of his own existence as he dives upon a hotly defended target. He must also have a lively knowledge of the possibility of non-existence as a mortal being.

These reflections are, of course, platitudes, but they are emphasised in order to contrast the motions of a robot machine with a piloted one as the former would strike the mind of a man or woman who had never flown in an aeroplane, or who knew nothing about aero-mechanics and dynamics and the possibilities of internal automatic, or externally applied, control. Few, it is thought, would doubt that such an observer would assume, to the point of dogmatism, that there was a mind *aboard* the robot, or an evil spirit, since aeroplanes unhappily have become associated with destruction rather than with creation.

But what of the anatomy and behaviour of a pilotless robot? The first point to remember is that such a machine could, if necessary, be designed so as to be indistinguishable externally from a piloted one.

The next point is that the robot would be found, on anatomical investigation, to contain strange organs that would be entirely redundant in a piloted machine. These delicate and complicated 'organs' would be unintelligible to an aeronautical novice, but an aeronautical engineer would soon discover that each one actually performed a function that a pilot *would* perform with his mind-controlled hand without the aid of these novel mechanical organs. They are in the robot to take the place of thought, and action based on thought.

And what can they achieve? In an aeroplane they can, or if Man's purpose so required could, be made to cause an aeroplane to steer a steady course or a variable one. If necessary it could be made to 'home.' They can, or could, maintain a steady height, or a variable one. They could make the robot drop a bomb or a mail-bag, or even seed a prairie, at will according to the 'species,' so to speak, of the robot. They can, or could ring bells, whistle, or play a tune at a selected position on the 'run.' They can, or could, zigzag or turn circles over Dover, and then steer straight on to London, circle the metropolis and return home. There are few things that they cannot, could not, or will not be made to do if Man with his great but finite, and too often diabolical, ingenuity so wills. A robot may yet be made to re-fuel itself—that is to say to feed.

So much for the internal automatic machinery. But what of external forces which even human pilots absolutely require if they are to navigate, find their way, or 'home' without visible leading-marks in a moving atmosphere—that is to say in a wind—a matter on which more has yet to be said in connection with butterfly 'migration and 'instinct.'

There is no need to go in detail into the ramifications and marvels of 'wireless,' radiolocation, and all the capabilities of electro-magnetic discoveries—actual and potential. All that need here be said on this matter is that robot flying machines can be made sensitive to invisible external agencies: furthermore, even in a machine with a human mind aboard, external agencies do, and must always do, for the pilot what he could not and never will be able to do for himself by the sole exercise of his air-borne mind. This will readily be confirmed by expert pilots.

So far the author thinks that his readers will concede that he has steered clear of fantasy, but he must now run the risk of being tedious by enumerating a few specimens of internal automatic devices, or external and invisible forces, that give mere mechanism the appearance of self-consciousness and deliberate action.

Hydrostatic valves, sensitive to a change in water pressure imperceptible to human beings, enable a torpedo to maintain exactly a fore-ordained depth. The torpedo 'feels.' Minute changes in temperature can be made to perform automatically a variety of functions, again by 'feeling.' Delicate electrical contrivances in early petrol-driven submarines lit a red light and rang a bell when vaporised petrol volume reached a tiny percentage of the air content of the compartment. The senses of 'tasting' and 'smelling.' The shadow of the hull of a ship can be utilised to operate the pistol of a torpedo—susceptibility to the 'feel' of interrupted light rays. Sonic vibrations can set mechanism in motion which will explode a mine or, if desired, perform a useful function—mechanical 'hearing.'

Sound vibrations can even make a little robot dog walk out of its kennel if the voice is correctly modulated or 'tuned'—a selective 'hearing' sense. High-frequency supersonic waves can cause to be automatically recorded by echo the five-mile depth of the Pacific Ocean to an accuracy of a few feet. An aeroplane can be exactly located 100 miles away. A combined sense of 'touch' and 'hearing.' Anyone who has used and examined the anatomy of a gyroscopic compass, and its 'repeaters,' will not only marvel at its capacity to replace the magnetism of the Pole, but will be almost aghast at the ingenuity and complication of its internal 'organs.' Heavy modern self-adjusting machinery, a linotype machine for example, gives the full impression of being itself sentient. The 'sense' of reflection.

On the natural external forces that Man can equip his machines to 'sense' there is no need to enlarge. Even though we have grown accustomed to some of them they still almost overawe us.[1] We are, by common consent, entering into what is called colloquially a robot age, in which, to an ever-increasing degree, machinery and contrivance perform functions which, since the earth was re-formed,[2] have heretofore had to be performed by man present in the flesh, where, that is to say, he could perform them at all.

We are now beginning, it is thought, to get down to bedrock on this matter of butterfly 'senses.' But before drawing conclusions there are yet one or two points that deserve consideration. Every one of these internal automatic devices and externally applied forces, which Man has contrived and employs in a thousand ways, can be made to give rise to a train of automatic *reactions*, sometimes trivial, sometimes far-reaching, complicated and various, through systems of what are called 'relays.' In other words, robot machinery is made highly sensitive, and it is fair to say that it is endowed with mechanical 'senses' which enable it to perform perfectly reasonable functions of which, in itself, it is incapable. Such 'senses' are purely physical. But what of Man's senses? Some, as doctors and physiologists emphasise, and laymen understand, are quite automatic and non-volitional, and for their functioning special organic agencies are required. But such senses can better be described as natural and automatic reactions to external forces, and are relatively few.

When, however, we speak of seeing, hearing, smelling, tasting, feeling, we in all cases do so with our minds—when, that is to say, we are in a self-conscious state—and thus see, hear, smell, taste and feel objectively and analytically. Our physical eyes no more see than do spectacles or a microscope. We can see accurately with our mind's eye a loved one in Australia;

[1] In this connection Job xxxviii. 35 is startling: "Canst thou send lightnings that they may go, and say unto thee, Here we are?" Unlike Job, Man to-day might be tempted to answer this Divine question with "I can," but he would be well advised to speak humbly, and with many qualifications!

[2] The word "re-formed" is used advisedly to draw attention to the unknown and perhaps vast gap in time that separates verses 1 and 2 of Genesis 1. Catastrophe clearly intervened between the two events.

we can hear accurately and poignantly a voice that is still; we can actually smell a last year's chrysanthemum; we can taste all too well the fruits and delicacies of which the war has deprived us; we can feel some acute pain now happily past. In other words, we *remember*, we *foresee*, we *know*—I think, therefore I am.

But at the risk of being tedious there is one other important point which must be stressed if the argument is to be complete. Our own organs, though fearfully and wonderfully made, are relatively simple when compared to those of butterflies in their four stages, as the lens has so dramatically revealed. These human organs control *automatically* those reactions needed, for the most part, for the preservation of life. But the senses which we consciously employ, those in fact which are reasonable, become operative through the agency of *relatively* simple machinery directed by the indwelling will and intellect.

This characteristic is repeated in the larger species of man-made machinery. Where his directing mind is aboard, as on a railway engine, in a bomber, at the handle of a steam-hammer or saw, the organic design of the machine can be relatively simple, indeed the simpler the better. When, however, we come to robot machinery, with the will and intellect external, and often far removed, operation of the machine by reactions and relays requires, and is given, incomparably more delicate, complicated and numerous organs than those necessary when the mind and will are on or in the machine.

Enough, and perhaps more than enough, has now been said to formulate a sound conclusion on the 'senses' of butterflies and other winged creatures.

The butterfly, in its ordinary *routine*, is a living machine actuated by purely physical sense-organs over which it can exercise no control, and of which it has no consciousness. These organs do automatically for the butterfly what man's mind does for him when it reacts to the sensations set in motion by the senses in question. Because there must be innumerable natural forces with which Man is unacquainted, it is therefore reasonable to conjecture that butterfly organs, which ramify far beyond the point at which the human eye aided by powerful lenses can penetrate, are sensitive to external forces, or to internal chemical reactions of which we are and must remain ignorant.

In short, in every sphere in which a butterfly adopts and pursues its normal habits from the moment it is born to its final act of reproduction, it is an automaton. But there are still certain actions, of which 'migration' and navigation provide examples, where seemingly there must be some glimmer of a mind to make decisions which cannot apparently be explained by automatic reactions to external or internal forces. This matter must be reserved for future consideration in the chapters dealing with aerial parasitism, 'migration,' and 'instinct.'

Chapter VI

MIMICRY

Of all the curiosities of nature, none is more remarkable and generally observed than is 'mimicry.' The close resemblances, under certain circumstances, of the colour and markings of some creatures to those of their immediate environment, and of members of another species, is to be found in animals and fish, and to some extent in birds.

One of the best-known examples of 'mimicry' is the variation in the colourings and markings of cuckoo eggs, which tend to match those of the many different small birds in whose nests the intruding egg is deposited. This extraordinary phenomenon, even more pronounced in Asiatic species than in English, has been considered in *The Cuckoo and other Bird Mysteries*, and will therefore not be considered here. But among all orders of living creatures none tend to harmonise more closely with their surroundings, sometimes to the point of being indistinguishable from them, than do butterflies in all three stages of their metamorphosis.

Volumes have been written on the facts of mimicry, as well as on the theories claimed as interpretations of the facts. It is not therefore easy within a small compass to sift the wheat from the chaff or, indeed, to deal concisely with the wheat when so sifted. The matter, however, is of such interest and importance, philosophically as well as scientifically, that the author will try to illuminate the phenomenon, and offer a solution of it, in a single chapter.

The theory of visible mimicry as a means of protection against innumerable enemies in the fight for survival pervades the whole problem, and in modern treatises may be said to govern it. Hand in glove, so to speak, with visible 'mimicry' is the theory of scent and taste mimicry as alternative protective devices of nature. These two forms of alleged *invisible* mimicry as natural protective devices are linked up with the antithesis of *visible* mimicry —violent contrast—which is so evident a stumbling-block in the otherwise plausible doctrine of the survival value of close visible resemblance.

First let us consider some of the well-known facts of close visible resemblance between a butterfly, in its three states, and its environment.

Even casual observers of our most lovely and brightly coloured butterflies—Red Admirals, Peacocks, Tortoiseshells, and many others—have noticed the striking difference of the undersides of the wings which, when closed and thus exposed to view, so far from contrasting with the surrounding foliage, as do the upper sides, almost exactly correspond to it. We may see a brilliantly painted butterfly alight among leaves and a moment later fail to locate it, though our eyes are searching within a few inches of where it is now perched, with closed wings, on a leaf.

The same is true of most caterpillars as they crawl or lie along the leaves which constitute their food, and which they devour on so prodigious a scale.

So with many of the chrysalids which hang suspended by their silken bands from a leaf, a twig, or the bark of a tree. Many striking examples of this close 'mimicry' in all three states are recorded in Part II of this book.

Here, in the case of caterpillars and chrysalids, is a phenomenon which undoubtedly protects them in these two states from the prying eyes of Man, thereby depriving collectors of many opportunities of making a perfect collection of perfect specimens reared to the finished butterfly state in captivity. Little wonder that the view has generally prevailed that this extraordinary natural visible mimicry is a form of calculated protection for weak creatures against their innumerable enemies.

But unfortunately for the theory of *objective* protective visible mimicry we are faced with many startling exceptions in which the creature, so far from being coloured and marked 'protectively,' is in violent contrast to its environment at the period during which it is supposed to be in the most urgent need of protection. A striking counterpart of these startling exceptions to a fairly general rule is to be found in the case of cuckoo-egg mimicry, to which an allusion has been made. Cuckoos' eggs laid in hedge-sparrows' nests with bright blue eggs are almost always, if not quite always, of strong contrast. And yet, as the greatest authorities on that strange bird admit, there is no more reliable 'fosterer' than the hedge-sparrow. In other words, the complete lack of mimicry by the intruded egg has no ill effect on the survival of hedge-sparrow cuckoos.

The same is true of butterflies in their three stages which contrast instead of coalescing with their environment.

To meet this obvious objection to the theory of colour-mimicry as a source of objective protection, the hypothesis is propounded that in cases of contrast the creature has acquired, or adopted, the taste or smell of another species which is objectionable to that particular creature's enemies. Thus it is argued that butterflies in their three stages may adopt one of two devices: they may resemble objects in which their pursuers take no interest, in which case the resemblance tends to concealment; or alternatively they may resemble insects of other species which their enemies have learnt by experience to leave alone. Here there is no attempt at concealment. On the contrary, the bolder the advertisement of its presence the more likely, it is argued, is it to deceive, and the more effective therefore its protective power.

The whole hypothesis of mimicry by concealment or by deception is well summed up by Eltringham: "The casual observer," he writes in *Butterfly Lore*, "is familiar with very few caterpillars because many are so perfectly hidden that even for an expert collector they are difficult to find. Some are literally hidden, in that they conceal themselves by day, and come out to feed only at night. Others are concealed very effectively though fully exposed to view, and I have endeavoured to show to interested friends caterpillars which they could not see though they were near enough to be touched. Others again are very conspicuous. Often they are brightly coloured and lie fully exposed in strong daylight, as if bent on advertising their presence to all who may pass that way." So much for facts. Now for hypotheses in reply to the question: "Why should the creatures be so seemingly careless of their life and risk destruction when they might so easily hide?" Why indeed, the layman will ask. Let Eltringham tell us in his own words. "We owe the original *explanation* of this phenomenon," he writes, "to the late Alfred Russell Walace, to whom Darwin referred the question. His *suggestion* was that such conspicuous creatures were *probably* nauseous to their enemies. If this were so it would be a great advantage to advertise themselves as much as possible so that birds and other creatures would the more quickly learn to recognise them as unpalatable. This is known as *the Theory of Warning Colours*."

But in order to show the lengths to which Man will go in concocting hypotheses agreeable to a fixed idea, and at the risk of being tedious, a reference must be made to what are called the Batesian and Mullerian theories of mimicry. Bates, apparently, was the first to call attention to the wonderful resemblance between butterflies of *different families*, and at the same time to suggest an explanation. He noticed that the *Heliconius* butterflies of South America were accompanied by others of totally different families, and even by many kinds of moths, all of which, while departing widely from their usual family patterns, had adopted the very different and striking livery of the *Heliconius*. His explanation was that the latter, which were numerous, careless of pursuit, and apparently but little attacked, possessed some property such as distastefulness which accounted for their comparative safety, and that the others benefited from the evil reputation of their *models*. In this way was established the hypothesis since known as the Batesian Mimicry, the supposed conditions of which were that a distasteful species, very numerous by reason of its protection, was accompanied by numbers of other and widely different species, which, though in reality perfectly edible, escaped destruction owing to their outward resemblance to their unpleasant models. "Soon, however," according to Eltringham, "a new difficulty arose. It was observed that different species of distasteful butterflies mimicked each other, and of this phenomenon no explanation was afforded."

To meet this new difficulty Muller obligingly stepped in. He pointed out that "if there were two kinds of butterflies, both distasteful and of quite different patterns, *we might suppose* that a certain number of each would be sacrificed to the experimental tasting of inexperienced enemies. *Suppose further* that each species lost 100 individuals in this way, 200 individuals would be destroyed. If, however, the two species were so similar in appearance as to be mistaken for one another, 100 casualties would still suffice for the enemies' *education*, and hence each species would lose only fifty individuals. It would thus be a great advantage that the two species should resemble each other, since their losses would be halved."

Eltringham, to do him justice, admits that there are difficulties in both these theories of invisible mimicry advertised by 'warning colours.' By the Batesian hypothesis, an edible form mimics a distasteful one, whereas in the Mullerian, two distasteful forms mimic one another! He points out that both theories overlook the fact that there are probably degrees of distastefulness! He says that from many experiments, notably those recently published by Swynnerton, we know that there is probably no such thing as absolute distastefulness. As though exhausted with these accommodating hypotheses on mimicry, all of which develop flaws requiring a new hypothesis, Eltringham concludes with the sensible if unscientific conclusion that the destruction of any species of butterfly by birds depends simply upon *the state of their appetites*. But even here there is a flaw, because it has been established by endless observation, including careful stomach-dissection, that birds are very rarely butterfly eaters.

He might have added that, in their finished flying state, butterflies can seldom be the victims of other insects as they are in their caterpillar stage. In other words, butterflies have few if any *living* enemies with which to contend, except possibly when hibernating in sheds, when mice are said to eat them. The perfect mimicry of the undersides of the wings is therefore not needed for protection, and some other reason for the mimicry must be sought.

There, at some length, but as shortly as possible, is the whole hypothesis of 'protective mimicry,' whether by visible likeness, by 'warning colour,' or by smell and taste. Mimicry, in short, whether for deception or concealment, is alleged to be a necessity of survival, and is treated as *objective*.

Now there are many objections to this theory, but we will content ourselves with a reference to three. First and foremost is the question as to the source from which this objective or planned mimicry is derived. All but a very few biologians agree that it cannot emanate from the insect itself, because even if it were endowed with an intellect it would, in the first instance, have needed a prophetic sense exceeding in prevision that of the prophet Isaiah. If mimicry is claimed to be the outcome of natural selection, this *process* of selection—if it is to be regarded as a process—must be capable of thought and prevision, very particularly in the case of scent or taste mimicry as expounded by Bates and Muller. But a process cannot think or select. Hence such ever-recurring expressions as "Nature has made provision"; "Nature in her wisdom ordains"; "Nature is not at a loss." But such expressions, if words still have precise meaning, attribute to Nature a mind, and thus a personality—making Nature a Planner rather than a Plan, and thus worthy of temples or shrines in her honour in the modern world as there were in the pagan, where God was nicknamed Pan and represented as a satyr. In short, current mimicry theories require a Selector.

But leaving out of account the very obvious philosophical difficulties, what of the physical ones?

If the creature, even *subjectively*, needs protection in the case of colour mimicry by *concealment* from view, and, in the case of colour contrast by deception, its potential enemies, excluding Man, must be endowed with senses of sight, scent and taste which differ only in degree and not in kind from human senses. This question has been considered in some detail in the last chapter, and will not therefore be reopened. But the fatal objection to the whole theory of mimicry as a means of protection, and the one that makes all other objections superfluous, *is its lamentable failure to protect*. How complete is this failure of mimicry, whether as a caterpillar or pupa, to do what is claimed for it is emphasised by Eltringham himself when he says: "The caterpillar and pupae are eaten in millions by birds and other insectivorous animals, whilst butterflies and moths are themselves the food of many enemies. Measured over a long series of years the average surviving offspring of two moths (or two butterflies he might have added) is no more than two; if it were more the increase would result in race suicide through starvation; if less, the species would gradually become extinct"—as in fact the Large Copper, for example, has—and for reasons totally unconnected with inadequate 'mimicry.'

The protective theory of mimicry therefore invites us to believe that this vast system of mimicry, and of the mimicry of mimicry, has been 'evolved' in order to save two of the progeny out of the 500 or even 1,000 eggs a single butterfly may lay at a single shedding, or laying.

How the balance of nature is chiefly maintained in the world of winged creatures it is hoped to show in due course. But by Eltringham's own admission, if protective mimicry did what is claimed for it the balance of nature would be upset, and butterflies in the course of years would have filled the earth to suffocation.

It is often said that destructive criticism is easy, and that criticism, unless it is constructive, is valueless where it is not positively harmful. But surely the truth is that criticism should be judged solely on the ground of correctness or otherwise. All just criticism must, in effect, be constructive because it clears any problem of *lumber*. It is better to have no theory than a demonstrably false one. But in the case of mimicry there is an alternative explanation so simple that it can hardly fail to impress those to whom simplicity is not, as is too often the case, a source of stumbling. Let all therefore who can put prejudice aside consider the following facts.

In the case of human beings, on the physical side we talk of men who live as much as possible on beefsteak as being 'beefy'; excessive beer drinkers as being 'beery'; sailors, to their disgust, as being 'breezy'; vegetarians, perhaps unjustly, as being 'weedy.' We say playfully to our children that if they eat so many sweets they will become walking sweet shops, or in the case of ices, shall we say, walking glaciers. None of these expressions is meant literally, but everyday speech indicates a perfectly natural train of thought which, in the cases quoted, is that the natural body takes on the nature, to some extent, of what it feeds on. So even with scent or smell, where a particular food or drink is indulged in to excess. If this is true of human beings with a varied diet, what should we not expect of a caterpillar which in a few days multiplies itself fifteen-fold on a particular or closely allied form of leaf? Can we not say that it is more than 'leafy'; that it is almost literally a crawling leaf? Should we not therefore expect its chemistry, and the physical manifestation of its chemistry, to resemble closely that of the leaf of which it is exclusively built? Certainly the author would. Should we not expect the caterpillar, in its 'dead' state—the chrysalis—to assume, as it so often does, the appearance of the leaf in *its* dead state?

And what of the ultimate form of the caterpillar—the butterfly? The construction of a butterfly's wing has already been described. It will be remembered that on its emergence from the chrysalis it consists of two extremely fine and separated membranes which, after expansion by the circulation of what can better be described as sap than blood, become glued together and form one wing. Any layman who has studied the composition of a leaf can hardly fail to be struck by the similarity of the construction. The well-known Indian Dead Leaf butterfly is a striking example. Some caterpillars, before pupating, separate the membranes of the leaf and, when between them, sew themselves in with their own silk.

Again, the upper and lower sides of innumerable leaves differ in colour and marking much as do those of a butterfly's wing, the lower membrane being generally duller and often variegated.

Another curiosity is the wide variation of the undersides of, for example, the Marbled White, to which an earlier reference has been made. It will be remembered that in this species, unlike most, the eggs are laid haphazard on various types of herbage, and that the food-plant, in many other species, is variable within these clearly defined limits.

Reverting to the construction of the butterfly's wing: it has not been possible to discover from any anatomical analysis from where the bases of the upper and lower membranes emanate; all that is emphasised is that they are quite distinct until they become one by being glued together. The factors, therefore, that govern the colouring of each membrane of the wing are likely to be as different and similar as those which govern the colouring of the upper and lower membranes of the leaf which is the exclusive food-plant of that particular species of butterfly.

Let us now turn to the smell—or taste, which is so closely allied—of butterflies as they strike the sense of scent or taste of human beings. Many readers may be surprised to learn that thousands of butterflies, mostly foreign ones, have been carefully smelt, and the results recorded in

Butterfly Hunting in Many Lands, by Professor J. B. Longstaff, F.R.E.S., who was assisted in his researches by Professor Dixey, F.R.S.

Muller (author of the Mullerian theory of mimicry already described), Dixey and Longstaff are at one in dividing the scents of butterflies into two categories: (1) attractive and more common in the males, and (2) repulsive or protective, common to both sexes and often stronger in the female. Dixey has called attention to what he calls the somewhat surprising fact that the scents that are *believed* to be attractive to the opposite sex are agreeable to the average human perception, whereas those that are *believed* to be repulsive, and therefore protective, are for the most part disgusting. Here we see the common practice of assuming the senses of Man and butterflies to be the same in kind when such an assumption suits a theory, though lay readers are repeatedly and rightly warned against such an assumption when a theory does not require it, or is upset by it. The method of smelling butterflies practised by Longstaff and Dixey was to take up the insect with forceps and to pinch the thorax till the wings opened, and then to bring the nose close to the upper surface. But a warning is given to beware of *faecal odours* due to pinching the butterfly, a warning that a smeller of the Purple Emperor, for example, would do well to heed in view of the food which this creature seems to eat, occasionally, as a sort of tit-bit!

Now the noteworthy fact about these records is the immense variety of scents recorded. Here are a few: coffee, cocoa, vanilla, cinnamon, ginger, and various other scents described as spicy in countries where these plants are native: verbena, honeysuckle, violet, syringa, freesia, stephanotis and many other flowers or shrubs common to those countries where the experiments were made.

Anyone interested in this matter will find in *Butterfly Hunting in Many Lands* a long series of these amusing butterfly smelling experiments and records. But the remarkable feature of these painstaking experiments and records, apart from the humour of them, is that there is not a single reference to the food-plant upon which the butterfly being smelt feeds. Only once is there a reference to the possibility that the insects obtain their characteristic smell from their characteristic food. This very natural, and indeed obvious, connection was put forward by Onslow, but is dismissed by Longstaff, though he does grudgingly admit the possibility. He prefers to think, however, that the varying scents are derived from the opposite sex of the species in question, because this hypothesis supports the theory that butterflies find their mates by their sense of smell, a theory which he is attempting to prove and one that has already been considered and shown to be impossible if the smeller is to windward of the smelt. But apart from this, there is no suggestion as to how the butterflies acquired their various scents, except that in the course of millions of years they *adopted* them for protective and reproductive purposes. Surely Onslow's conclusion that butterfly scents resemble those of their characteristic foods is one of that ordinary good sense, "which only is the gift of Heaven, and though no science, fairly worth the seven." In this connection readers are referred to the Swallow-tail in Part II, which, when pinched, smells strongly of fennel, and whose food-plant *is* fennel!

The conclusion, therefore, to which the author is inevitably drawn is that the butterfly's mimicry, in all stages of the insect, whether of colour, scent or taste, is the direct outcome of the chemistry that goes to the making of the creature's specialised and characteristic food, just as the construction of its wings is already in harmony with the construction of the leaf upon which it feeds. Furthermore, the extreme sensitivity of its wings to the rays of the sun, causing them to open like the petals of a flower and to close when the sunlight fades, still further brings them into line with the vegetable kingdom. So with their development from seeds (eggs), which in some cases 'flower' as butterflies the same year, like annuals, and in others the second year, like biennials. If butterflies are in fact the product of their food in those respects considered in this chapter, most of the mysteries of geographical variations in the same species fall harmoniously into line. How a variation of food alters the colouring and markings of butterflies, much as varying types of soil and water change the colour or shade of hydrangeas and other plants without altering their form or habit, is emphasised by Eltringham in *Butterfly Lore*. Mimicry, in short, is a *subjective* and not an *objective* phenomenon.

If in the future, skilled young botanists, without any preconceived ideas on the question of origin, would include the study of butterflies in their study of plant-life, it is confidently predicted that many butterfly *mysteries*, including mimicry and variation, will be solved, and new aids to classification will be found. But if certain 'mysteries' are soluble, the *miracle* of the butterfly, so far from being eliminated, becomes plain for all with eyes to see and minds to reflect.

Chapter VII

AERIAL PARASITES

UP to this point we have been considering what may be called the biological aspects of butterflies. Whether in the development of the finished insect in its preliminary stages, or in the problems of the sense-organs and mimicry, there is ever present the mysterious and imponderable phenomenon which we call Life, that strange Essence which the mind of Man can see in action, but which he cannot define, let alone create or even analyse. Any conclusions about the behaviour of butterflies in any department into which Life enters must inevitably, therefore, be based on circumstantial evidence. Conclusions so reached may be valid, or at least partially so, but they are always liable to be challenged by those to whom the circumstantial evidence seems incomplete, or by those with some fundamental prejudice which no circumstantial evidence, however strong, will shake. And perhaps it is best that this should be so. No argument, however cogent, is going to persuade everybody that butterflies do not, to some extent at all events, feel as we feel and think as we think. Indeed, if everyone became convinced that butterflies are automatons and semi-vegetables, many would lose all further interest in them. Indeed, every branch of natural history, especially in modern times, owes its interest for most students, amateur or professional, to the speculations about the whys and hows of the animal, bird, fish and insect worlds.

This was not always so. Solomon, whose wisdom excelled the wisdom of all the children of the East country, and all the wisdom of Egypt, "for he was wiser than all men," was, with the possible exception of Adam who named all living creatures, the greatest of naturalists. It is recorded of him in 1 Kings iv. verses 32 and 33, that he not only spoke three thousand proverbs, and that his songs were a thousand and five, but that he spake of trees, and of beasts and of fowl, and of fishes, and also of insects which include butterflies. If, as we must suppose, his natural history knowledge was as profound as his proverbs were wise, his songs lovely, and his worldly wisdom unique, we may be sure that in his natural history books, which are lost to mankind, he would have settled, once and for all, many of the questions so far considered in this book.

The words 'for many' are used advisedly, because Solomon as a God-fearing, though very erring, man studied nature as a visible manifestation of the marvellous works of a personal and designing Creator, an approach which rules out so many biological theories of these latter days.

Now in passing from the miracles and mysteries of the butterfly world which have up to this point been considered, to the phenomena connected with butterfly distribution and 'migration,' we are passing from a realm with an imponderable element in it to one of known and verifiable law which is capable of exact analysis. And yet, strangely enough, the problems we now have to consider are almost universally treated as mysterious, whereas those that involve 'instinct,' the nature of the senses, and even origins, are regarded as straightforward and capable of precise solutions and definitions. Without more ado, therefore, we will get down to the ascertainable laws, and deducible facts, which always have and always will order the mobile life of butterflies *on the wing*.

Anyone who has made a wide study of authoritative entomological books and treatises will recollect, on reflection, what little reference is made to the environment in which flying creatures in general, and butterflies in particular, spend so much of their time—the air. And yet any investigation of the life-history of flying creatures must lead to wrong conclusions if the air and its movements are left out of account, or worse still, if the effect of an invisible moving medium on creatures operating in it is misinterpreted or unknown.

In his recent book on birds, and the mysteries supposed to surround their migration and distribution, and other phenomena, the author has made a thorough investigation of the laws of air-currents as they affect the life-history of birds. The effect of air-currents on airborne creatures was demonstrated by diagrams, and the mathematical implications of what is known to physicists and mathematicians as 'the parallelogram of velocities' were expounded in detail. It is not therefore proposed in this book to repeat all that was there set forth, or to reproduce the flight diagrams. Instead, the consequences of flight within a moving medium will be set out as facts which no physicist or mathematician has disputed, or in future will dispute. If any student of butterflies, or any reader of this book whether student or not, is sufficiently interested in the question to verify the proofs of the facts here re-stated, or is disposed to challenge them, such a one is respectfully referred to *The Cuckoo and other Bird Mysteries*.

The First Law of Currents, which governs the movement of all flying creatures on the wing is this: no bird, butterfly, moth or winged insect in flight is subject to any pressure from the uniform movement of the medium by which it is supported and in which it is flying. Such airborne bodies in free flight feel only a dead calm so far as wind-pressure is concerned. They can feel neither the force nor the direction of the wind except for a momentary sensation due to change of inertia if, in the immediate region of the minute area they occupy, a sharp variation in speed or direction of the wind—a sudden gust—occurs. In the open and unobstructed spaces of the atmosphere it is doubtful if such sharp and sudden variations occur.

It may seem a hard saying, but it is not on that account any the less true, that birds and insects in flight are the only living creatures (with the exception of submerged fish) which never feel a breath of wind. So with fish in their watery environment: no fish can feel the pressure of the water-current in which, or across which, it is swimming. The only draught which birds, butterflies or bomber pilots feel when flying is that caused by their own proper flight speed through the moving atmosphere, a draught for all time and in all circumstances between their eyes, or in other words from right ahead. This is true whether the wind is a gentle breeze of 5 m.p.h. or a mighty gale of 60 m.p.h. In the case of fishes swimming in water-currents, the only sensation they feel is the water-pressure on their noses appropriate to their own swimming speed through the moving water, which, so far as sensation is concerned, is calm or stationary water.

Now if we set a four-engined bomber, a great gas-inflated airship, a swallow, a butterfly or a gnat, flying in a straight line on the same course through a cross-wind of, say, 40 m.p.h., at the end of a minute or an hour all would still be in a straight line, though the distance between each unit of the procession would be proportional to the proper flight speeds of each unit through the 'wind,' or, as we should say, the air-current.

To many it may seem almost incredible that so frail a creature as a butterfly should, in a gale which roars in our ears, be as free from pressure or discomfort as when flying about a sunlit garden on a calm summer day. Anyone who may have overlooked this fundamental fact will, however, on reflection, recall that the infinitely delicate wings of a butterfly, if sighted flying in a strong wind, are still perfect, though the lightest touch with the hand is liable to mar this perfection. Damaged wings are due, not to wind, but to contact with fixed objects. So much for the fact. But what of its implication?

This simple little fact of absence of wind-pressure has a bearing upon butterfly life in general, and upon migration and geographical distribution in particular, out of all apparent proportion to the simplicity of the fact, and some explanation of the matter and of its implication may be as little out of place in the case of a butterfly as it was in the case of a bird. A butterfly flying in a strong adverse wind, even if of gale force, feels nothing of the pressure of this wind, neither does it feel the pressure of a wind blowing in the same direction as the butterfly's direction of flight, nor yet of a wind at any angle across its direction of self-propelled progression. To a butterfly in flight there is, in truth, no such thing as 'wind,' the butterfly being in a dead calm, *but a moving one*, so far as pressure is concerned. Airborne bodies, whether giant airships, aeroplanes, albatrosses, tiny birds, bees, gnats, a puff of smoke or butterflies, become integral parts of the medium in which they are supported and operating. All, in short, are atmospheric parasites, whether still or in motion, just as man and quadrupeds are terrestrial parasites as the earth travels silently in its atmospheric shroud through space. This being so, the idea that the wind has a relation to the outspread wings of a butterfly or bird in any way analogous to the action of wind on the sails of a ship or a kite is incorrect. The wings of butterflies, like those of birds, are *oars*, not *sails*, with all the fundamental consequences that the distinction involves.

The expressions 'a following wind,' 'a head wind,' or 'a side wind,' always used in entomological books and articles when, as is seldom the case, wind is mentioned at all, have no true meaning though they convey a false one. These so-called winds are, to a creature supported by them, and flying in them, in reality *currents*, and their movements relative to all airborne bodies are non-existent. A butterfly, like all airborne bodies of whatever size or weight, feels only a draught exactly equal to its own speed of flight *through* the moving atmosphere, a draught always and for all time from right ahead, between its eyes and on its antennae or proboscis.

Though the butterfly *feels* no wind-pressure, the effect of air-currents on its movements over the ground is always great, and at any time may become overwhelming and dominating, as a simple example will demonstrate.

Let us assume a butterfly to have a flight speed of its own of 15 m.p.h., and let us assume three conditions of the atmosphere in which it is flying:

(*a*) A calm, that is to say still air.
(*b*) A favourable current of 20 m.p.h.
(*c*) An adverse current of 20 m.p.h.

For the sake of simplicity, and with an eye on the future consideration of the phenomena of 'migration' and distribution, let us suppose the butterfly to fly for 12 hours on a course which renders the current, if flowing, to be directly favourable or adverse. With these simple assumptions, which can be varied infinitely to meet all cases of butterfly movement in space, we arrive at some remarkable discrepancies as to the ground covered in each case, though the distance flown through the moving air (a moving *calm*), and the effort expended by the butterfly, are identical in all cases.

In case (*a*), the butterfly covers 15×12 miles $= 180$ miles over land or sea.

In case (*b*), the butterfly covers $(15+20) \times 12$ miles $= 420$ miles over land or sea.

In case (*c*), the butterfly covers $(15-20) \times 12$ miles $= -60$ miles over land or sea.

Thus in this deliberately simplified example, if the 20 m.p.h. 'wind' was from the south, as in the late spring and summer in England it generally is, and if the butterfly was endeavouring to reach its 'home' in England from the south, it would make good towards its home over land or sea 420 miles in 12 hours. If, on the other hand, it was already *at* its 'home' in England, and was trying to remain at it, it would drift, willy-nilly, 60 miles away from its 'home' to the north in 12 hours.

If, however, it was at 'home' on a warm, calm, summer day, it could cover 180 miles in the infinite number of directions assumed while feeding, *and still remain at 'home.'*

At the risk of being tedious by repetition, it must again be emphasised that in all cases the butterfly experiences no sensation from the wind whatever. So far as the creature can be aware, through its *senses*, of what is happening to it, it is flying in dead calm air with a draught on its antennae or proboscis of a strength appropriate to its own flight speed—15 m.p.h. This sensation therefore never varies. It cannot know, except by recognition and observation of landmarks, in what direction or at what speed it is being translated by the *moving calm* in which it is operating. The extremely simplified example that has been given can be varied by readers to suit any butterfly and wind-speeds they like to postulate, including, of course, cross-winds. They will, in fact, be working out problems in what, as already mentioned, is the well-known 'parallelogram of velocities.'

In short, a butterfly is as parasitical to the atmosphere in which it flies as it was parasitical to its appropriate food-plant when, as a caterpillar, it crawled. In other words, a butterfly is both an aerial and a vegetable parasite—just that.

What this means, and the 'mysteries' that these two facts will go a long way to solve, will be considered in due course.

Chapter VIII

THE SENSE OF DIRECTION

In the last chapter it was shown that butterflies in flight are parasites of their aerial environment, and, in the absence of any regular and coherent control, the butterfly world would therefore be a drifting chaos, subject to no law. But because there is perfect order in nature, and because the atmosphere is unpredictable, unstable and infinitely variable in its motions, there must be some factor in the creature itself which brings natural order into the world of butterflies.

The wind bloweth where it listeth, and we cannot tell whence it comes, or in other words *starts*; or whither it goes, or in other words *ends*. Our next step therefore is to look for an order-producing factor which will automatically give direction to flight within a moving, variable and incalculable medium. Let us, for a moment, return to the case of a man-made flying-machine which, as already shown, is as much a parasite of the moving air in which it flies as is the frail butterfly. In the absence of the external aid of radiolocation, the pilot of a bomber crossing seas, oceans or deserts, would be as ignorant of his *drift* as would be a butterfly, if, that is to say, the speed and force of the wind in which he set out, and which he could therefore obtain at the start from ground observations, and by sextant angles of balloons in the upper strata of the atmosphere, changed. In other words, a reasoning pilot, flying in winds, has no means, under certain circumstances, of exercising his reason. Under such conditions Man himself is helpless, and at the mercy of the air-currents which he cannot gauge. A magnetic compass will not guide him home if he cannot calculate his 'drift,' except in one imaginary case which is illuminating.

Let us suppose that the pilot's ultimate destination, his 'home' we will call it, is at one of the Magnetic Poles of the earth. Let us also suppose that he can obtain fuel and food at any spot upon which he lands his aeroplane for rest or refreshment. Now, if this pilot continues to steer a compass course north or south, he will eventually reach his home if his fuel—his flying endurance—does not lapse over the sea or over a foodless desert. His *course* to his 'home,' for which he is always heading, will be on a curve, or on a series of curves, which will be governed by the relation between his own proper flight speed and the speed of the moving atmosphere *through* which he flies, but the movement of which he can no more feel, or sense, than can a butterfly.

The mathematical demonstration of the curves of flight assumed by any airborne vehicle or creature heading for a fixed spot through intervening air-currents is, like the *First Law of Currents,* contained in the author's recent book on birds, where he has called the law governing these curves *the Second Law of Currents.* Anyone can check the mathematics of this law by watching an inexperienced person in a boat rowing for a fixed destination through a water-current. Instead of allowing for the current, as would an experienced or reasoning person, he keeps the bows of the boat continually heading for the destination, with the result that he rows an unnecessarily long distance; makes a curved instead of a straight course to his destination, and finally reaches it exactly head on to the current through which he has been rowing. So with a water-rat crossing a stream to its home on the other bank. Anyone who has watched these creatures 'homing' across a stream will have noticed the curve which the swimming rat pursues. The fact that the rat swims on a curve instead of swimming *straight* for its home as it would do if it *allowed* for the current, proves that swimming creatures, like flying ones, do in fact continually orientate themselves for the spot in space which they have an urge to reach.

And here it may be well to refer to a characteristic of a butterfly's eyes mentioned and emphasised in Chapter V. It will be remembered that they are *fixed*, so that the body itself must be directed towards the spot for which it is heading. Thus if sight, in the sense that we understand that word, is the means by which a butterfly makes for a *visible* alighting spot, it must of necessity behave like the unthinking person in the boat, or the water-rat. It must, therefore, fly on a curve, and equally it must arrive at the alighting spot exactly head to wind, as it invariably does. Thus a butterfly's very anatomy precludes reasoning as an aid in its navigation.

The only exception to this curvature of flight, in the case of a pilot heading for the magnetic pole, would be in the case of a dead calm all the way, or of the wind being dead ahead or dead astern from the point of departure to the 'home.' Only in these three almost inconceivable circumstances would his flight be straight as the crow is *reputed* to fly, but doesn't, or as the straight bee-line which the bee is *reputed* to take for its hive, but again doesn't.

Again, no two such flights to the Pole would ever cover exactly the same ground. If made at widely separated times of the year—winter and summer—the courses to the 'home' might diverge by thousands of miles, thereby rendering flight by recognition-marks impossible. Furthermore, the length of the flights reckoned in *air* miles, and thus in the time taken or effort expended, might differ by thousands of miles according as to whether the air-currents in which the flights were made were favourable or adverse, as shown in cases (*b*) and (*c*) in the last chapter. If consecutive flights were made at short intervals, the respective courses, though much less divergent, would never be the same, owing to the variations of the air-currents.

Nevertheless, the airman would always reach his 'home' in the absence of an exhaustion of his fuel over the sea, or over a foodless tract of country, or of a mechanical breakdown of the machine while in the air. And he would always reach it from leeward, that is to say he would be seen approaching his home exactly head to wind.

It will be seen from the foregoing facts that the pilot's navigation from the point of departure to his 'home' is not accomplished by reasoning or calculation because his environment precludes their use. All he has to do, and what he must do, is to keep his machine headed magnetic north or south by compass; and his arrival at his 'home,' barring one of the accidents mentioned, is automatic, the time of the arrival being dependent upon the relation between the force and the direction of the wind or winds in which he has flown, and the speed of the machine itself. If the speed of his machine is 150 m.p.h., 150 m.p.h. is the draught that he will have felt without cessation, and always from right ahead regardless of the strength or direction of the 'wind'—the air-current.

Here, then, is an example of successful 'homing' by a man-piloted flying-machine in circumstances under which reason is inoperative, even though it is available at the helm. All that is necessary is a determination, or *urge*, by the pilot to reach his 'home', and an infallible 'sense of direction of that home', in this case supplied by the attraction of the earth's magnetic pole for the aeroplane's compass-needle which, when over the pole, would, if free, dip vertically. What we have now to determine is whether butterflies have this double sense of urge and direction for any fixed spot, or 'home,' on earth, as a piloted aeroplane has for the earth's magnetic pole in the imaginary[1] case considered; and if so, what *is* the 'home,' or 'Pole,' of a butterfly?

In his remarkable book, *The Reign of Law*, the late Duke of Argyll discussed the unchanging nature of law in the physical universe and, he might have added, in the spiritual. In this connection, in referring to 'the First Law of Motion' in particular, he wrote on page 111 as follows:

"Like many laws of the same class, it was discovered not by looking outwards, but by looking inwards; not by observing, but by thinking. The human mind . . . by careful reasoning . . . is able, from time to time, to reach now one, now another, of those purely Intellectual Conceptions which are the basis of all that is intelligible to us in the Order of the Material World."[2]

Here, then, is some warrant for a seaman, such as the author, or for any airman, physicist or mathematician, to pit his thinking against the observation of highly—sometimes too highly—specialised biologian, and to contrast the conclusions reached by the two different methods.

Bearing the words of the Duke of Argyll in mind, the surest proof that butterflies *are* so endowed with a sense of direction and urge lies in the fact that if they were not, the butterfly world, instead of being subject to law, would be chaotic. But as mathematical reasoning is less

[1] Since this analogy of an airman flying for the magnetic pole was originally drawn sixteen years ago in *This Bondage*, an R.A.F. pilot has recently made this very flight in a Lancaster bomber. Over the pole the compass needle 'dipped' 90°.

[2] Quoted in *The Cuckoo and Other Bird Mysteries*.

convincing to those who are neither physicists nor mathematicians than is observation, let us examine briefly the *observed* facts which actually do support the mathematically demonstrated necessity of a sense of direction, and a homing urge in butterflies, if law, and not confusion, is the order of nature.

Let us first consider a few analogies.

To test experimentally the existence of an imponderable sense of direction and urge in birds for 'homing,' *brooding* Terns were removed in closed baskets from the Tortugas and taken on board steamer for hundreds of miles into a waste of unknown waters. When released, a variable percentage returned home in safety. That in some cases the birds did not reach home is attributable to an adverse variation in the mean speed or direction of the intervening air-currents on those particular oceans on those occasions, and the consequent failure in *endurance* of the birds, rather than to a variable accuracy in their urge and sense of direction.

On the same authority, a pigeon returning to its nest will fail to retrieve its eggs which have been removed from the nest to a distance of *two inches*, a fact which well illustrates the exactness of the mechanical sense of direction, but which excludes recognition and thus reasonable action based on recognition. Homing pigeons released far from their fixed dovecots return to their homes.

Swallows, martins and other long-distance 'migrants' return over great tracts of land, sea and desert to the same nest—if, that is to say, any members of the several last year broods survive the hazards of 'migration.' There is no need to multiply examples of the inherent sense of direction in birds, which is almost universally accepted as proved from daily observation. Not only have they the necessary sense of direction, but, reinforcing this sense, all birds, hardy or otherwise, have what Sir Herbert Maxwell has described as "an invincible habit of returning to their birthplaces to nest"—an inveterate urge.

The same is true of fish which, through a waste of waters, return to the same pool or loch to breed, and probably—though this has not so far as the author is aware been verified by observation—to the very spot in that loch or pool at which the creature was born.

If this sense of direction, and the urge to return home or to stay at home, is an observed fact in birds and fish, is it likely to be absent in insects?

What of bees, which are said to make a 'bee-line' for their hives, though this line is in reality curved and not straight as is generally supposed. If in the bee's absence a new and different hive is substituted for the one it left, the bee will return to the strange hive unconcernedly, *provided it stands on the identical spot on which stood the old hive which it left*. Retain the old hive *but move it a very short distance* and the bee will be nonplussed, a fact which well demonstrates the exactness of the insect's sense of direction and the absence of any form of *recognition* as a guide in its 'homing.'

In the *Nineteenth Century* of October 1928 the late Mr. T. A. Coward gave an account of the amazing, indeed infinite, accuracy of this imponderable sense of orientation in the lower forms of life.

It will thus be seen that observation and experiment provide the evidence of what mathematical reasoning postulates—an inherent sense of direction in all creatures that operate in a moving medium to which they are themselves parasitic; that is to say fish, birds and flying insects, which include butterflies.

We may therefore conclude this analysis of the flight of winged creatures by postulating that butterflies, as aerial parasites, must be, and therefore are, endowed with a perfect sense of orientation which human beings have not got; and that reinforcing this sense is an urge to remain at home or to return home to the spot from which, as aerial parasites, they have unconsciously been drifted by the moving atmosphere which is to them a moving calm. The 'home' is that spot in space, or its immediate neighbourhood, upon which the creature was born.

Armed with what some may prefer to regard as possibilities, some as probabilities, and the author as certainties, we will now approach the mysteries of migration and geographical distribution with the facts of aerial parasitism, instead of fancies, as our major premises.

Chapter IX

THE 'MIGRATION' OF BUTTERFLIES

IN his recent book on the cuckoo and other bird mysteries, the author dealt in considerable detail with the problems of bird 'migration' in all their forms, and the explanations which he offered of these age-old mysteries have not up to the present been challenged. Though the phenomena of bird and butterfly 'migration' are fundamentally the same, their manifestations are more complex in the latter case. As a first step, therefore, we will examine as shortly as possible some of the reasons for the greater complexity of butterfly 'migration,' because the contrast will in itself do something to illuminate our problem and to clear the ground.

In the first place it must be emphasised, at the risk of being tedious, that all movements on the wing of flying insects and birds are overruled and dominated by the two laws of currents enunciated and explained in the last chapter. Butterflies and birds are alike absolute parasites of the atmosphere and of its every motion. That is a mathematical fact, in the light of which every problem of 'migration' and distribution must be approached. The existence of an 'urge' to return 'home,' and a perfect, though imponderable, sense of the direction of the 'home,' have been *postulated* on the evidence which has been given. But although the unseen forces which govern the movement on the wing of birds and butterflies are the same, the mean *effect* of these forces will often differ, and for two reasons. Firstly on account of the flight factors of the creatures themselves; and secondly on account of the very different circumstances of their respective life habits when not in flight.

Let us first consider the flight factor. No one can say exactly what are the flight speeds of the various species of birds and butterflies in absolutely still air. What, however, we can say with confidence is that the average speed on the wing of the bird-world is higher than that of the butterfly world. Not only is this a matter of ordinary observation, but it must almost inevitably be so, because the speed required to keep a relatively heavy bird from stalling is greater than that needed for the lighter creature.

Now the bird-world is divided broadly into two groups in this matter of flight. One group, all strong fliers, live in daylight on the wing or in exposed localities where, in both cases, they are continually exposed to the full speed of the wind. The other group consists of sedentary birds which pass their existence for the most part in sheltered surroundings. The first group owing to their flight powers, and the second owing to their life habit, can generally remain 'at home' during the normally quiescent months. When, however, the strong winds set in, the former inevitably become 'migrants' or 'vagrants' from home—the birthplace. So with butterflies. Some are inevitably 'vagrants' or 'migrants,' while others, the majority, are regular 'stay-at-homes' because they have sheltered habitats, spend all but a fraction of their short summer careers as immobile eggs, caterpillars, or chrysalids, and furthermore cease to fly in rain or when the sun is obscured—that is to say in unsettled weather conditions.

From the foregoing it follows that, in the summer, vagrancy from home is more apt to occur among the strong-flying butterflies than among their counterparts in the bird-world, a strong summer breeze being to them what a strong autumn wind is to birds. The more numerous 'stay-at-home' butterflies on the other hand will, owing to their habits, and in spite of their weak flying powers, remain in the immediate vicinity of their 'homes.' Hence the extremely local distribution of most butterflies, a subject upon which more has yet to be said.

Observation confirms this conclusion, because those of us who have perseveringly chased a rare strong-flying butterfly with a net in our gardens, have seen it elude us with despair, knowing that it is most unlikely we shall ever see it again. Most of the common and generally weak fliers, on the other hand, we expect to find, and do find, remaining and flying about in the precincts of their near-by and verifiable 'homes'.

The inevitable vagrancy of some butterflies on the wing, and the stay-at-home habits of most, are therefore no mysteries.

So much for the flight factor—the dynamic one—in its bearing upon 'vagrancy' and fixity in all their varying degrees and aspects. Let us now turn to those aspects of the problem which so immensely complicate the analysis of butterfly movement, and which have baffled, and still baffle, the keenest observation of experienced and highly skilled lepidopterists. Birds have nests—'homes'—which can generally be easily found and watched. The life of those that survive the breeding season and 'migration,' which is the chief balancer of nature in the world of wings, is prolonged for several years. Birds can, if necessary, be ringed, but the most important point of all is that they have no intermediate stages between the egg and the winged product. It is these characteristics which make accurate observation of, and conclusions about, birds comparatively simple, and which if correlated to the mathematical certainties of the two Laws of Currents, and of the homing-sense, enable us, in all their major aspects, to reduce the mysteries of bird 'vagrancy' and 'migration' to exactly explicable phenomena.

But what of butterflies? Their eggs, no bigger than small seeds, are laid on one or a few of thousands of identical leaves, and are thus difficult to find. Some butterflies lay single eggs on a large number of leaves. Others lay clutches on one; sometimes, as in the case of Tortoiseshells or Clouded Yellows, for example, four hundred or more are laid in piles. Some are single-brooded, others two- or three-brooded. Some eggs become butterflies within a few weeks of being laid early in the season; others at the latter end of the season, and others not until the next year. Thus when a rare butterfly is sighted in the spring, early summer, or autumn, it is difficult, if not impossible, to say whether it is a 'vagrant' or whether it is a 'native' that has hibernated in one of its stages at home. Sexual maturity, or the reverse, may be a guide, but it does not appear to be an infallible one. Some species of butterflies, as previously shown, hibernate as eggs, some as caterpillars, some as chrysalids, and some as butterflies. The length of the hibernation period, in all four stages, varies with species and with weather conditions.

Variety in marking and colouring is another source of confusion. Is an unusually marked or coloured butterfly of a particular species a native of foreign lands that has 'immigrated'; of another locality in Britain from which it is vagrant, or is it a home-produced variety?

Here are some of the many difficulties which so often reduce the observational side of butterfly migration and vagrancy to guesswork, and which account for the many conflicting opinions of experts which, in the case of birds, do not arise. The truth of this can be checked by anyone who has carefully studied standard works on birds and butterflies, and notably that masterpiece of butterfly observation—the *Migration of Butterflies* by Williams,[1] or *Natural History of British Butterflies* by Frohawk. But perhaps the greatest obstacle to the complete solution of butterfly 'migration,' 'immigration,' and 'vagrancy' problems has been the short life-cycle of the creature—approximately one year as a maximum in all but very few cases. This factor, taken in conjunction with the other features of butterfly life which have been enumerated, is apt to make confusion worse confounded, as Williams emphasises. In short, whereas with birds we have a point of departure, so to speak, for analysing their life-history, in the case of butterflies these points of departure are incomparably more complex as well as being variable according to temperature and other environmental factors.

Is it possible, or profitable, it may reasonably be asked, to attempt under such circumstances to unravel the secrets of butterfly movement, whether described as 'migration,' 'immigration,' or 'vagrancy,' with so many uncertainties in the problem? The author thinks that it is, in so far, that is to say, as the general aspects of the phenomenon are concerned. And for this reason. Among all the variables there are three constants: (1) the butterfly's parasitism on the atmosphere and particular food-plants; (2) its sense of direction and natural urge to reach or stay at its home when not engaged in its prior necessity of feeding, and (3) the fact that in all cases where it hibernates as an egg, a caterpillar or a chrysalis, it cannot be a regular 'migrant' in the generally accepted meaning of that

[1] C. B. Williams, M.A., formerly Entomologist to the East African Agricultural Research Station; Stevens Lecturer in Agricultural and Forest Zoology, Edinburgh University.

very confusedly used term, because its life-cycle is only one complete season. Such species *must* therefore be 'resident natives.'

This last fact enables us to remove the majority of butterflies from the ranks of those commonly styled 'migrants'; that is to say from those that leave our shores in the autumn and return like the swallows in the spring or early summer to breed, and a few days after this act of reproduction, to die.

Let us first consider a species of British butterfly that is known and accepted as a true 'migrant,' or regular 'immigrant,' because, though breeding here, this species does not winter in England in any stage. After careful study of the two species (or three if we treat the Pale Clouded Yellow as a distinct species and not as a variety) that come under this heading, the author has selected the beautiful Clouded Yellow in preference to the Painted Lady because the facts about this creature seem, on the whole, to be more clearly established and more circumscribed. The following assertions, stated as facts, about the life-history of this butterfly are taken from Frohawk's standard work and have been checked from others.

1. The Clouded Yellow (*Colias Edusa*) is a *native* of North Africa and of the Mediterranean region, whence annually in early spring it migrates over Central and Western Europe and generally reaches the British coasts in varying numbers during April, May and June.
2. This species has no hibernating stage.
3. It is powerful and rapid on the wing.
4. Upon arrival in Britain it *wanders* over the country, resorting to clover and lucerne fields, the food-plants to which it is parasitic, that is to say the plants upon which its egg is laid and upon which its caterpillar feeds.
5. These early immigrants lay their eggs in the spring soon after arrival, and then die. This first brood become butterflies in fifty-four days.
6. These butterflies of the first brood in turn quickly pair, lay eggs and die, leaving to succeed them a late autumnal brood if the weather remains sufficiently warm.
7. The Clouded Yellow is adversely affected by our climatic conditions, which are fatal to its existence, and the species becomes *extinct* in this country until fresh immigrants reach our shores.
8. This butterfly lays as many as 500 eggs, and in suitable summers after the arrival of many immigrants in the spring it becomes abundant in various parts of the country.
9. A freshly emerged specimen, which was carefully watched, laid 494 eggs between August 27th and September 4th. She died on September 5th, when dissection showed that her abdomen was empty.

10. The time taken in hatching out the caterpillar from the egg varies from six days to ten days, depending upon the temperature. The longest period is at the end of the season.
11. This butterfly is subject to great variation.

Here, then, is the life-history of a true 'migrant,' or 'immigrant,' British butterfly which, if the facts as given are correct, is capable of sure analysis, and which may be treated as a criterion of all butterflies that can be so classed, whether among British species, or foreign species of Tropical and sub-Tropical butterflies, or those of the Temperate regions of the Southern Hemisphere. Few, it is thought, will be disposed to dispute the legitimacy of treating the laws which regulate and ensure the 'migration' of one species of 'migrant' as being strictly applicable to all 'migrant' species.

But first we must refer to the three words italicised in the extracts from Frohawk's life-history of this butterfly, because they reveal a misinterpretation of facts.

The Clouded Yellow, it will be noticed, is said to be a *native* of the Mediterranean. But because 'immigrants' lay their eggs in England and in Central and Northern Europe, they are *natives* of the localities where they are born—as swallows are. In the South, like swallows, they are not natives but *vagrants*.

Again, the Clouded Yellow is said to *wander* when it reaches our shores. So, to the eye, do swallows, and yet in the absence of strong winds they in fact remain at 'home' until they vanish altogether. So does this butterfly.

Again, the Clouded Yellow is said to become *extinct* in the autumn. So, *apparently*, do swallows, but in fact they do not. They merely move to warmer climes and survivors return with the sun.

Having corrected what the author claims with the utmost respect to be three serious misinterpretations of facts, we can now set about explaining the 'mystery' of this 'migration' phenomenon which, as already said, must serve as a criterion of so-called butterfly 'migration'—that is to say of the regular seasonal passage of certain species of butterfly to their birthplaces in the north from the south in the Northern Hemisphere, and to their birthplaces in the south from the north in the Southern Hemisphere.

Now the following features of the Clouded Yellow's short life-history correspond to those of the relatively long-lived swallow.

Both arrive in England from the south and south-east about the same time.

Both are non-hardy and unable to weather the cold.

Both are inveterate fliers, and strong on the wing.

Both pair and lay their first clutch of eggs on arrival. But whereas the swallow survives all its egg-layings the Clouded Yellows survive none.

Both vanish from their native land in the autumn.

The two key differences are:

(1) The butterfly dies after laying its one clutch of eggs. This is true not only of the spring 'immigrant' itself but also of the first winged progeny of the 'immigrant' which breeds as soon as it comes to maturity as an imago.

(2) The butterfly's eggs or seeds depend upon the temperature of the air for hatching. The latest batch may need double the time of the earlier batches, from which it is clear that an unusually cold or early autumn may prevent the eggs hatching, or alternatively kill the caterpillars or chrysalids. Herein is a strong resemblance between butterfly's eggs and *flower seeds*, and a complete difference from birds' eggs which, within very narrow limits, have a fixed period for incubation, as have the eggs of mammals, including man. Furthermore, the temperature essential for germination is, in the latter cases, fixed and constant by natural means. In the case of butterfly and plant seeds, germination is stimulated within a wide range of temperatures. Butterflies are thus characteristic of the vegetable rather than of the animal world in this vital matter of reproduction.

From (1) it is clear that it is the butterflies of the last brood which alone migrate to warmer climes, and it is these which return sexually mature in the spring, complete their laying, and then die. Furthermore, it is only the last brood whose life-cycle is approximately eight months. The remainder never live through a winter.

From (2) it is plain that an early and cold autumn will prevent the bulk of the last brood of eggs from maturing as butterflies, just as late-sown seeds of annual flowers may fail if the weather is unpropitious. The plentifulness of Clouded Yellows in the following season will thus depend upon the weather conditions of the *preceding* autumn and not on those of the current spring and summer. Hence the great periodicity of the appearance in numbers of this beautiful non-hardy butterfly, a characteristic which has been noted since Entomology became a serious study. It also discloses that the 'homes' of the Clouded Yellows that are seen in England are *in* England—that is to say the 'home' of this butterfly, as of all butterflies, is the birthplace, as it is for birds. They are true natives of Britain, not of North Africa, just as well-to-do folk who go to the Riviera for the winter still remain native Englishmen.

With the mechanics of the departure and return of the Clouded Yellow it is proposed to deal quite shortly, because to do so in detail would necessitate repeating almost word for word the explanation given in the author's recent book on birds of the swallow's 'migration.'

During the relatively stable conditions of the atmosphere in the summer months, the creature, with its strong flight powers, will be able to remain and breed at home. As the atmosphere grows unstable in the autumn, a tendency to drift to leeward of its home will develop. In the summer, also, strong winds will cause temporary vagrancy, frequently from the south to the north. Let us suppose that one autumn day the mean speed of the wind rises to 15 m.p.h., the Clouded Yellow's own flight-speed being, say, 20 m.p.h. Remembering that the butterfly is flying in a moving calm, and thus unconscious of any wind pressure, it will fly indiscriminately in search of its food. When it darts 'down-wind' it will be covering the ground at (20+15) m.p.h.=35 m.p.h. When it darts 'up-wind' towards its home, which is its natural orientation when not actually feeding, it will make good over the ground only (20−15) m.p.h.=5 m.p.h. Multiply such darts hither and thither by scores in the course of the day, and it will readily be seen that by the evening it will be far to leeward of its home.

This process of drift will continue so long as the butterfly is under the influence of adverse winds, and will increase or decrease in proportion to any increase or decrease in the wind-speed. If the wind-speed exceeds the insect's own flight-speed it will be unable to alight and must keep on the wing. When the butterfly reaches southern climes where its food-plant, or a variety of it, is thriving, as it was ceasing to do in England when its southerly drift set in, it will become a homeless *vagrant*, but still with an urge for its northern 'home' when not engaged in hunting for its food. But adverse winds will prevent this urge from becoming effective. As the English spring approaches, that is to say when the mean movement of the intervening atmosphere is from the south towards the north, the Clouded Yellow will begin to approach its home in England at a speed which is, broadly, the *sum* of its own flight-speed and the wind-speed, whereas the speed of its drift to the south was, broadly, the *difference* of these two speeds. In other words, the outward 'migration' was much slower than will be the 'immigration,' as it is in the parallel phenomenon of 'migrant' birds.

Thus migration is unvolitional. The butterfly, so far from deliberately flying south to suitable conditions of which it can know nothing, and of which it has had no experience, endeavours to resist this southerly and south-easterly drift. A perfect natural harmony, or order, ensures that the creature *must* move to localities where the necessities of its life will be encountered. Furthermore, its blind effort to stay at home where, if the effort succeeded, conditions would lead to its extinction as a species, is the means by which its departure to an agreeable environment is perfectly regulated, ensuring perfect *timing*.

Before leaving this specific case of the 'migration' of the Clouded Yellow, there are one or two further points of interest that should be mentioned.

The first has to do with mating. If the weight of the two sexes differs, the lighter or smaller sex will have a slightly lower flight-speed. This implies that during the non-breeding season the sexes from the same place of origin will be separated, the weaker flyer drifting farther afield and thus reaching 'home' later. Thus the female Clouded Yellows, which are considerably larger than the males, will reach home first. In this connection, great flocks of 'migrating' male butterflies have often been encountered over the seas of South America without a female in the flock. Williams records the same phenomenon in Ceylon and elsewhere. Gätke records the extreme separation of the sexes where millions of winged males have been seen 'migrating' while the wingless females of the same species necessarily remain 'at home.' These cases, recorded in the *Entomologist* of February 1937, perfectly demonstrate the wind-parasitism of winged creatures. In those rarer cases where males and females of the same species form part of the same flock, generally with one sex greatly predominating in numbers, we shall find either that the two sexes have the same flight-speeds or, alternatively, that the two sexes have 'drifted' from different localities and are thus overlapping and mixed up. Herein lies the key to this sex separation mystery during the winter and to the general problem of the mating of migrants on reaching home in the spring.

Let us now suppose that fifty male and fifty female Clouded Yellows of the last autumnal brood blossom into butterflies in England at the same 'home.' Their 'migration,' or as we should say, 'drift,' to the south will be as described, as also will be the 'immigration' in the following spring of the survivors. The sexes of this particular brood will not meet again until they reach 'home'—the same spot in space for the few survivors of that last autumnal brood. This accounts for the otherwise inexplicable meeting of a mature male and a mature female immigrant. What would be the chances of such a necessary encounter, if the species is to be preserved, if in a year when Clouded Yellows were rare they had to rely on scent or sight for purposes of meeting and mating? There might well be no males or females within many miles of one another, and scent, as already pointed out, does not travel to windward! The fact that these immigrant butterflies *do* meet, and *do* mate, provides additional evidence that the birthplace is the home for which all wild flying creatures ceaselessly strive when not engaged in feeding—feeding and reproduction being the overruling purpose of their brief lives.

Another point to be remembered is that Clouded Yellows are widely distributed and, compared to swallows, generally rare: 480,000 Clouded Yellows distributed equally over the British Isles would provide one pair to every square mile. These figures are worth remembering, as is the fact that there is not, in all probability, one skilled observer or expert lepidopterist in every fifty square miles. We should therefore expect them to drift away to the south unobserved as single spies rather than in battalions, and so to return.

The 'migration' of butterflies in all parts of the world is so vast a subject, involving as it does many hundreds of species, that no attempt can here be made to deal with the phenomenon in all its aspects and variations. Williams, in his great work *Migration of Butterflies*, admits that even he has done little more than open up questions for further investigation. But what can be done, and what the author has tried to do in this one case of the Clouded Yellow, is to demonstrate that the 'mysteries' surrounding the 'migration' of any selected species, in any part of the world, can be solved by applying the unvarying laws that govern the movement of flying creatures in a moving environment, provided the habits of the creature *when at home*, that is to say at the birthplace, are known.

All students of butterflies, as of birds, have hitherto advocated the multiplication of observations and records as the only means of learning the secrets of 'migration' and distribution. Indeed they offer advice exactly the opposite to that of the late Duke of Argyll in his *Reign of Law* where, as already quoted, he exhorts students of nature not to look *outwards*, but *inwards;* to do *less* observing and more thinking.

The soundness of the Duke of Argyll's advice becomes immediately apparent from a study of Williams' *Migration of Butterflies*. Here are hundreds of recorded observations, almost all of which differ in some respect, but any *one* of which, when carefully analysed, will be found to conform either to the 'migration' of the non-hardy Clouded Yellow, when the different circumstances of wind and life habit of the insect are taken into consideration, or to the *vagrancy* of such hardy butterflies as the Red Admiral, Brimstone, or Comma.

A most striking example of this conformity is provided by the 'migration' of *Danaus plexippus* or, according to Frohawk, *Anosia plexippus*, which breeds throughout the summer in the U.S.A. and Canada, and as far north as Hudson Bay. Williams deals at considerable length with the 'migration' of this foreign species known variously in the vulgar tongue as the Black-veined Brown, the Milk-weed, and the Monarch. As the facts recorded about it are verified from many sources, this butterfly will serve as a suitable corroboration of the author's explanation of butterfly 'migration' in general, and that of the Clouded Yellow in particular. Here is Williams' general account of this famous regular long-distance 'migrant': "In the autumn the adult butterflies collect together in large bands and, when conditions are suitable, move in large masses to the south until they reach areas, usually about the Gulf States, in which they are able to pass the winter. They remain in these localities in a state of semi-hibernation, generally in large numbers on trees, usually dormant, but occasionally flying round on warm days if disturbed. In the spring these hibernating groups break up and individuals move slowly and steadily to the north, laying eggs on the food-plant on the way."

The first thing to be emphasised about this long trek of the Black-veined Brown is that it takes place at the same times, and seems to follow much the same route, as that of the American golden plover, a chart of which appears as a frontispiece to the author's recent book, *The Cuckoo and other Bird Mysteries*. The migration route on this chart was obtained from the National Geographic Magazine, and the winds from Pilot Charts of the U.S. Navy Department.

It is true that the behaviour of this American butterfly at the southern limits of its southward migration seems to be rather different from that of the Clouded Yellow which is not recorded as undergoing semi-hibernation at the southern end of its 'range.' It is also true that in its southern drift it 'packs' very much more than does its English equivalent. The former difference, however, is a matter of life-habit overruled by temperature, and not one of migratory movement. The latter is a consequence of the greater plentifulness of the insect over the whole of North America, and of the inevitable tendency of the northern natives to come down as aerial parasites upon the more southerly ones, the north wind reaching the southern natives later. Or in other words, the more northerly natives automatically join up with the more southerly natives as wintry conditions travel south. This is borne out by the fact that years of observation have established that *the surviving butterflies of the last summer brood in the north* (the same generation, it should be noted, as in the case of the migrant Clouded Yellow) begin to move (drift) south about the middle of August to the middle of September, whereas the natives in the latitude of New York start drifting south late in September, and those native to Oklahoma and Texas in October. These American butterflies are all multi-brooders, fourth broods occurring, as would be expected, at the southern limit of its range. Yet only survivors of the *last* brood, over their whole vast range, 'migrate.' All the others, like the Clouded Yellows, die after breeding. During the 'migration' to the south the butterflies will be found flying *against* the northerly wind, that is to say *drifting backwards while striving for home.* On the return to the north in the spring they will be flying *with* the south wind, laying their eggs on the appropriate food-plant as each reaches the place of its birth in the previous autumn. Having laid its eggs it will die, and the life-cycle of the species will continue as in the case of the Clouded Yellow and of all other non-hardy migrants.

Here are a few additional interesting facts about *Danaus plexippus* while winter *vagrants* in the south.

Individuals from the hibernating flocks go out on the wing feeding, but they always return before nightfall to their hibernating, or 'roosting,' quarters.

These butterflies are not harmed by occasional *light* frosts or by storms, thereby showing that there is a precise temperature which causes a butterfly to become dormant and also one which will kill it. They are never attacked by birds.

About the first few days of March a few at a time begin to disappear. The known localities of hibernation, as opposed to semi-hibernation, are all on or just south of a mean January temperature of 50°F.

The author has now analysed the 'migration' of two well-known species of butterfly—one British and one American. All the facts recorded about the 'migrations' of these two particular species harmonise exactly with the laws of flight which have been postulated, and which form the major premises upon which the author's explanation of 'migration,' whether of birds or butterflies, is based. Before, however, concluding this analysis, it may be of interest to give some of the general suggestions on the whole subject of Butterfly Migration which have been tentatively put forward by Williams, all of which only need the basic laws enunciated in this book to bring his observations and the author's explanation into line.

With regard to what has been called the homing *urge*, Williams underlines this description by calling it an 'ecstasy' or 'hysteria.'

Of the 'sense of direction' inherent in butterflies, as in birds, Williams gives many remarkable examples, one being the wholesale disappearance of a host of migrating butterflies into a railway tunnel, the unnaturally black mouth of which was on the direct flight route. Observers all over the world have recorded the persistence of the uni-directional flight of migrating butterflies, some of whom remark that it is as though the insects were 'flying by compass,' an expression which will recall the author's description of an imaginary flight by an airman to a home at the earth's magnetic pole.

In concluding this chapter on the migration of butterflies, it may be of interest to quote the words used by Williams in summing up his general conclusions on *the origin of the migratory habit*. He writes: "Any remarks on this subject can only be conjectural. *It appears that two things are necessary at present to bring about a migration—a suitable condition of the environment and an ability to respond in the animal.*" The words italicised are correct in a sense, but in a sense exactly opposite to that which they convey. The terrestrial, or geographical, environment of the butterfly becomes *unsuitable*, but the cold northerly winds of approaching winter which make the geographical environment unsuitable provide a *suitable* aerial environment for translation to a new geographical environment which *will* be suitable. When this is reached the suitable aerial environment for the necessary translation of the butterfly becomes a *barrier* to its return until the northern geographical environment is again becoming suitable. This is brought about by the aerial *barrier*, the northerly winds, turning to an aerial *conveyor*—southerly winds.

The insect's response to the aerial environment is absolute, because it is an aerial parasite, but so far from responding by deliberate flight from an unsuitable geographical environment the creature strives to cling to an environment that would, in fact, lead to its extinction. Williams continues thus: "It is impossible to believe that the ability to respond in this particular way has always existed as a part of life itself, but that only recent conditions became suitable to liberate it in a few species. Therefore we must suppose that it is the inherited ability to respond which has developed in certain species as evolution proceeded, and that there was once a time when migration did not exist." Then follow references to the 'ice ages,' and modern theories of Continental Drift, which have been suggested as causes of prehistoric migrations which have become fixed in the migratory butterflies, though the originating causes have now ceased to operate. These evolutionary theories of migration are commonly applied to birds and butterflies alike, and as they raise the whole question of the world-wide geographical distribution of butterflies and of 'species,' 'genera,' 'geographical races,' and 'varieties,' they will be considered in the next chapter.

Chapter X

GEOGRAPHICAL DISTRIBUTION AND DISPERSION

In the last chapter the 'migrations' of two species of butterflies were examined in some detail, and it was shown that their seasonal movements, or drifts, to the south in the Northern Hemisphere, and to the north in the Southern Hemisphere, were as automatic, inevitable and seasonal as is the flow of the atmosphere which accompanies winter conditions in temperate lands. Similarly, that the reverse atmospheric movement which heralds summer conditions in the temperate belts brought about the seasonal 'immigration,' or return of butterflies. Indeed, the 'migrations,' 'immigrations,' and 'drifts' of the butterfly world may be said to be governed by the aerial tides and currents of the world, just as in some cases are those of fish by the tides and currents of the seas, oceans and rivers.

The term 'migration' is generally applied to the regular two-way passage of non-hardy species to and from the precise localities where they originated—to which, in other words, they are *native*. But all butterflies caught on the wing must drift from their native haunts when the atmospheric 'tide' assumes a certain relation to the butterfly's own flight-power. Some of these butterfly movements are slight and generally unperceived; some are over great expanses of land and sea, resulting in the unusual appearance of species or varieties in countries to which they are not *native*. In other lands, and especially in the tropics, species move in great flocks to and fro over comparatively small areas. Many detailed observations have been made of different species steering in flocks, in small groups, or singly, on opposite or divergent courses at the same time and in the same place. Many of these various distinct and observable movements are recorded in *Migration of Butterflies*, from which Williams concludes, with his customary lucidity of reasoning, that 'migration' is a very loose term, and one that may in some respects be applied to almost all butterflies of all species and varieties in all parts of the world. It may therefore be of interest to examine briefly the general distribution of butterflies, and the comings and goings of those which are not generally classed as migrants proper.

Now Williams and other entomologists have frequently drawn attention to the close parallel that exists between the 'migration' of birds and that of butterflies, a well-known example being that of *Danaus plexippus*, quoted in the last chapter, which closely resembles that of the American golden plover. They are unquestionably right, and as in his recent book on bird migration the author has carefully explained the causes that govern the dispersal and distribution of birds, locally as well as continentally and hemispherically, he will repeat that explanation much as it was originally written with butterflies substituted for birds.

The dispersal and distribution of butterflies, as of birds, is often explained by assuming that both forms of life underwent wholesale extermination in pre-glacial, inter-glacial, pliocene and pleistocene ages, during which periods, in the fabulous past, migration was supposed to be non-existent. Indeed, in his discussion of some general problems of butterfly migration Williams writes, as quoted in the last chapter: "We must suppose that it is the inherited ability to respond which has developed in certain species as evolution proceeded, and that there was once a time when migration did not exist."

Arising out of these alleged disasters in the twilight of the world, present migrations are attributed to the constant endeavour of what we are asked to regard as relics of such exiled life to regain and 're-people' the areas that they once occupied in prehistoric pre-glacial time. 'Extension of Range' is treated as an indication of the gradual success of this constant endeavour, while the trend of birds and butterflies northward in the Northern Hemisphere, and southward in the Southern Hemisphere, at the breeding season is advanced by many biologians as a proof of inherited memory and love of home passed on to succeeding generations in the form of instinct, 'sexual urge' being invoked as the 'trigger' which sets this train of inherited memory in motion. The main routes of migration are linked up with, and indeed are said to provide evidence of, long vanished land-masses over which the seas and oceans are now alleged to roll.

But all such theories and speculations have arisen through a failure to appreciate that all flying creatures are pure aerial parasites and therefore absolutely subject to the aerial environment in which they fly. The laws of dynamics, and the parallelogram of velocities, which have been enunciated, enforce and control the dispersal of butterflies as they do that of birds. Butterfly life on the wing must be dominated by the winds of the world, which in their turn are set in motion by temperature. Temperature is thus the originating cause of migration, as it is the regulator of the food supply of the migrants. Not only do the winds govern the movement of butterflies about the world, but they demarcate for all time the regions to which some species are rigidly confined and from which others are permanently excluded.

How great is the influence of the winds of the world upon the distribution of butterflies is well shown in the two charts here reproduced from the Comparative Atlas. These charts are, of course, on a very small scale, and they are thus of no assistance in estimating the effects of local and variable winds. They are also for the months of January and July (mid-winter and mid-summer) instead of for spring and autumn, which are the great migration and vagrancy periods. These could not be obtained, but the ones reproduced do give a bird's-eye view, so to speak, of the world-wide

CHART SHOWING PERMANENT, PREVAILING AND PERIODIC WINDS OF THE WORLD (JULY)

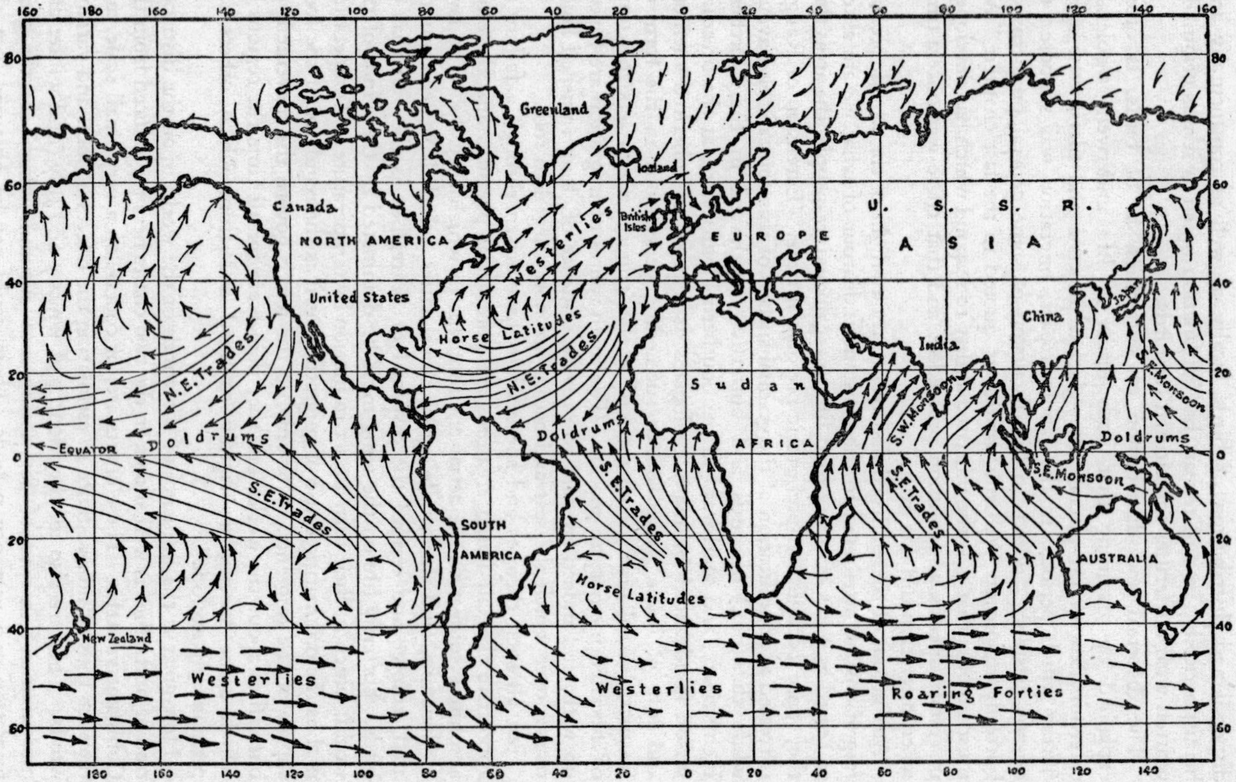

CHART SHOWING PERMANENT, PREVAILING AND PERIODIC WINDS OF THE WORLD (JANUARY)

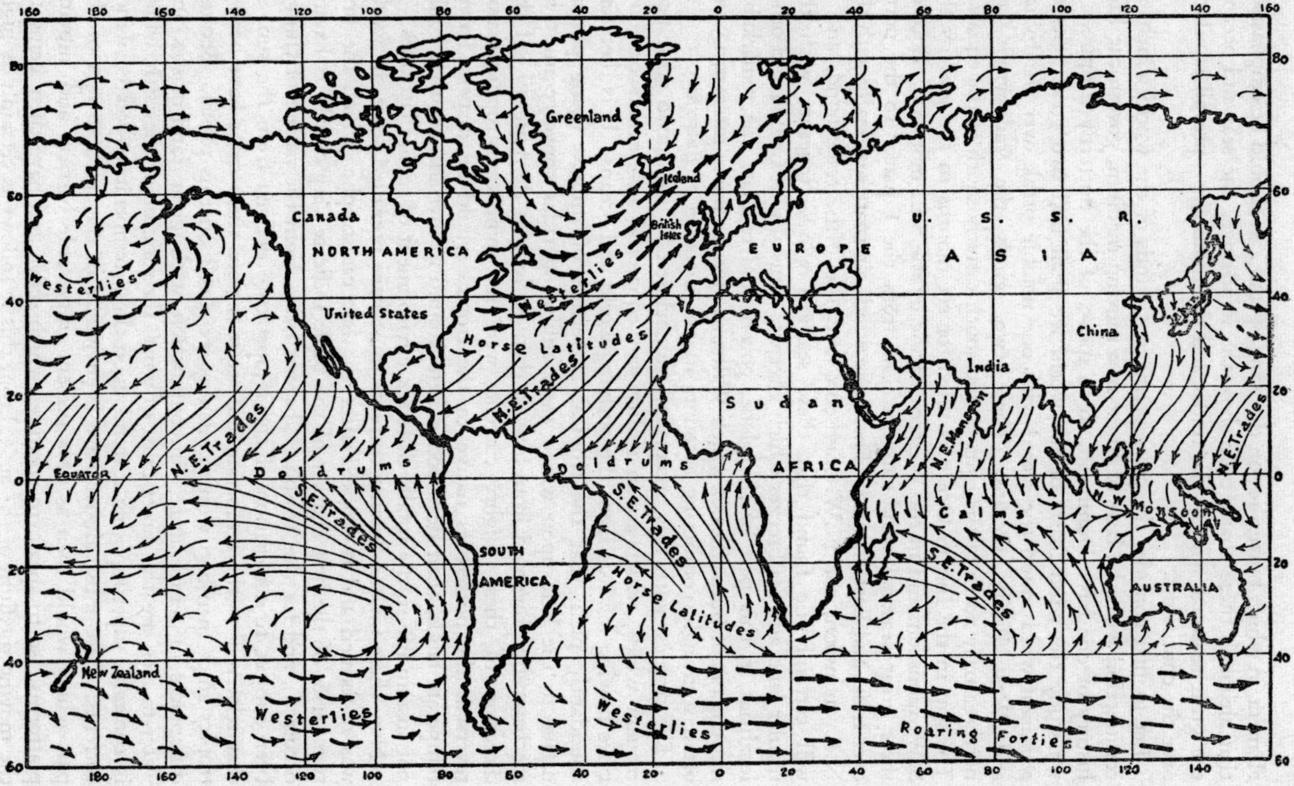

element in which butterflies on the wing operate. It should be emphasised that although these charts only show the winds over the seas and oceans, the great seasonal winds—the trades and the monsoons—prevail similarly over the continents.

Let us first consider the great permanent winds of the world which, in conjunction with the laws of flight in a moving medium, govern the life-history of one large Dominion, so to speak, of the Butterfly Empire. If we study the wind-charts of the world we shall find two great belts of *permanent* wind round the world with one notable break over the Indian and West Pacific Oceans. These two winds—the trade-winds—are north-easterly north of the equator and south-easterly south of the equator. The gap in the Indian Ocean is filled for six months in the year by the S.W. monsoon, and in the Western Pacific by the S.E. monsoon. Both of these great seasonal wind-currents flow from the Equator to the north over India and Eastern Asia. These two winds alternate seasonally with the N.E. monsoon, the N.W. monsoon, and the N.E. trade-wind, and it will certainly be found that these seasonal winds, together with the regular land and sea breezes which alternate diurnally in Ceylon and other localities in this part of the globe, govern and regulate the remarkable movements of butterflies of which Williams gives so many interesting and often seemingly conflicting accounts in his *Migration of Butterflies*.

The tropics, with this exception, are enclosed by these two great permanent winds, which are in reality vast equatorial air-currents or aerial tides flowing inwards from the outlying world and oceans. It is therefore abundantly plain that the tropical butterflies of limited flying powers native to the belt upon which these inflowing tides converge must be mechanically prevented from leaving them so long as they prevail. If the direction of these mighty currents were for some catastrophic reason reversed, the butterflies native to the tropics would be dispersed over temperate lands, their dead bodies being found in myriads, for they could not sustain life in the totally different environment of higher latitudes.

Now these inward-flowing currents must have prevailed since the world was re-formed and re-stocked after the last catastrophe (which the first two verses of the first chapter of the Bible indicate very clearly as having occurred), and for this reason. The earth has, from the nature of things, been subject to a variation of the temperature derived from the sun, so that relatively to the temperate and arctic regions there must have been a tropics since men and women such as we dwelt on this planet. Because differences in temperature, in conjunction with great land-masses and water-masses, are the direct cause of wind, the rotation of the earth, which is constant, superimposing a trend upon these temperature-created wind-currents, there must always have been winds in the farthest ages of the past which would then as now present impassable barriers and 'moving platforms,' so to speak, to creatures which move and have their being in the moving medium of the air. From this it follows as certainly as night follows day that species of butterflies *native* to the tropics, like native tropical birds, cannot have had a common origin with those of temperate climes. In other words, they cannot have come into being by natural selection of favourable variations. Further references will be made to this matter when we come to a consideration of the vexed question of 'species,' 'genera,' 'families,' 'races,' and 'varieties,' and of classification generally.

Turning from the inevitable and permanent confinement of native tropical butterflies native to the tropics and their immediate neighbourhood, we can definitely exclude the butterflies of the northern half of South America from Northern Africa and Europe, because of the utterly impassable barrier of the trade-winds. This barrier was graphically illustrated in the case of the migration of the golden plover in the author's recent book on birds. The impassability of such a barrier becomes apparent when we reflect that the geographical—the absolute—distance from Cape St. Roque to Cape Verde of 1,800 miles becomes 7,200 miles to a butterfly of such a strong flight-speed as 20 m.p.h. if we assume the average speed of the N.E. trade-wind to be as low as 15 m.p.h. at average flying heights.

Leaving the neighbourhood of the tropics and passing to the temperate regions of both hemispheres, we find the prevailing wind over vast oceanic areas to be westerly and often of great strength. We should therefore expect to find, as in fact we do, different geographical races or varieties of the same species of butterfly appearing in areas separated by thousands of miles. Because in the great easterly and westerly belts of temperate lands prevailing winds within prevailing winds exist—that is to say prevailing local winds—there is a tendency, though only a tendency, for particular species to be confined permanently to particular areas, a tendency which, however, is modified by frequent or occasional 'invasions' from other areas, sometimes very distant ones, owing to the variability of temperate winds. This exceptional drift is more frequent from west to east, a well-known case being, in the case of birds, the not infrequent appearance in Britain and Europe of American and Canadian species. A drift from east to west, though rarer, has been recorded of British birds, and of a Brown-tail moth in the early 'nineties by Lutz. A striking example of transatlantic crossings is the occasional appearance in this country of that beautiful American butterfly, the Black-veined Brown (*Danaus plexippus*). This butterfly provides such an admirable example of *one-way drift*, or vagrancy, as well as of the *two-way seasonal* 'migration' considered in the last chapter, that some account of its vagrancies will serve as a criterion of many other well-known cases of vagrancy of foreign butterflies.

In his most interesting account of the history of the Black-veined Brown (*Danaus* or *Anosia plexippus*), Frohawk records the following facts.

Its occurrence in England and Europe is certainly due to immigration from North America.

Its occurrence in Britain has almost always been in September.

The habits of this species are similar to those of the Painted Lady and of all the other members of the genus *plexippus*, and, it may be added, to those of the Clouded Yellow, whose migrations and life-history have been examined in some detail in the last chapter.

None of its food-plants is indigenous in this country, and the creature cannot consequently produce a single brood in Britain. It is not therefore a native, and for this reason it should not be included among British butterflies. The Black-veined Brown, as already shown, produces many broods in the southern portion of the United States and in Central America. It annually 'migrates' northwards in the spring and breeds over Northern United States and far northward in Canada. Stray specimens have been captured at sea hundreds of miles from land, and specimens have been recorded as far east as the Malay Archipelago and Sumatra.

So much for the facts: what of the interpretation of them? This becomes simple and plain when these immense drifts or vagrancies in the north to the east, and in the south to the west, are referred to the north and south migration-route of the butterfly in North and Central America and to the wind charts of the world. These charts show the liability of migrants on the easterly edge of the regular north and south migration route in Canada and North America to be carried across the Atlantic to Europe in the westerlies, and particularly in September when the great movement of the species to the south sets in.

Similarly, these butterflies on the western fringe of the migration route are liable to get involved in the N.E. trades and to be carried, willy-nilly, towards the Far East where they will later get involved in the S.E. monsoon.

One other important point must be stressed. It has always been assumed that these long-distance vagrants, like the short-distance ones in the East Indies and that neighbourhood, have headed towards the localities where they have been surprisingly found. The truth is that they were, during the passage of these great ocean spaces, heading for their 'homes,' just as were their fellows who successfully passed south or north instead of west or east on their regular seasonal migration route. They in fact drifted *backwards* across these ocean spaces while flying *forwards* through the oppositely moving atmosphere. The speed of the crossing was, roughly, the difference between the wind-speed at the elevation at which they were flying, and their own proper flight-speed through this adversely moving *calm*, as it would feel to the butterfly. Assuming the exceptional speed of the wind on these occasions of long-distance vagrancy to have been 40 m.p.h. and the butterfly's own flight-speed to have been 20 m.p.h., the butterfly would drift about 500 miles a day. If the wind was 60 m.p.h., as it well might be at the times of the year in question, the daily drift to leeward would be about 1,000 miles.

A careful study of the wind charts and 'wind-roses' of Britain, North-western Europe, and Scandinavia will extinguish at a glance the speculation as to the reason for the periodical appearance of foreign species, such as the Camberwell Beauty, and of continental varieties of our native species, in this little corner of the world.

To trace the innumerable 'sub-species,' 'races,' 'varieties,' of a single species or *kind* of butterfly that are to be found in great belts of countries and continents of approximately similar physical conditions is quite beyond the scope of this book. Indeed, a whole book—and a large one at that—would be needed to analyse fully the life-history of a single widely distributed species. It need hardly be said that latitude is only the roughest of guides in tracing out such belts. Arctic species of butterflies are found on mountain-tops in New England and Alberta. The same species are found along the Andes and Rockies from Patagonia to San Francisco. Temperature, the arbiter of wind and particular forms of vegetation, the two things to which butterflies are parasitic, is modified by terrestrial considerations of elevation, equatorial and arctic currents, and other features of this planet, as well as by the *origin* of external temperature—the sun. These affect the latitudinal consequences of solar temperature in historical times, much as the earth's own surface, or near surface, temperature must have modified, though uniformly, the differential solar temperatures of tropical, temperate and arctic belts in prehistoric times. Now, as then, however, the trends of the winds must be of such a nature as to provide permanent barriers and to and fro avenues for butterflies in their passage about the world. These barriers and avenues ensure that while butterflies of various species cannot trespass or helplessly drift into regions in which unsuitable conditions would lead to their extinction as a species, they can drift about the world where physical conditions, which must include a suitable food-plant if they are to survive their enforced vagrancy, are agreeable to the preservation of life.

And here it may be of interest to consider briefly that remarkable butterfly, the Painted Lady, which is to be found in almost every land, from the Arctic to the Antarctic, in the tropics, and from China to Peru. Indeed, it appears to be as ubiquitous as the mosquito. At first sight it might seem that the world-wide prevalence of this particular creature was a refutation of the effectiveness of any barrier which wind can present to butterflies; and some might argue that the Painted Lady provides a proof that butterflies have some say of their own, so to speak, in their 'migratory travels,' wind or no wind. This is not so, but it is true that the Painted Lady presents an exceptionally interesting and instructive problem in butterfly movement and distribution, as Mr. Compton Mackenzie has emphasised. For example, he asks: "Why is the Painted Lady in St. Helena of the South American and not the South African type?"

Here, it will be noticed, Mr. Compton Mackenzie uses the term 'type,' and there is evidently no doubt in his mind that the Painted Lady found in St. Helena is immediately recognisable as of South American origin. Mr. N. D. Riley, the curator of the Department of Entomology at the British Museum, on the other hand, has written as follows: "It seems in fact that only one species of Painted Lady occurs in St. Helena, and this is the same insect as we get in this country and of which the correct name is *Vanessa cardui*.[1] Nobody has ever claimed to recognise any geographical races in this cosmopolitan species, and the specimens we have from St. Helena certainly seem quite typical.

"We have no specimen of any other Painted Lady from St. Helena, and the only paper on the Lepidoptera of St. Helena known to us does not record any Painted Lady other than *Vanessa cardui*. All this does not preclude the possibility of one of the South American species occurring there, for the evidence is entirely negative."

It will be noticed that though in the first paragraph Mr. Riley claims that there is only one species, or indeed geographical race, of the Painted Lady, in the second paragraph he refers to "one of the South American species," which implies that there are several Painted Lady species, races, or varieties. Thus the Painted Lady presents an interesting study in classification as well as in migration. In this connection Morris mentions the capture of a North American *species* of the Painted Lady (*Cynthia Huntera*) in South Wales in August 1828, which he had in his collection, and this specimen is noticeably different from the English 'species,' 'race,' or 'variety.' This North American variety, if it is a variety, race or species of the Painted Lady was, like the Black-veined Brown in England or the Malay Archipelago, a drifted vagrant. Without entering into the seeming contradictions about the identity or otherwise of Painted Ladies in different continents, but assuming that, as Mr. Mackenzie says, the St. Helena specimens *are* from South America, the explanation is as follows.

The wind charts for the various seasons reveal that in the South Atlantic, as in the North Atlantic, the fast-flowing *westerlies* impinge on the eastern fringe of the north and south migratory route of the South American Painted Ladies of the southern hemisphere, some of which will inevitably be drawn into the vortex of the westerlies until, nearing the longitude of St. Helena, they will be carried through the Horse Latitudes of the S.E. trade-wind to that island. The absence in St. Helena of the African Painted Lady will be plain from a study of the large-scale wind charts of the intervening sea-space at the appropriate time of year.

Again, if the trade-winds provide an absolute barrier against the penetration of butterflies native to the tropics into temperate lands, how comes it, it may reasonably be asked, that the Painted Ladies native to

[1] The Painted Lady has been variously classified as follows by well-known authorities:

Cynthia cardui.—Kirby, Stephens, Duncan, Westwood.
Vanessa cardui.—Godart, Latreille, Meyer, Hubner.
Libythia cardui.—Lamarck.
Papilio cardui.—Linnaeus, Fabricius, Haworth, Lewin, and six others.
Pyrameis cardui.—Newman, Frohawk.

Among so many differing authorities, a layman is justified in confessing himself to be a little at sea on this scientific matter (see page 104).

the tropics are found in temperate lands? The answer is that those that are in reality *native* to the regions upon which these great inflowing equatorial air-currents converge do not, in fact, leave them for temperate climes, though they may drift thousands of miles *longitudinally* in the westerlies, as do the North and South American Painted Ladies to Britain and St. Helena, or the Black-veined Brown to England and the Malay Archipelago. In the latter case it is the 'type,' or 'variety,' or 'race' of the Black-veined Brown which breeds in the north of the U.S.A. and Canada which sometimes drifts as a vagrant to England, whereas it is the 'type,' 'variety,' or 'race' which breeds in the south, in or near the tropics, which drifts as a vagrant to Malay—the former in the westerlies, the latter in the trade-winds.

The Painted Ladies to be found all round the world breeding in the northern and southern temperate zones 'migrate,' in the two-way sense, *towards* the tropics in the winter and from them in the summer, just as does the Clouded Yellow or the Black-veined Brown. The migrations or wanderings of the type, variety, race or species of Painted Ladies which breed *in* the tropics, and are thus native to them, if such there be, will be found to be confined to the 4,000 mile belt enclosed between the tropics of Cancer and Capricorn.

Experts on the 'migration' and distribution of foreign butterflies will be able to give innumerable examples of butterfly movements in vast battalions, or as single spies, which apparently are at variance with the general laws the author has endeavoured to expound, and with the particular examples he has used to demonstrate his case. He is confident, however, that any expert on the butterflies of any particular part of the world who is willing to accept as correct the laws governing the movement of flying creatures within a moving and all-embracing medium will, with the aid of accurate meteorological charts for the locality in question, be able to solve problems which have hitherto baffled him. Nowhere will such a study be more fruitful than in that part of the world in which the four seasonal winds—the S.W., N.E., N.W., and S.E. monsoons—prevail, and where, in addition, regular land and sea breezes are prevalent, as is so notably the case in Ceylon where they often dominate locally the monsoons.

There is, however, one phenomenon of butterfly movement which for hundreds of years has astonished all who have witnessed it. This is the appearance of massed formations of these insects flying steadily and unswervingly on a steady course head to wind or, as we should say, through an adverse air-current. A remarkable example of such a massed flight of *Danaus plexippus* is given in *Migration of Butterflies*. Within a zone of 40 miles wide by 432 miles long is contained about 17,280 square miles, or 11,059,200 acres. It was estimated that there were about 300 butterflies per acre, so that in the course of about three days 3,000,000,000 had passed in the 40-mile wide zone. What force or 'instinct' caused these myriads of a very common butterfly, normally spread over vast territories during the breeding season, so to congregate and to maintain a steady course against the wind with a determination which, elsewhere, Williams describes as something akin to hysteria?

The explanation is this: The wind that puts the 'migration,' or backward drift, in motion sets in first at the extremities of the butterflies' range, be it in the north in the Northern Hemisphere, in the south in the Southern Hemisphere, or east or west in more circumscribed local migrations. As this bodily movement of the atmosphere extends south, north, east or west, as the case may be, the hosts of butterflies over the vast moving fronts are carried along with it, picking up and mingling with the hosts that were still clinging to their homes while circumstances allowed them to do so. The effect of such a coming-down of one front upon another front, which when they overlap will move uniformly, must inevitably strip area after area bare of butterflies of the same flight capacity, a process which will terminate in the packing of the butterfly content of perhaps a continent in a relatively small area. In this case of the drift to the south of the *Danaus plexippus*, a glance at the map of North and Central America will disclose at once how this packing naturally takes place in the late autumn, and why, in the return flight to the north, the 'unpacking' of the myriad host proceeds apace though less noticeably, as each unit heads for its own birthplace, perhaps as far apart latitudinally as Hudson Bay and Washington, and as far apart longitudinally as Boston and Calgary. In the case of birds, the same phenomenon is observed in England on a small scale during the autumnal departure of the swallows which we see in tired flocks on telegraph wires. Like the butterflies, each swallow endeavoured to stay at its particular home, but was carried south on top of other swallows still trying to do the same.

If we regard each longitudinal butterfly 'front' as a butterfly tidal *wave*, it is easy to understand the process of mass formations of moving butterflies by watching the ripples of an ebb tide in a harbour or bay as they make contact with water previously still. Even more marked is the 'building up' process if the main ebb encounters a contrary tide or eddy, or one that is divergent to the general ebb, as in seaman's language it begins to 'make.'

So much for a vast north and south seasonal migration of non-hardy butterflies. But the same 'packing' phenomenon will inevitably occur in localities where relatively strong local winds occur and alternate. For example, on an island like Ceylon, rich in butterfly life, strong land breezes alternating with strong sea breezes will tend to drift butterflies seaward, those drifted farthest to sea coming landwards again with the sea-breeze before those still subject to the falling land-breeze have reversed their direction of progression. There will be a time and a place where a mass of butterflies are flying against the wind and with the wind, but the most noticeable of the two flights will be that *against* the wind, because the flight with the wind will more quickly disintegrate into individual flights as each insect reaches or approaches its individual 'home.'

Enough has been said to indicate the general principles governing butterfly dispersion, distribution, 'migration' proper, 'local migration,' drift and packing. In every country, and in the case of every species, these phenomena will vary. But the author is convinced, as he has already said, that if skilled students of the butterfly world, wherever their observations and records are made, will relate them to the *constants* which have been indicated; and if, furthermore, they will obtain the interest and co-operation of skilled meteorologists or navigators, most if not all of those 'mysteries' of butterfly life which are connected with movement will be well on the road to solution.

Chapter XI

DISTRIBUTION AND VARIATION OF BRITISH BUTTERFLIES

UP to this point we have been chasing butterflies about the world in order to elucidate the general principles which govern all winged life. We will now turn to the study of some of the problems which British butterflies in particular present. And at the outset it may be well to re-emphasise that the miracles and mysteries that surround the life-history of any single species in the world are common to the whole of the butterfly creation, whether in the realm of migration, distribution, the senses, mimicry or generation. Every species of butterfly manifests some variation in the application of the laws common to them all, just as every unit of a well-managed railway system, though obedient to the rules governing the creation and operation of the system as a whole, has its own characteristics, whether in design of engine, speed, colour, distribution, endurance, and so forth.

Just as in all other parts of the world, British butterflies confront their students with the following problems:

1. What should determine the claim of any species to be British, that is to say a native of Britain?
2. Which of the British butterflies are true native 'migrants'?
3. Why is the distribution of some species, though geographically wide, strictly, and sometimes very narrowly, local?
4. What determines the periodic plentifulness and scarcity of certain species?
5. Why have some species apparently become extinct, and is there any possibility of such species reappearing as natives?
6. To what cause, or causes, are we to attribute variations of particular species?

For the sake of clearness each of these much discussed problems will be examined independently, though it may well prove that some of them are interdependent and thus help to interpret one another.

1. *What should determine the claim of any species to be a 'native' of Britain?*

The answer to this depends upon whether it is true that the 'home' of every butterfly, like every bird, is the place of its nativity, and that this place is a fixed spot in space or its immediate vicinity, at which the creature was not only born but at which it endeavours to remain, or to which it strives to return if drifted from it. To the author's mind the evidence in favour of this assumption is conclusive, as indeed it is to the mind of many if not most expert lepidopterists. From which it follows that any butterfly whose egg is found in Britain, irrespective of the stage in which it hibernates, or in the case of regular migrants does not hibernate, is a natural British subject of the butterfly kingdom. From many lists of British butterflies we should therefore remove foreign *vagrants*, such as the Black-veined Brown which is a drifted American species and without an appropriate food-plant in Britain, and the Camberwell Beauty which, though its food-plant is here, does not breed in Britain. They are strangers in a strange land; they cannot by any means be treated as naturalised British subjects, even though so great an authority as Frohawk elects to give them, so to speak, naturalisation papers. These are not valid under any laws of 'naturalisation.' By this system of 'classification' or 'grouping,' the number of true British species of butterfly is reduced from Frohawk's 68 to 63 or 62, the rejected species in his list being the Black-veined Brown, Bath White, Queen of Spain Fritillary, Camberwell Beauty, Long-tailed Blue, and (doubtfully) the Short-tailed Blue. The Large Copper, extinct for 100 years, must also be eliminated, unless the Dutch variety, now said to be introduced artificially, is given 'naturalisation papers,' as it deserves. How far the reduced list should be still further reduced by classifying some of the smaller butterflies, now given the status of species, as varieties of the same species, is a matter that will receive further attention in due course.

2. *Which of the British butterflies are true native 'migrants'?*

This is simply answered: All those which lay eggs in Britain, but which, except in very rare and generally uncertainly recorded instances, do not hibernate with us. These regular seasonal 'migrants' and 'immigrants' are thus, like swallows, martins and other species of native British birds, *non-hardy*. A regular characteristic of these species is that they are always double-brooded and sometimes triple-brooded, from which it follows that because the creature's life ends with its egg-laying, two out of three of the generations of such butterflies have an existence of only about two months covering all four states. The survivors as butterflies of the last clutch of eggs—the last autumnal clutch—complete about a nine months' life-cycle, approximately six of which are spent in warm southern lands. These are laid as eggs, say, about mid-August; they emerge as butterflies about fifty-six days later; they then drift south and return as immigrants to their native haunts, say, in April; they mate with a male of the same autumn brood in the place of their mutual nativity, and then die. By the foregoing reasoning there are thus three species of true British migrants: the Pale Clouded Yellow, the Clouded Yellow, and the Painted Lady.

3. *Why is the distribution of some species, though geographically wide, strictly and sometimes narrowly local?*

Here we come to a problem which has exercised the minds of expert students from the earliest times, and nowhere has the author found any explanation in which its own propounder seemed to feel any confidence. The reason for the absence of conviction on this phenomenon is the lack of generally accepted universal laws which govern the life-history of all butterflies, and which have a bearing on this mystery in Britain as in all other lands.

If, however, certain propositions which the author has laid down as laws are accepted as valid, which by some whose views command respect they may not be, light is at once thrown on this baffling problem we are now considering. It has been assumed on the evidence set forth that:

1. A butterfly like a bird clings to its 'home,' the spot where it originated, the place of its 'nativity', with a tenacity second only to its supreme need of feeding.
2. That if it is drifted from this spot it will endeavour to return to it whenever it is not engaged in its prime necessity of feeding, this overruling need being the chief factor in causing it to drift from home in the first instance, as shown in Chapter IX.
3. That a butterfly like a bird has an inherent sense of the direction of its home which is infallible.

In further support of the validity of these three propositions it may be of interest to give two examples taken from the life-history of two kinds of British butterfly as recorded by high authorities. The first is that of the Small Blue which is widely distributed throughout the British Isles. In England there are only four counties in which it has not been recorded. But in spite of its widespread distribution it is usually extremely local and is generally found frequenting a very limited space of ground, where it occurs year after year in the same spot. Its haunts are *sheltered*. The habit of regularly congregating at the same spot, a stick or leaf of the food-plant, has been observed in the case of the Silver-studded and other Blues. In his book, *Complete Book of Butterflies*, Frohawk records how "a particularly solitary tree, usually a wych-elm, will remain its home year after year."

But a more striking example of the fixity of the birthplace as the home of a butterfly, and its ability to return to it from any distance or direction when the atmospheric currents are favourable, is provided by the Painted Lady. According to Frohawk, "the early immigrants are generally met with singly, frequenting a particular patch of ground, often a space of a few yards by some hedgerow, by the side of a wood or field, where it seems intent to remain, taking short, rapid flights to and fro and settling on the bare ground with expanded wings to bask in the sunshine. If disturbed it dashes away for a short distance, but almost immediately returns to the same spot; this it will do time after time. This habit seems to be peculiar to the vernal immigrants; possibly they may have selected a certain spot for egg-laying and there remain until they have deposited. These early butterflies seem much less attracted by flowers than those appearing later in the season, which delight in feasting on blossoms of various kinds." The first point to be remarked is that this careful record of observed fact supports the author's contention that the mating of separated butterflies is brought about, not by a sense of smell, but by the mechanical function of the return to an identical spot of any survivors of a particular brood to which that spot was native.

As already recorded, Eltringham emphasises that *on the average* only one pair ultimately survives out of perhaps 500 eggs that were originally deposited at the same spot. It may well happen that none of the fruit of the 500 eggs at one or more spots survives the winter, whereas several pairs may survive at other spots in widely separated and more favourable localities. This would account for the widely varying plentifulness of species in different parts of the country in different years, which is a matter of such general observation.

Returning to the question as to why the distribution of some species is strictly and often narrowly local, the answer seems to be this. In the case of those butterflies whose habitat is in sheltered spots, as is that of the Blues quoted, survivors will not only be able to deposit their eggs at the ancestral spot, but during the short period they are on the wing, in what is normally the most quiescent part of the season, they will not drift far afield and thus be mistaken for natives of a new locality. It must also be remembered that the majority of butterflies do not fly when the sun is obscured or when it is raining—that is to say in unsettled weather. Other species, on the other hand, whose habits are different, will be sighted as 'vagrants' all over the country, though their *birthplaces* are equally confined to particular spots in particular localities. In other words, most species of butterflies, like many birds, are able to be regular stay-at-home residents, as all winged creatures *endeavour* to be, whereas others are forced by circumstances to be what in the bird world would be regarded as 'partial migrants,' or 'passage migrants,' but which in reality are enforced vagrants from home. Examples of these are Brimstones, Commas and Red Admirals. In the case of the permanent stay-at-home residents, unfavourable local conditions at the breeding season might destroy complete clutches, thereby still more narrowly circumscribing the future geographical distribution of the species, even to the point of extinction. An interesting example of this was provided by the Large Copper nearly 100 years ago, and about which more will be said in due course. The same may well be true of Camberwell Beauties, long since extinct as *natives*, though not infrequently appearing as foreign vagrants.

4. *What determines the periodic plentifulness and scarcity of certain species?*

Generally speaking this phenomenon is confined to, or at least most noticeable in, those species which do not hibernate in any state in Britain; that is to say the non-hardy 'migrant' Clouded Yellows and Painted Ladies. To a less extent it is true of hardy 'partial migrants' such as Red

Admirals and other species which spend the winter in the winged state. The non-hardy migrant natives are subject to the same considerations as the hardy resident and partially migrant natives; survivors will still return to the same spot to mate and lay. But as the clutch of late autumnal eggs from which the surviving immigrants spring are more liable to decimation by unfavourable weather conditions than are those of hardy residents or hardy partial migrants such as Red Admirals, the liability to a great thinning out of the native population in any but exceptionally propitious years is correspondingly marked. This will be readily conceded. But what is the cause of a sudden and great increase in the number of these creatures in a particular season, and after the lapse of perhaps many years? Here the explanation lies in one of two causes, or in a combination of both.

An exceptionally favourable autumn will ensure that all, or nearly all, of the numerous offspring of single pairs thinly distributed over the country will survive at their birthplaces and 'migrate,' thus ensuring that a large proportion of *ultimate* survivors will immigrate the following spring. Where this cause is operative it is therefore *the weather conditions of the previous autumn*, and not of the subsequent year of visible plentifulness, that leads to the plentifulness. In his account of two famous years of multitudes of Painted Ladies, 1879 and 1903, Frohawk treats as remarkable the fact that both these summers were among the *wettest* on record. He manifestly connects this plentifulness with these wet summers; but if records of the autumns of 1878 and 1902 are still available, it will be found, according to the author's reasoning, that they were exceptionally favourable to the fructifying of the last autumnal eggs of the native Painted Ladies of those two years. Again, according to the author's reckoning, Painted Ladies were probably extremely rare in 1880 and 1904 because of the recorded unfavourable weather of 1879 and 1903. Had the autumn of this year, like that of the previous one, been also propitious for the last broods, there would have been something like a plague of Painted Ladies in 1880 and 1904.

The second cause of a bountiful year will very occasionally lie, not in the weather conditions of the previous autumn, but in the weather conditions *immediately preceding* the sudden appearance of great numbers. These contemporary, or nearly contemporary, weather conditions clearly cannot account for the birth of great numbers of the *natives*, but they will account for a great influx of *foreign vagrants*. If in the usually quiescent summer a most unusual and strong easterly wind occurs, the natives of France, and even of Germany, will, willy-nilly, be drifted backwards to the west across our shores, such foreign vagrants remaining with us until the wind-conditions allow them to return, as every butterfly and bird strives to do, to their native haunts, which, in the case of foreign vagrants, are on the Continent. A careful study of the history of the British 'migrants' reveals how, periodically, the slightly differently coloured variety of the Continent appears in large numbers in Britain. To either or both of these causes we may therefore confidently attribute the respective phases of plenty and scarcity in the non-hardy migrant species.

In this connection it may be of interest to give Frohawk's further account of the phenomenon of Painted Ladies which appeared in hosts in the famous year of 1903. "Frequently," he writes, "years may pass when only single specimens, or a very few, are met with in isolated localities." Then a year may come, such as in 1903, when a sudden and great autumnal *invasion* occurs. The butterflies arrived in hundreds of thousands along the southern and eastern shores and dispersed throughout the British Isles. In that year the great migratory flight was so vast that it extended from the Shetlands to the most southern parts of England and Ireland. The butterflies occurred in swarms along the whole eastern seaboard from Durham to Kent, and whenever observations were made along the Scottish coast they appeared abundantly. It is therefore probable that these butterflies extended in an unbroken line along the entire eastern coast of Britain.

"The first specimens of this vast swarm arrived about September 18th, 1903, and the flight continued for five or six days. Either on the following day, or early on the 20th, they arrived in many thousands, and during the next few days their numbers increased. On September 20th at midday, large numbers of these butterflies suddenly made their appearance over two patches of devil's-bit scabious in full bloom growing in the hollow of a meadow at Hockley, Essex, a few miles inland, where none were seen earlier in the day. The Painted Ladies feasted on the blossoms in company with many other species, including Red Admirals, Peacocks, Brimstones, Browns, Heaths, Small Coppers and Common Blues. (See exceptional drift of Argus Browns, page 90.) Altogether this great assemblage of butterflies formed a charming scene. But this was eclipsed on the 24th, and again on the 25th, when the same plants were covered with them in such profusion that they formed a fluttering mass." So much for the facts. Frohawk's interpretation of the facts is recorded in the following sentences:

"Occasionally great numbers reach our shores in the spring months of certain years, resulting in an abundance of British-born specimens appearing about the end of July and August; and then, during such favourable years, a great and general migration takes place, and autumnal flights of these butterflies arrive on the southern and eastern coasts of Britain; these aliens then mix with the home-bred individuals.

"But the enormous swarms of this species which occasionally and suddenly make their appearance in this country are entirely composed of immigrants from the continent of Europe."

From the foregoing it is clear that in Frohawk's view hosts of butterflies, for no known reason, periodically desert their native territory and fly north, south, east or west, as the case may be, into foreign lands, and there generate their species or variety. But this interesting account and interpretation of the 1903 phenomenon, though rich in facts, lacks any major premise which would bring all the facts into harmony, and bring order into a phenomenon which, as Frohawk leaves it, is chaos. If, however, we apply the laws governing butterfly movement which the author has enunciated elsewhere, the 1903 phenomenon ceases to be mysterious and becomes plain, and not only plain but corroborative of his general thesis. What happened was this.

The unusual numbers of native spring immigrants sprung from the last 1902 broods gave rise to vast numbers of 1903 second broods which were on the wing in September all over the British Isles. In that month, exceptional westerly winds drifted the entire population of Painted Ladies, as well as Red Admirals, Peacocks, Brimstones, etc., from their birthplaces towards the East Coast and beyond. As in the case of the American Black-veined Browns already described and analysed, all the butterflies on a north–south line would come down upon those farther to the east with the inevitable effect of *massing*. The whole host would, however, be found to be flying *towards* the west against the west wind in order to recover the birthplace of each individual of the host. The eastern fringe of the host would have been carried backwards across the English Channel, *and the French Painted Ladies to the east* by the prevailing westerly wind. As the westerly wind subsided, the whole Painted Lady world of France and Britain would begin recovering its lost ground, the easternmost fringe of the British section of it coming in over the sea from France, thereby giving to an observer the inevitable impression that the Painted Ladies of France were invading Britain, whereas in fact there had been a temporary enforced invasion of France by the natives of these islands.

One other point is of importance in its bearing on the Painted Lady population of the next year, that is to say 1904. Frohawk emphasises that it was the *second* brood which swarmed in 1903, that is the *grandchildren* of the numerous spring immigrants of the last 1902 autumn broods. But it is the survivors of the great-grandchildren which are the next year spring immigrants. The author therefore feels safe in deducing that the phenomenal weather conditions which overtook the second broods of Painted Ladies in this cold and wet summer of 1903 entirely upset the population of the critical third broods, thereby rendering 1904 a year of Painted Lady scarcity when, on the face of it, it should have been a year of plenty, if not of plague. So confident is the author in the correctness of this analysis of this famous example that if the records of the weather in the late autumns of 1878 and 1902, and of September 1903, and of a scarcity of Painted Ladies in 1904, show that his assumptions are wrong, he will admit that his whole argument with regard to migration, whether of birds or butterflies, is invalid. If, on the other hand, the records show him to be right, his explanation of the world-wide phenomena of bird and butterfly 'migration' and enforced 'vagrancy' will have been established as correct.

After the foregoing analysis of the Painted Lady phenomena of the years 1879 and 1903 was written, some of the author's lepidopterist friends, with justifiable caution, advised him, if possible, to obtain information of the weather conditions of late autumn in 1878 and 1902, and of September 1903. These have now been obtained through the kindness of the Meteorological Office of the Air Ministry, from which the following facts are established.

In 1878 the mean temperature in the autumn was above the normal with a range of as high as 40°. Gales over England were prevalent in October. In 1902, in the early autumn, the temperature was generally a little below the average, though in some districts it was above. In *October*, however, the temperature was above the normal over the whole of Britain, except on the south-east coast. In this month gales were frequent in the exposed coastal districts. Both temperature and wind were thus favourable to the production and drift of an exceptional number of potential spring 'immigrants' in the years 1879 and 1903, and thus to swarms from summer broods. In August 1903, strong westerly winds and rains and many gales prevailed throughout the month, but with many brilliantly fine intervals during which butterflies in normally sheltered spots, and those which only fly in sunlight, would emerge on the wing. In early September a westerly gale of exceptional severity swept Britain, and particularly the south; reaching its peak on September 10th, when much damage was done on land and sea. This was followed by a short spell of cold northerly and north-westerly winds with night frosts in many parts of the country. These must have exterminated the bulk of prospective parents of the third broods of Painted Ladies and Clouded Yellows, thus ensuring that 1904 was an exceptionally poor Painted Lady and Clouded Yellow year instead of making it, as would be expected, a year of plague of such insects. Between September 23rd and 26th the weather turned fine, during which time the vast drifted butterfly population would be recovering its lost ground and reaching home.

In short, the official records show that the weather conditions which the author *assumed* in his analyses of the 1903 phenomenon were, in fact, exactly as he had calculated that they must have been.

A further striking corroboration of this analysis of the Painted Lady 'invasion' of 1903 is provided by Newman in the case of an 'invasion' by Camberwell Beauties in the year 1820. He records that Wailes, in his *Catalogue of the Lepidoptera of Northumberland and Durham*, wrote: "Our fellow member, Mr. William Backhouse, informed me that about the year 1820 he saw vast numbers of this species strewing the seashore at Seaton Carew, Durham, both in a dead and living state. Now, continues Mr. Wailes, it is surely more reasonable to suppose that these specimens had been blown from the land than that they had crossed a sea at least three hundred miles. . . . Mr. Backhouse informs me that it has been repeatedly found near Seaton, Durham, and often floating on the river Tees."

Mr. Wailes was mistaken in thinking that a sea passage of 300 miles is any obstacle to an oversea invasion. In this case the Camberwell Beauties had, as he says, been 'blown' from the land, but the land was Norway or Northern Europe where these butterflies were native. The finding of large numbers of these butterflies floating on the sea, a common experience, was due to the exhaustion of the insects in their vain effort to reach their *foreign* homes from which they had been drifted by exceptional north-easterly winds. Subsequent invasions of Camberwell Beauties have been due to similarly exceptional weather conditions. Every butterfly, like every bird, has a precise limit to its power of sustained flight, and it is owing to this fact that myriads of birds and butterflies perish annually, a process which is a large if not principal factor in maintaining the balance of nature in the world of winged creatures.

Another remarkable 'invasion' of England, this time on the south coast, is recorded by Morris of Small Whites on July 5th, 1846. On this occasion the mass was so great that it obscured the sun from people on the cross-Channel steamers, and the butterflies strewed the sea. Morris records that "the flight reached England about noon and dispersed themselves inland and along the shore. During the sea-passage of the butterflies, the weather was calm and sunny with scarce a puff of wind stirring. But an hour or so after they reached 'terra firma,' it began to blow 'great guns' from the south-west, the direction whence the insects came." In this case a vast population of *native* Small Whites had been drifted across to France by a northerly wind. As this slackened the butterflies began to recover their lost ground and would naturally arrive home ahead of the south-west wind which replaced the northerly one.

Another point should be noted. This host, like that of September 1903, included many other species, which proves conclusively that there was one compelling cause governing the drift of them all simultaneously—the wind.

5. *Why have some species apparently become extinct, and is there any possibility of such species reappearing as natives?*

The best-known example of an extinct British species is the Large Copper which was common in the Fen District in 1830, but which gradually vanished during the 'forties. Its extinction in England is generally attributed to the drainage and reclamation of the Fens. But this seemingly natural and sufficient explanation of the total disappearance of the very local variety of this species, a variety of which is common in Holland and elsewhere on the Continent, is not apparently the complete one. In an article in *The Times* of September 3rd, 1928, it was disclosed that in the early 'forties an old professional collector, Mr. Harding, visited Holme Fen where he found a thriving trade by old and young in the caterpillars which fed on the Great Water Dock. He confessed, in 1883, to having himself bought two dozen for 9*d.* and to having retailed them at 1*s.* each! A few years later he revisited the ground. Holme Fen was, and apparently still is, there, as is the food-plant, but the Large Coppers had vanished and have never since returned. Here, therefore, seems to be the true explanation of the extinction of the Large Copper at what was once its metropolis.

Now it is of interest to note that in years subsequent to its extinction as a *native*, a few specimens of the *Continental* variety have been taken in Britain. These were *vagrants* carried across the Channel from their native haunts on the Continent. But because the native British variety has not been taken in this country for nearly a hundred years it is clear that the vagrants from other lands, even though conditions in this island have been proved to be suitable for them, do not *naturally* breed here. This fact not only supports the conclusion that every butterfly like every bird naturally breeds at its birthplace, but it seems to prove that if the offspring of any native species of butterfly is killed off gradually, or in a single season by some adverse circumstance, that species will almost certainly, *without the intervention of Man*, become, as a *native*, as extinct as the Great Auk.

But here the question arises—can a Continental variety be naturalised as a native by artificial means? In this connection the same article in *The Times* furnishes most interesting information. Apparently in 1913 Captain Purefoy had successfully established a German variety of the Large Copper on a private marsh in Ireland *after introducing the German food-plant*. In 1925, a committee of the Royal Entomological Society, encouraged by Captain Purefoy's Irish experiment, prepared a 'sanctuary' in Norfolk, and in it let loose females of the Dutch variety obtained from Holland. These laid their eggs; and the young larvae emerged, weathered the winter, and the first butterfly "gleamed over the sedges on June 29th." On July 17th, the first females were appearing, "courted e'er their wings were dry by ardent suitors." Everywhere over the fen flew dozens of *males*. "Since then," the narrator goes on, "*batavus* (the Dutch variety) has been appearing in numbers, and the females were laying their eggs till late in August."

There *The Times*' story of this interesting experiment ends. The author has since been told that the Large Copper is now established in this experimental sanctuary, but he has been unable to determine: (1) whether the imported *batavus* is laying and feeding on the English food-plant or on an imported food-plant; (2) whether the Dutch Variety, if it is feeding on the English food-plant, has recovered its ancient English markings. The one thing, however, which is clear is that without artificial interference the Large Copper would still be extinct as an English butterfly, even though the environment is still available for it. The Dutch variety, only a short way across the sea, remained at home till forcibly translated. In this connection, the experiment with Swallow-tails reared in England, in captivity *on the German food-plant*, recorded in Part II, is of interest, as also is Mr. Lorne Campbell's attempt to found a colony of Speckled Woods in the Isle of Canna.

There is, however, one very exceptional set of circumstances under which a local native variety, or even a foreign one, might get established *naturally* as a native in a new locality; or in which a species or variety for a very long time extinct in Britain, or in a particular locality in Britain, might reappear. If immediately after mating, and before the egg-laying took place, a foreign or distinct local variety or race were drifted from its home, and were prevented from returning to its birthplace before the necessity of egg-laying asserted itself—a period which seems to be four days or more—the eggs would perforce be extruded. In this connection a curious case of egg-laying enforced on 'migrating' butterflies is mentioned by Williams. In describing such a flight at Trincomalee, Ceylon, he records that "several bushes of the food-plant in the line of flight were covered with eggs, as if handfuls of sago had been thrown at them . . . the process of laying eggs was totally contrary to what one usually observes—there was no attempt to choose a suitable leaf, no deliberation displayed about the operation at all, but every female seemed possessed with the one insane idea of getting rid of her eggs with the utmost expedition, regardless of the fate of the future larvae, *and then madly continuing her flight*"—that is to say towards the spot where the eggs *would* have been laid if the creature had been able to reach it.

Now Williams makes it clear from numerous records of observations that normally a migrant butterfly's migratory flight, or 'ecstasy' as he calls it, immediately ceases on laying its eggs, thereby confirming that it is the effort to reach its birthplace which is the driving force of the immigration. When this spot is reached the migratory urge ceases, and thereafter the butterfly flutters about in the immediate neighbourhood feeding, and as already shown, clings tenaciously to the neighbourhood of this spot. He also emphasises that at the commencement of a 'migration,' or 'immigration' as it would be more accurate to say, the butterflies are immature, their maturity developing normally at the conclusion of the migratory flight. All these observations confirm the author's case that normally the original birthplace of the butterfly is the 'magnet' for immigration and reproduction. The abnormal example quoted—and there are other such cases on record[1]—seems to show, however, that circumstances occasionally arise in which the creature's necessity to extrude its eggs occurs when it is absent from its birthplace though still striving 'madly' to reach it. Whether the phenomenon recorded by Williams resulted in establishing a new home is not stated. In that case, the flood-plant was almost certainly extremely common and widespread, so that the enforced and premature egg-laying on a suitable food-plant was almost assured. In the case of butterflies with an extremely common food-plant in Britain, the same cause may lead to the establishment of new colonies, as in a case recorded by Mr. Lorne Campbell in Canna where woods which did not exist seventy years

[1] A striking example of the natural establishment of new colonies of normally resident natives is provided by the White Admiral. (See page 144.)

ago have now become the haunt of appropriate *moths* which, according to South, had not previously been recorded in the Hebrides. The list includes no butterflies,[1] and none of the six species recorded hibernate in the ova state. The conclusion therefore seems to be that the colonies were founded by homing vagrants, upon whom egg-extrusion was enforced as in the case quoted by Williams in Ceylon. The woods presumably consist of trees or shrubs which are the common and widely distributed food-plants of the new moth colonies, and which would thus occur on the vagrant's route without any divergence from that route for the purpose of 'looking for' the appropriate food-plant. (See pages 25-6.)

This seems to be the only set of circumstances in which new colonies of butterflies can become native to new localities, or in which a native British species that had become genuinely extinct for the reasons already given could be restored *naturally* by the naturalisation of a vagrant foreign variety of the same species. That this has not occurred naturally in the case of the Large Copper seems to harmonise with these considerations. In the case of the famous foreign vagrant, the Camberwell Beauty, the food-plant (willow, sallow, birch, elm) *is* widely distributed, and it might therefore be expected that an influx of these vagrants would lead, as in the case in Ceylon, to the enforced egg-extrusion on the appropriate food-plant, and thus to the naturalisation of a foreigner. But these rare influxes always occur *in the autumn,* and the Camberwell Beauty is apparently single-brooded. These drifted specimens are thus immature, and will not mate till the following spring, by which time survivors will be back at their foreign homes.

As the sexes actually mate at their mutual birthplace the question of the possibility or otherwise of cross-mating between the 'varieties' or 'races' of the same species of different lands, or localities in the same land, does not here arise. The barrier which prevents the compulsorily extruded eggs of a vagrant from perpetuating themselves in a foreign environment, and thus re-establishing an extinct native species or variety, must, by the author's reasoning, generally be attributed to the scarcity of the appropriate food-plant on the homing route. For the foregoing reasons the conclusion seems to be that the prospects of the *natural* re-establishment of an extinct native butterfly by the naturalisation of a foreign variety of the same species is extremely remote, though not, as far as can be judged, beyond the bounds of possibility under circumstances such as have been recorded in Ceylon and considered here.

6. *To what cause, or causes, are we to attribute variations of particular species?*

Here we are entering a realm in which the greatest biologians are at variance. Indeed the question has an intimate bearing on the whole vexed question of classification on which the authorities so widely differ. On

[1] See the case, page 158, since recorded of Speckled Woods taken for the first time in Canna, and from which Mr. Campbell hopes to be able to found a colony from progeny of these vagrants reared in captivity.

this matter, involving an exhaustive knowledge of genetics to which the author lays no claim, he will not rush in where even genetical experts tread warily. How vexed and uncertain is this question will be readily appreciated by any layman who tries to trace the common or popular name of any particular species of butterfly from the scientific classification of experts. For quite a long time the author was unable to discover, for example, the homely name of *Vanessa cardui*, as generally used for the Painted Lady, and for reasons already shown.

Avoiding, therefore, the wider aspects of butterfly classification, the author will stick to the narrower aspect of variation as it has occurred from time to time in earlier chapters of this book, and as it will constantly recur in Part II.

First of all, what is a *species*? This, as has already been said, has been settled once and for all by Sir Edward Poulton, F.R.S., when he defined a species as "an interbreeding community," or, in the language of Genesis, creatures after their own 'kind.' How rigid are the bounds of species, or interbreeding communities, and how wide the possible variations within this ring-fence of 'kind,' is well illustrated by the breeding experiments undertaken with a view to bringing into being a new species by crossing variations of that species with the wild form. A notable experiment of this nature has been carried out by many experts with the fruit fly, *Drosophila melanogaster*. An egg of this fly laid in the first day of a month hatches out and produces offspring which themselves lay eggs on the fifteenth of that month. Thus 24 successive generations can be raised in a year, and some 800 generations of it have already been selectively bred in the attempt to transform some of its offspring into a new species. By exposing these creatures to X-rays, the rate at which marked variations, or *mutations*, appear is greatly increased. All these experiments have brought into being over 100 *varieties* of *Drosophila*, many of them more divergent in appearance from one another than they are from other species; and yet all these variations are perfectly fertile when crossed with the wild form, or with one another, and infertile with all other species and *their* varieties, no matter how alike in appearance. On the other hand, wild 'species' or 'families' rarely if ever interbreed *naturally*, and when they can be induced to cross by the machinations of Man the result is either no progeny or offspring sterile with one another, though not in all cases with one of the species which produced the hybrid offspring. Dewar has pointed out that there seems to be some fundamental difference between the varieties produced by Man and nature.

Now these exhaustive experiments with *Drosophila* have produced results which should throw light on the mystery of slight variations, and of mutation, in butterflies of the same species—or 'kind,' as the author prefers to express it. In considering this question we will confine ourselves to British butterflies, because what is true for them is likely to be true for all foreign kinds. In order still further to simplify the inquiry, we will select a well-known species which shows marked geographical variations—the Brown Argus.

This butterfly is distributed widely throughout Britain, and with such marked and permanent local variations that 100 years ago some of the local varieties were variously classified as distinct species. Both Newman and Morris, however, came to a reasoned conclusion, finally accepted by their contemporaries, that they were "geographical *races* of the same species." Newman records the perfectly distinct markings and colouring to be found in the south, in the Chalk district; in the Midlands; in the Manchester district, and in Scotland. So clear-cut are these differences that an expert could tell at a glance from which district the particular variety came, just as an expert can tell with certainty what species or kind of butterfly will develop from a particular kind of egg. It will be remembered, and in Part II it will be seen, that there are extreme differences in the eggs of every true species of butterfly, and that the egg of every true species remains constant. Frohawk, in his beautiful illustrations, shows on the same plate the wide variations of the Brown Argus, but only one *egg* for them all. Indeed, a careful study of the illustrations of most of the eggs of the native British Blues and Whites, for example, must almost inevitably raise in the mind of many the suspicion that they should be classified as *geographical races* of the same species rather than as separate species. In this connection it is noteworthy that in the view of Newman, the *earliest* and not the *latest* stages of a butterfly's life are the most likely to furnish us with permanent characteristics. Or, in other words, that the egg determines the species or kind; and the variations, whether in the caterpillar, chrysalis or butterfly, the effects of geographical and other environmental influences. And here it may be well to emphasise that although the eggs of the various Whites and Blues, for example, are similar in form, they vary in markings and to some extent in colour. This is exactly paralleled in the bird world where, for example, the Indian *black drango* lays three differently marked and coloured eggs in three distinct localities in India. The variations in the colour and marking of the eggs of birds which are native to distinct localities are emphasised by Dewar,[1] and all are shown, conclusively, to be geographical races of the same species and not distinct species. Further reference is made to this matter in Part II when considering some aspects of classification.

How great are these environmental influences on the appearance of butterflies in their later stages is well illustrated by Eltringham, who records that the caterpillars of the same brood of the Common Peppered moth, if reared on white twigs, became silver grey; on black twigs, black; and in bright green surroundings, bright green! Still more remarkable, says Eltringham, is the way in which caterpillars kept on speckled lichen-covered bush develop not merely the colouring but the very pattern of their surroundings. Earlier references to this environmental appearance

[1] Douglas Dewar, F.Z.S., author of *Birds at the Nest*.

and variation have been made in the chapter on mimicry, and will constantly recur when dealing in Part II with the life-histories of British butterflies.

One, and only one, confusion appears to exist between these geographical variations or races of the Brown Argus, and that is on the border in the neighbourhood of Newcastle. Here, according to Newman, "they appear to be mules, or hybrids, between the two species, partaking in some degree of the characteristics of both." It should be noted that in this quotation Newman, always most careful in the choice of his words, has slipped into the use of the term *species* in spite of his previous emphasis on the fact that these varieties of Brown Argus were "geographical races of the *same* species," just as are Hottentots and Englishmen. This constant tripping in the use of the term 'species' is not confined to Newman. It occurs in every authority the author has studied.

But as Newman and Morris are relatively ancient authorities, it may be well to stress that Frohawk, apart from his classification of the Brown Argus as *Lycenae astrarche*, accepts and confirms the conclusions of Newman that the distinct local variations of this butterfly are geographical races and not distinct species. Frohawk, however, does not mention the possibility of the variety found near Newcastle being a *hybrid*. Enough of the facts of this butterfly have now been given for an analysis to be made of these variations in the light of what the author has pointed out earlier on the question of distribution *as governed by the laws of flight*, to which no reference has been made by the authorities he has consulted.

The first point, and one made several times before in other connections, is that the natural home of a butterfly is its birthplace, and that this is the spot at which any descendant of an individual butterfly endeavours to remain when not feeding in its neighbourhood, and at which, through close propinquity, the sexes meet and mate. If this is correct, as the author is convinced that it is for the reasons given previously, the distinctive geographical variations will remain constant; furthermore, butterflies like birds must be close *inbreeders*. In cases where the Brown Argus of one distinctive variation, or race, have been found in the localities of another distinctive variation, or 'race,' as they are reported to have been on rare occasions, the explanation is that these were rare *vagrants* which returned to their native locality when the air-currents that drifted them away permitted such a return. Such an exceptional drift of Browns and Blues and other inveterate stay-at-homes, was well exemplified in the famous 1903 phenomenon when, it will be remembered, Heaths, Browns, Small Coppers, and Blues, were associated with the vast swarms of Painted Ladies, Red Admirals, Brimstones and other regular migrant or vagrant butterflies.

The markings and shades of the particular geographical races of the same 'kind' are readily attributable to the local characteristics of the environment, particularly of the food-plant, which is affected by soil and temperature. On the analogy of the *Drosophila*, whose variations are so affected by X-rays, we should expect the strength and frequency of the sun-rays to have their effect on differentiation, and this we do find to be the case as will be shown in many instances in Part II. Indeed, when we consider the influence of temperature on a local environment, it seems as natural to look for distinct and identifiable variations among local resident natives in the British Isles, from Land's End to John o'Groats, with a difference of latitude of about 10°, as among those which occur between Continental and British varieties.

In short, the laws which normally confine particular butterflies to particular spots will inevitably tend to keep the geographical 'races,' or 'varieties,' distinct, so that cross-breeding between the geographical races or varieties will not occur naturally. Fantastic as the analogy may sound, the same is true of the human species under natural conditions, which was made of one blood or 'kind,' to dwell upon the face of the whole earth. This *natural* segregation of the varieties, or 'races,' of human beings has been overcome by Man's *will*, by the use of which he has not only developed *means* of overcoming the natural geographical barriers that separate, shall we say, a white man from a black, yellow or red woman, but by the use or misuse of which will he has, in the case of some human varieties, *determined* to interbreed. The rarest cases of this determination to cross-breed are to be found in the English, German, Scandinavian and Japanese, varieties of man which still remain, generally, 'true to type,' though this tendency is diminishing. Herein, as the author sees it, is the cause of the noteworthy difference that exists between the man-ordained *chaos* of human race variation, and the natural *order* of butterfly race variation in any particular species or 'interbreeding community.' Whether Man's deliberate hybridisation of his unique species is a good or bad thing is a matter of opinion, in the case that is to say of different colour and habit. But whatever opinions we may hold on this question, the gulf between man's deliberate race-mixing and butterfly race-purity under natural conditions, exists, and the reason for the gulf is that man has mastered his environment, whereas natural law, mainly through the wind and the 'homing instinct,' is the master of butterflies.

But to complete the argument, there are two other points to be made. Variations *in* a geographical race, as distinct from variations *between* geographical races, is to be expected—just as distinguishable physical variations exist in a local community of human beings whose habitual food and drink varies. Further, individual human variations within such general local variations occur owing to marriage. If, therefore, we take any local 'race' or 'community' of the Brown Argus, or other species, whose food-plant and other local circumstances vary slightly, as in the case of the different grasses upon which the caterpillars feed, we should expect to find *local* variations within the still distinct *geographical* variation of the same species of butterfly.

The other point is this: Do hybrids between two geographical races occur *naturally*, as in the alleged case of 'hybrid or mule' specimens of the Brown Argus in the Newcastle area as suggested by Newman, and to which a reference has already been made? In the first place, Newman is in error in his expression 'hybrid or mule,' because, as shown in the breeding experiments of the *Drosophila* fly, the hybrids between the variations are not mules. On the contrary, such hybrids are perfectly fertile with any of their own 'kind' or 'species,' but infertile with any other species, or variety of an alien species.

In the second place, Newman's suggestion that the Newcastle Brown Argus is a hybrid is admittedly only a surmise, and it seems more likely that in this latitude, on the border between England and Scotland, the northern and southern environmental conditions merge with a consequent tendency for the parasitic caterpillars of the two varieties to reveal characteristics of both geographical environments. If, on the other hand, this curious blending of the northerly and southerly variations of the Argus Brown *is* brought about by cross-mating under natural conditions, it must be due to some external natural force which brings the two varieties into intimate association by propinquity, just as hybrids of the same species of plant, or *Drosophila* fly, can be brought about by man's intervention, though in a state of nature they seldom, if ever, occur. Indeed, so closely are butterflies associated with their local food-plants that inter-pollination of these food-plants by different varieties of the same butterfly might be expected to be reflected in the butterflies themselves.

The author's conclusion on variations and mutations, and on their causes, is therefore this. In all but extra-abnormal circumstances the variations of the geographical races of the same species, or 'kind', of butterfly are due to environmental causes such as sun-rays (*vide* X-rays in the artificial breeding experiments with *Drosophila melanogaster*), variation of the food-plant and cross-pollination, and not to cross-breeding, except in one case. The exception is in the case of double or multi-brooded butterflies where a member of a first brood breeds with a member of a second brood which, owing to temperature conditions, is differently marked or coloured. In this connection see Comma, page 216. At the same time, if any particular species of butterfly could be selectively bred in captivity for scores of generations, exactly the same phenomenon could be produced as in the test case of *Drosophila*. In other words, Man artificially can selectively produce variations which nature, left to herself, seldom produces for the mechanical reasons inherent in the laws of dynamics governing the movement of butterflies on the wing. In this respect, as in so many others, butterflies reveal their kinship to the vegetable kingdom where the same laws govern plant and vegetable species and varieties to which the appropriate butterflies are parasitic.

Butterflies were created after their 'kind,' just as were "the grass and herb yielding seed after his kind . . . whose seed was in itself, after his kind." This, as already shown, has been confirmed by Sir Edward Poulton, F.R.S., in his decisive definition of species as an interbreeding community, which definition in its turn has been remarkably confirmed by the selective breeding experiments with *Drosophila melanogaster*. In his book, *What is Life?* published by the Cambridge University Press, Erwin Schrödinger confirms the accuracy of the author's brief account of the experiments with this scientifically famous insect. He emphasises the analogy between the effect of X- and Y-rays, as applied by man, and the more modest 'dosage,' as he calls it, by nature. Man's artificially produced *mutations* may be sufficiently drastic to inflict sterility on the mutated victim; though as yet this has not, apparently, been achieved. But if this sterility *was* induced, the result would be to extinguish such an abortion of that species, not to launch a new species. "One set of chromosomes," writes Schrödinger, "is from the father, one from the mother. Neither chance nor destiny can interfere with that." Farther on he adds: "We know definitely to-day that Darwin was mistaken in regarding the small, continuous, accidental variations, that are bound to occur even in the most homogeneous population, as the material on which natural selection works. . . . Selection has no effect because the small continuous variations are not inherited." Again he writes: "The whole (four dimensional) pattern of the 'phenotype,' *the visible and manifest nature of the individua*', is reproduced without appreciable change for generations, permanent within centuries—though not within tens of thousands of years." In short: the fixity of species is proved by experience, and confirmed by experiment, within historical times. Instability of species is *assumed* in prehistoric times, that is to say in fabulous times. But events alleged to have taken place in fabulous times are, manifestly, fables. Organic evolution is a myth.

From all of which we must conclude that within the ring-fence of 'kind,' necessary for the preservation of *order*, the Creator, in His infinite wisdom and goodness, provided scope for His supreme creature, Man, made in His own image, to co-operate with Him in the development of that infinite variety of beautiful variations of animals, flowers, plants, shrubs and trees with which the world has been enriched. And if this is true, we may be sure that the most beautiful and profitable variations, and hybrids, will be 'pro-created' by those who approach nature with the reverence, awe and praise, which Man owes to the Creator of all things, including himself.

Chapter XII

INSTINCT

We have now reached the point at which something should be said on the mystery or miracle of mind and 'instinct.' Have butterflies any gleam of understanding or intellect, or are they in every aspect of their wonderful life mere creatures of blind 'instinct,' bound to act as they do, and without knowledge of their own existence? On this complex matter no one who has studied closely, and with an unprejudiced mind, the works of ancient and modern natural historians can have failed to detect an inconsistency in both. Let us first consider the attitude of the modern school of thought on this seemingly insoluble question.

It has already been shown that modern biologians are loath to allow any reasoning mind to a butterfly, not even self-consciousness or a knowledge of its own existence. And yet, from the language they all employ, and from the causes to which they attribute certain phenomena of butterfly life, they do implicitly endow the creature with some power of intelligent discrimination, and an appreciation of cause and effect. The theory generally holding the field is that the 'mind' of butterflies, like that of birds, is a combination of primitive 'intelligence' and 'instinct.' Some treat their powers of navigation, particularly in the sphere of 'migration' and 'homing,' as falling within the 'intelligence' sphere; their feeding and reproductive activities being relegated to 'instinct,' which is treated as a sort of 'potted memory' derived from bygone ages and now evolved into instinctive, or automatic, habits. Others reverse the two spheres of 'intelligence' and 'instinct.' But however much they may deny, and even reprobate, the attribution of 'mind' to butterflies, they do in fact allow the creature a 'memory,' whether of the 'potted' or still active variety. But memory implies reflection, and action based upon it is intellectual deliberation from memorised facts. In other words, butterflies are still being credited with a mind that differs in degree but not in kind from that of their fellow-creature, Man.

The endeavour to surmount this difficulty by 'potting' the memory till ıhas evolved into 'instinct' is merely to antedate the implied common denominator, in the highest sphere, between a man and a butterfly. If millions of years ago a butterfly had a memory upon the promptings of which it acted, it was clearly then a higher order of creature than it has since become; if, that is to say, deliberate and calculated beneficial action is superior to 'instinctive,' or automatic, action—as most will allow. In which case evolution so far from having led to the development and improvement of creatures has degraded them, in the highest sphere of existence, from sentient beings to automata—mere slaves of their environment.

But let us turn from the modern school on this question of 'mind' and 'instinct' to what may be called, for lack of a better name, the Classical School; and of this school, to those two great thinkers, Kirby and Spence, who were not only the writers of the great work, *Introduction to Entomology*, but who were also devout and profound believers in the traditional account of Creation, and in a Creator Who specially created butterflies and all else, perfect in the first instance, and once and for all.

Anyone truly interested in the analysis of acts performed by instinct as distinct from those prompted by reflection based on memory, or on the promptings of the senses, should, if he has not done so, read the two letters XXVII and XXXVII in the *Introduction to Entomology*. In these letters either the Rev. William Kirby, or William Spence, reveals not only the most profound thought on the subject with which he is dealing, but brings to his subject a wealth of information on the astonishing performances of insects which cannot fail to hold the attention and excite the admiration of all his readers. It is significant, however, that one of these two famous and perfect collaborators goes out of his way to dissociate himself from the conclusions on instinct of his partner in the great work, and that this is the only disagreement which is disclosed in the four volumes—a fact which well shows the extraordinarily mysterious nature of the power by which so humble a creature as a butterfly orders its existence.

The conclusion reached by one of these two profound philosophers is this: Although in almost every operation which an insect performs it can be demonstrated beyond question that automatic reactions, without any gleam of intellect, are the controlling forces—not excluding variations in the normal way of behaviour which are often cited as proofs of mind—there remain, however, a few of its actions which in his view cannot be so explained; and these, he concludes, we *must* attribute to a reasoning faculty which differs in degree, but not in kind, from that of Man. These reasonable actions he divides into two spheres: the first is that of selective action derived from the senses of sight, smell and taste, and the second is an insect's power of *navigation* from a distant spot to its home, his argument being, as it is to-day, that the creature homes by *recognition* of familiar objects, implying *memory*, which in its turn, and as he stresses, implies *mind*. In other words, flight guided by recognition of landmarks based upon memory is the means by which, in his view, a bird reaches its nest, a bee its hive, or a butterfly its 'home.'

With regard to the first reason for attributing mind to a butterfly—the conscious selective use of the senses—all that need be said is this. The assumption is based upon the assertion that a butterfly's senses are, in fact, of the same order as our own, an assumption which, as Newman emphasises, we have no ground whatever for making. Indeed, this assumption by Kirby or Spence is in contradiction with the elaborate proof by both of them that all the functions of architecture, whether in building a nest, making a honeycomb, spinning a pad of silk for the support of the chrysalis, and other such phenomena, are purely *instinctive*, *mechanical*, or *automatic*. But in these architectural functions, on the face of it, the sense of selective sight must play as great a part as in feeding and reproduction, whether in the siting of the nest or pad or in the erection of the building. Indeed, with the most sympathetic and admiring attitude towards the argument of Kirby or Spence, it is impossible to disregard the inconsistency on this matter of instinct and mind which nowhere appears in any other subject with which they jointly deal.

But it is when we turn to the second sphere of insect existence that the fallacy of attributing 'mind' to a butterfly passes from speculation to certainty. There is no need to repeat what has been said on this matter at considerable length in preceding chapters. Here the author will content himself with saying that the unawareness of the immutable laws which govern the movement of flying creatures of limited flying capacity within a moving and all-embracing medium has necessarily led to a wrong interpretation of the phenomenon of migration, and of 'homing' to a fixed spot through intervening air-currents. Hence the assumption of recognition, implying memory, and deliberate action based on recognised landmarks. It is a remarkable fact that the laws of flight, as revealed by the parallelogram of velocities, have been excluded from the study of bird and butterfly life from the days of Aristotle and Virgil up to the present time. The explanation is to be found in the over-specialised approach to their problems by students of nature in general and of biologians in particular.

We will now face the question, "What *is* Instinct," in the light of the considerations which have been brought to bear upon the subject in this book, and in the author's previous book, *The Cuckoo and other Bird Mysteries*. In order to clarify the issue, the first need is to decide whether there is any one aspect of butterfly existence which must be attributed to a determining mind possessed by the creature *itself*.

1. Does a butterfly disclose any self-conscious determination in its reproductive cycle from the egg to the perfect imago? No. This is almost universally conceded by authoritative natural historians.
2. Do the mechanical motions of the butterfly on the wing necessitate a mind in the flying-machine itself? No, as expert engineers will almost certainly confirm for the reasons given in Chapter VI.
3. Do the 'senses' of a butterfly differ in degree or in kind from our own? They differ in kind, because they themselves *perform* the appropriate actions whereas Man's senses, in all but a few cases, transmit sensation to his mind and thence to his will which becomes the deliberate executor of the appropriate action. *Some* of Man's sense reactions are, however, as automatic as are *all* those of butterflies.
4. Is there any ground for attributing to a butterfly calculated action in migration, immigration, or distribution of butterflies? No. (See Chapters VIII–X.)

5. Is it possible for butterflies to employ recognition as an aid to their navigation? No; neither is there any need for it. (See Chapters VIII–X.)

Having reached the reasoned conclusion that a butterfly has, as expressed in the book of Job, been deprived like the ostrich of understanding, and as Eltringham and other authorities concede, of self-consciousness, let us turn from an insect to a man, and ask ourselves: "What is Man?"

Man is, or can be, a tri-unity—the *whole* man consisting of spirit, soul, and body (1 Thessalonians v. 23). The three components, though perfectly distinct, are so perfectly and delicately compounded that the lines of demarcation are sometimes apt to be confused. The Bible enables us to trace 'scientifically' the clear distinction between spirit and soul. The spirit is that part of Man which *knows*—his mind (1 Corinthians ii. 11). The soul is the seat of the *affections* and *desires*, and so of the *emotions*, and of the active *will*—the self (Matthew xxvi. 38).

Because Man is 'spirit' he is capable of God-consciousness and of communication with God (Job. xxxii. 8; Psalm xviii. 28; Proverbs xx. 27).

Because he is 'soul' he has self-consciousness, and thus personality and individuality (Psalm xiii. 2; xlii. 5, 6, 11).

Because he is 'body' he has, through his senses, world-consciousness, or physical environmental consciousness. Thus Man is, or may be, if he does not succumb to materialism, a trinity in unity and a unity in trinity. Sunk in materialism he approximates to a duality—soul and body, but non-spiritual.

If the foregoing is the correct answer to the question: "What is Man?" the next question to ask ourselves is: "What is a butterfly?" Eliminating spirit which implies God-consciousness, and soul which implies self-consciousness, a butterfly is left with its body through which it has world-consciousness, just as Man has through *his* body. Here we are back once again on the different nature of the senses of Man and insect. As already shown, there are *some* senses in Man which compel action agreeable to the sustenance of life, automatically and without reference to his spirit or his soul. Over-exertion, for example, makes him pant, and increases the speed of his heartbeats. His eyelids react instantly to any sudden exterior threat to his eyesight, be it from particles of matter or excessive light rays, just as a butterfly's wings react to the shining or obscuring of the rays of the sun, and as do the opening and closing of the petals of an evening primrose and other flowers. Doctors and surgeons could no doubt make a complete list of automatic sense-reactions which Man has in common with the animal and vegetable worlds. But apart from these life-saving and health-preserving senses which automatically *perform* essential functions, the bulk of sense-reactions in a man are brought about judiciously by reference to his mind or his emotions. These senses stand in relation to his mind and personality, his spirit and his soul, much as do the home and distant signals on a railway track to the driver and fireman of a train. An exception to this analogy is where machinery, or 'sense-organs,' linked to the signals are introduced, as on the Great Western Railway, which will automatically slow up, and finally stop, the train if the signals are against the driver who, either due to fog or mental aberration, has failed to react reasonably to the signal warning. In one case the signals react on the driver's *mind* and cause him to take appropriate action. In the other case the automatic machinery, the extra sense-organs, do for the train what the driver's mind would do if he were in a position to exercise it.

Now it has already been shown that the lower we go in the order of God's creatures (the term 'lower' being used in the spiritual sense), the more marvellous and complicated is the machinery of existence, and the multiplicity of organs, the one exception being the brain. In place of a brain, a butterfly has what are called ganglions, which are nerve-centres located in the various distinct parts of its anatomy, and which, as previously shown, enable that particular part of the anatomy to continue to operate 'reasonably,' though cut off from the remainder of the body. Thus the members of a butterfly's body are not, strictly speaking, as in Man members one of another. Each part is more highly specialised and isolated.

Any readers who have had the patience to follow the author's reasoning up to this point will now perceive clearly to where the argument is leading him. A butterfly is a creature which in every aspect, and at every stage of its life-cycle, performs reasonable actions which not only sustain it but which contribute their essential quota to the ordered existence of the vegetable kingdom, of which, rather than of the animal kingdom, it is itself a part. Emphasis is laid on this latter point—not only because it is, in the author's view, a fact, but in order to disarm any critic who may twist his argument from the *insect* kingdom to the *animal* kingdom which introduces different considerations, and in which the attribution of soul (self-consciousness) and spirit (mind) can be plausibly maintained.[1]

We have therefore reached, after some circumlocution, the crucial question: "What is instinct?" How can a creature derive the benefits of perfect reason, and itself express reason, if it is totally devoid of any reasoning faculty of its own?

Here we must revert very briefly to the analogy of Man's robot contrivances. It has been shown that Man's external mind, or spirit, can be materialised and made operative by the introduction into his 'creations' of automatic sense-organs which, so long as they remain intact, and therefore subject to the external influences to which they were designed to react, will obey his will. Furthermore, his will need not be continuously 'willing' the activities of his creature when it has been so equipped and launched

[1] Belief in a future life for animals is not confined to Ancient Philosophers, but was shared by such men as John Wesley, Archbishop Benson of Canterbury, and guardedly by Joseph Butler, Bishop of Durham, and author of *The Analogy*.

on its mission. It will continue to be obedient within strictly finite limitations. Man's mind and will, his spirit and his personality, *have been put into commission*. Thus, in his own little way, Man can endow his inanimate creatures with instinct which may be defined as the enforcement of an external will upon mindless creatures through the introduction of the appropriate 'sense-organs.' Each 'sense-organ' thus becomes reasonable with a reasonableness external to itself.

Turning from the creatures of Man, which move and function with the power of rapidly exhausted motive force, to those of nature which are powered with the motive spirit of life, need we flounder interminably in attempting to define instinct as revealed by so marvellous a creature as a butterfly? The butterfly is a fact. That it behaves reasonably, indeed with reasonableness and foresight which stagger us in their perfection, is a fact. That in many, literally, vital aspects of its life it can be proved that it has no volition of its own is a fact. That Man can compel mindless things to act reasonably and profitably (though all too often unprofitably) is a fact.

Is it not therefore in accordance with pure reason, without any buttress of Faith, to define the instinct by which the life of a butterfly is ordered as the necessity of acting reasonably, and therefore of obeying, absolutely, the will of its Creator Who, through a multiplicity of sense-organs which we cannot analyse, has put His will and good pleasure into commission for the benefit of His greatest but only erring creature—Man?

That, at least, is the author's interpretation of the miracle of instinct. Nature, like the Bible, is the Word of God made partially manifest, and in the early days of Man it was his only 'Bible.' If the Book of nature is to be searched with profit, as it is meant to be, and not to our undoing, it must, like the Bible, be searched humbly, and in the fear of the Lord which is the beginning of wisdom. Searched in such a spirit, both Books hold glorious revelations for the benefit and happiness of Man. Only from the spiritually blind is revelation withheld.

PART II

BRITISH BUTTERFLIES

Life Cycle, Distribution and Notes

INTRODUCTION

In the Preface to this book the author confessed his lay status as a lepidopterist, and acknowledged his debt to the great authorities for most of the facts in the marvellous life-histories of the various species of butterfly. During two periods of his life he has collected butterflies, and in both he felt the need of a book in which the salient facts of these life-histories were clearly set forth and disentangled, so to speak, from the general account of the butterfly in question. Remembering his own needs as an amateur collector, he has endeavoured to supply, in some small measure, what may be a similar need in budding lepidopterists.

Every effort has been made to ensure that the facts set down are indeed facts, and with this in view many authorities have been consulted. Where the authorities differ, those given by Mr. Frohawk have generally been adopted, though where necessary, contrary opinions are quoted. Mr. Russwurm has most kindly read and passed the *facts* as being in accordance with the latest knowledge.

In each short life-history attention is particularly concentrated upon the egg, and in this respect the author's description is drawn, in a condensed form, from Mr. Frohawk's classic work, *Natural History of British Butterflies*. The descriptions of the caterpillars, chrysalids, and imagines, are very abbreviated, and these are derived and condensed from various sources. To describe in words the details of the colouring, shading, and markings of the creature in these three stages would be interminable. Indeed, it has always seemed to the author that much printer's ink has been wasted in the past on such word pictures, which at their best are poor substitutes for such beautiful illustrations as those provided by Mr. Frohawk, or by Mr. Russwurm, F.R.E.S., in his recently published work, *The Butterflies of Great Britain*.

The only original part of the ensuing life-histories of British butterflies is the *Notes*. These, in all cases, are related to the general thesis contained in Part I which was written before a detailed study of the British species and races was undertaken.

In order to avoid undue prolixity it was decided to concentrate upon one standard work: Mr. Frohawk's was selected because of his unique study of the butterfly in its original state—the egg. These notes are thus, in the main, a commentary on the *Natural History of British Butterflies*. Though many of Mr. Frohawk's conclusions are questioned, the facts and illustrations which it contains provide, in the author's view at all events, remarkable corroboration of the general thesis contained in Part I of this book.

The 68 'species' of British Butterflies listed have been divided into five distinct groups—Hardy Native Residents; Hardy Native Vagrants;

Non-hardy Native Migrants; Foreign Vagrants; Extinct Native Residents. And here it should be re-emphasised that the term 'migration,' hallowed by usage in the case of birds as well as of butterflies, is an inappropriate term for the phenomenon. It implies *objectivity*, whereas the truth is that 'migration' *from* the birthplace of the creature is enforced 'vagrancy' brought about by the overruling movement of the atmosphere. In the case of non-hardy natives—the Clouded Yellows and Painted Ladies—this enforced drift to the south empties Britain of these butterflies in the late autumn, and is the means by which they are preserved from extinction. On the other hand, the Red Admirals and other butterflies which are hardy, which are on the wing in the late autumn, and spend the winter in the winged state, also drift to the south, but the more northern natives will in many cases drift to, and hibernate in, England, whereas the Southern England natives will drift farther south, and there remain on the wing, or hibernate, according to climatic conditions. All, however, whether hardy or non-hardy, will return 'home' to reproduce their kind in the spring when, in the Northern Hemisphere, the drift of the atmosphere from the south to the north sets in—for all species which hibernate in any stage other than that of the winged state are, from the nature of things, almost universally 'stay-at-homes,' or in other words hardy native residents. In this latter case an exception sometimes occurs where the insect is double- or multi-brooded, exceptional winds imposing vagrancy on the imagines of the last broods. The Bath White, Queen of Spain Fritillary, and Long-tailed Blue are examples of Continental residents whose last broods are occasionally drifted to Britain in the autumn.

A wotd must now be said on the vexed question of classification. Elsewhere in this book references have been made to the confusion that exists on this matter. Indeed, it may truthfully be said of butterfly classification—*Quot homines, tot sententiae*. The author has adopted that of Frohawk,[1] which seems to be that of Newman, but he must confess that he har been unable to determine upon what precise basis it rests. For example: the well-known Painted Lady, classified by Frohawk as *Pyrameis cardui*, has been variously classified as follows:

Cynthia cardui	Kirby, Stephens, Duncan, Westwood.
Vanessa cardui	Godart, Latreille, Meyer, Hubner.
Libythia cardui	Lamarck.
Papilio cardui	Linnaeus, Fabricius, Haworth, Lewin, Donovan, Shaw, Panzer, Wilks, Albin, Harris.
Pyrameis cardui	Newman, Frohawk.

In many other cases the second names ('species'), as well as the first '(genus)' are a complete higgledy-piggledy. In this connection Eltringham,

[1] The latest classification as previously stated in the Foreword, is printed as an Appendix.

in *Butterfly Lore*, writes: "The problem of reference to exotic insects which have no English names has been a difficulty. To the unscientific reader the Latin names used by men of science are uninteresting and, it may be, even meaningless. Every known creature has two Latin names, the first that of the Genus to which it belongs, and the second its own distinguishing name, the name of the Species." Contrary to Eltringham's assertion, the author, a layman, finds this scientific higgledy-piggledy in classification extremely interesting, because it shows in a most striking way that scientists are themselves still ignorant of the deeper mysteries of what constitutes a 'kind' of butterfly or moth. Many examples of this confusion occur in the life-histories of butterflies.

Mercifully for the lay student there is tolerable unanimity on the vulgar English name, without which he would be completely lost, as indeed would be the experts of different generations in which totally different classifications were in vogue. The reason for this confusion seems to be the almost universal conviction that similarities in appearance of the winged creature are the correct guide; whereas, as Newman urged, the surest means of correct classification is almost certainly contained in the *earliest* stage of the creature. Having little detailed knowledge of the eggs, Newman therefore used the next stage—the caterpillar—as his guide. Holland again and again says of American species "early stages unknown." Mr. Frohawk, however, has made the remarkable distinction of the eggs of true *species* plain for all to see, and without presuming to dogmatise on such a matter, it certainly seems that the egg and life-habit, rather than the appearance of the imago, should be the principal guides of the Classifier. By such a method, the number of British *species* would be greatly reduced, and many butterflies at present granted the status of 'species,' would be reduced to that of 'geographical races' of the same species. This applies, for example, to some of the Whites and Blues, whose eggs and life-habits respectively, though not identical, are strikingly similar.

The eggs of a distinct species of bird vary considerably, but not to the point at which there is any difficulty in deciding what kind of bird will emerge from the egg, unless we exclude some of the finches which the author has always found confusing. In this respect, therefore, there seems to be a close analogy between the eggs of birds and butterflies, though in all other respects butterfly eggs seem to be comparable to flower and plant seeds.

In the course of his study of the authorities, the author has frequently met the expression: "a distinct species but closely related." This is a contradiction in terms if we accept Poulton's definition of species as "an interbreeding community." It only has meaning on the assumption that butterflies are descended from some primitive common stock and that, in the course of ages, they have developed variations, or *mutations*, which eventually have become so distinct that they are now unable to interbreed with the parent stock—thus starting new but 'related' species. This theory, or, to be more accurate, hypothesis seems to be contradicted by the remarkable tenacity with which 'races' cling to their birthplaces, as well as by the experiments with the *Drosophila melanogaster*, to which a reference was made in Chapter XII. The complete dissimilarity of the eggs of species which are classified as 'related,' seems to confirm the original and continuing ring-fence of species, or 'kind.' Furthermore, butterflies with eggs which reveal slight variations, but which are still hardly distinguishable from one another, seem to fall naturally into the ranks of 'geographical races' of the same species, and which might therefore be capable of being interbred artificially, though in a state of nature they remain distinct on account of the inveterate 'home-keeping,' or 'home-seeking,' of all insects. A reference to this matter is also made in Chapter XI.

To conclude: The author hopes that his notes on the life-histories and life-cycles of British butterflies, read in conjunction with Part I of this book, may at least stimulate new interest and study among any who may feel disposed to join the happy throng of butterfly collectors. It is also hoped that the tabulated data at the beginning of each life-history may be useful as a handy guide to identification, and as an aid to the making of a collection of perfect specimens bred from the egg in captivity. The periods of egg 'germination,' and of the larval and pupal stages, are in all cases approximate, because climatic and other environmental conditions play strange tricks with butterflies, as they do with the flowers and plants to which they are parasitic.

HARDY NATIVE RESIDENTS

Swallow-tail	*Papilio machaon*
Black-veined White	*Aporia crataegi*
Large White	*Pieris brassicae*
Small White	*Pieris rapae*
Green-veined White	*Pieris napi*
Orange Tip	*Euchloë cardamines*
Wood White	*Leucophasia sinapis*
Silver-washed Fritillary	*Argynnis paphia*
High Brown Fritillary	*Argynnis adippe*
Dark Green Fritillary	*Argynnis aglaia*
Pearl-bordered Fritillary	*Argynnis euphrosyne*
Small Pearl-bordered Fritillary	*Argynnis selene*
Heath Fritillary	*Melitaea athalia*
Glanville Fritillary	*Melitaea cinxia*
Marsh Fritillary	*Melitaea aurinia*
White Admiral	*Limenitis sibylla*
Purple Emperor	*Apatura iris*
Marbled White	*Melanargia galathea*
Small Mountain Ringlet	*Erebia epiphron*
Scotch Argus	*Erebia aethiops (blandina)*
Grayling	*Satyrus semele*
Speckled Wood	*Pararge aegeria*
Wall	*Pararge megera*
Meadow Brown (Large)	*Epinephele ianira*
Hedge Brown	*Epinephele tithonus*
Ringlet	*Epinephele hyperanthus*
Large Heath	*Coenonympha tullia*
Small Heath	*Coenonympha pamphilus*
Brown Hairstreak	*Thecla betulae*
Purple Hairstreak	*Thecla quercus*
Black Hairstreak	*Fixsenia pruni*
White Letter Hairstreak	*Chattendenia w-album*
Green Hairstreak	*Callophrys rubi*
Small Copper	*Chrysophanus phleas*
Silver-studded Blue	*Lycaena argus*
Brown Argus	*Lycaena agestis*
Common Blue	*Lycaena icarus*
Chalk Hill Blue	*Lycaena coridon*
Adonis Blue	*Lycaena bellargus*
Holly Blue	*Cyaniris argiolus*
Small Blue	*Zizera minima*

Large Blue	*Nomiades arion*
Duke of Burgundy Fritillary .	*Nemeobius lucina*
Grizzled Skipper . . .	*Hesperia malvae*
Dingy Skipper . . .	*Nisoniades tages*
Small Skipper . . .	*Adopaea thaumas*
Essex Skipper . . .	*Adopaea lineola*
Lulworth Skipper . . .	*Adopaea actaeon*
Large Skipper . . .	*Augiades sylvanus*
Silver-spotted Skipper . .	*Augiades comma*
Checkered Skipper . . .	*Carterocephalus palaemon*

SWALLOW-TAIL

Papilio machaon

(State of Hibernation—Chrysalid)

Egg	*Chrysalis*
Size—9 mm.	Size—approximately 30 mm.
Incubation period—7 to 11 days	Pupation period—1 to 6 months
No. of Broods—2	
Food-plant—Hog's Fennel (See Notes)	

Caterpillar	*Butterfly*
Size—3 to 53 mm.	Wing-span—3 to $3\frac{3}{4}$ in.
Larval period—30 days	On the wing—June–October
No. of Moults—4	

MALE

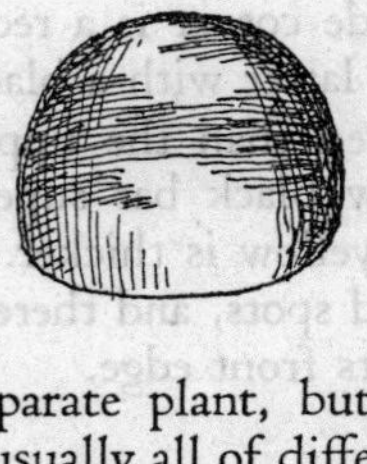

THE EGG

Each egg is laid on a separate plant, but frequently five or six eggs are found on the same leaf, usually all of different ages, denoting that they have been laid by separate females.

When first laid it is pale yellow; when a week old it is zoned irregularly with brown; in its final state it is a purplish grey with about a dozen longitudinal dark stripes.

In shape the egg is globular with a flattened base and a smooth surface.

THE CATERPILLAR

On emerging it is a leaden grey colour. After the fourth moult, before pupating, the ground-colour is a beautiful bright green with velvety black rings, dotted alternately with yellowish red. The entire surface, including the head, is densely sprinkled with short bristles, each being of the same colour as the surrounding ground. When pressed near its anterior part, Bonnet records that "it darted forth its horn as if it meant to push me with it, but it withdrew it as soon as I left off pressing it." Newman adds: "This horn smells strongly of *fennel*." (See Notes.)

THE CHRYSALIS

There are two types. One is light green, with yellow on the sides and the back. This is the female. The other varies from black to a light brown, having a darker line down each side and bordering the wing-cases. This is the male. The chrysalis is firmly attached to the stem of sedges and other fen plants by the black cremastral hooks and a silk band round the waist. Chrysalids are found in July and August, the later ones hibernating as such and emerging as butterflies in the following spring. The earlier ones emerge as butterflies in August and September, and sometimes as late as October. These lay, and their chrysalids also hibernate as such.

THE BUTTERFLY

The Swallow-tail is the biggest of British butterflies and one of the most beautiful. The female is the larger, but the colour and markings of the sexes are the same. The ground colour is yellow with black markings. The fore-wings have a large patch of black, dotted with yellow at the base, and the front margin is black with three large black marks. The nerves and hind-margins are also black, in which are eight yellow dots. The hind-wings are also yellow; the inner margin and a broad border on the outside, black—the latter with six yellow crescents above which is a thick sprinkling of blue dots. Near the inside corner is a red eye, margined with yellow beneath and blue above, the latter with a black crescent above it.

Underside: Lighter coloured than the upper, and the black markings are less extended. A narrow black bar supersedes the yellow crescents, above which the dotting of yellow is thicker. In the middle of the hind-wings are three triangular red spots, and there is another spot of the same in the yellow spot, next to its front edge.

Distribution

Now said to be confined to the fen lands of Cambridge, Norfolk, and parts of Suffolk. In the past thirty years specimens have been taken in Southern England. Although now confined to the fens in this country it is not a swamp-living insect on the Continent, where it is common in woods, fields, gardens, and even 6,000 feet up on mountains. In the Continental variety, the caterpillar feeds on many umbelliferous plants and on the cultivated *carrot*. (See Notes.)

Notes

Two interesting facts deserve special notice in the life-history of the Swallow-tail.

The first is the identity of the scent of the caterpillar of the British variety and its food-plant—hog's fennel (see page 41).

The second is the difference between the food-plants of the Continental and British 'varieties' or 'races.' In an article on January 19th, 1945, in *Country Life*, entitled "Butterflies in Captivity," the writer, a prisoner of war who took up butterfly collecting in Germany, says: "I remembered as a boy searching in vain for this rarity which, I believe, can only be found in the Fen Country, and we hurried out to see what we could find. It was an astonishing sight. The *carrots* seemed alive with Swallow-tails! Large juicy looking caterpillars clad in Old Wellingtonian colours."

Newman, in his life-history of the British Swallow-tail, records the following careful and precise observations: "Having in the spring of 1840 obtained a number of chrysalids from Burwell-sedge Fen, a male and a female emerged from them on the morning of the 27th of May, and were left near one another on the window-blind to expand and dry their wings. On my return from a short walk I was agreeably surprised to find them *in coitu*, and having a fine plant of the *marsh hog's fennel* growing in a garden pot, I placed it in the window of the room and confined the female on it as well as I could with the window-blind. On the 30th she had deposited fourteen eggs, but appearing nearly exhausted I supplied her with a little moistened sugar in a teaspoon, at the same time uncurling her trunk with a pin: she seemed to enjoy her feast, and being left with the sash raised about an inch made her escape. *The plant was returned to its place in the garden with the eggs attached.*

"The first caterpillar was hatched on the 10th of June and the others on the following day. By the 13th of July they had completely stripped the plant. Not being able to get a fresh supply of the food-plant I placed some carrot leaves in a small jar of water and introduced them amongst the stalks of the hog's fennel. *Contrary to my expectations*, the caterpillars fed on the carrot-leaves without any apparent reluctance, and by the end of the month were full-fed. Up to this time, although left in the garden day and night, they never quitted the food, but now it was impossible to keep them on it; and after one had been finally lost the others were removed into the breeding-cage, where they passed into the chrysalis stage on the 30th and 31st of July and the 2nd of August.

"The first butterfly was produced on the 14th of June 1841 and ten more in the course of a fortnight. One died in the chrysalis state and one continued in that state until this day, the 10th of May 1842, when a very fine and perfect female made her appearance. *I tried very much to continue the brood but was unsuccessful.*"

Here we have a careful and detailed account of the life-history of British Swallow-tails reared under conditions which transgressed the natural order of things in the following respects.

1. The original chrysalids were removed from their place of origin on their native food-plant at Burwell-Sedge Fen.
2. Immediately on emergence from the chrysalids in a strange place, a male and female, in artificially contrived intimate propinquity, mated at a spot foreign to the place of their nativity.
3. The eggs of this pair were then removed to a spot foreign to the spot at which *they* were laid.
4. The caterpillars hatched out at this foreign spot and fed on the *British* food-plant—hog's fennel.
5. By a skilful device they were induced to transfer their feeding from the British to the Continental food-plant, to the surprise of the experimenter, and they became full-fed on garden carrot-leaves instead of on wild hog's fennel.
6. Up to the point of being full-fed they had remained at a spot foreign to that of their nativity.
7. When full-fed, and just before pupating, they could not be held to the feeding-spot. Instead, they began to 'wander'—home? In fact, these caterpillars behaved like all caterpillars which, just before pupating, as Newman puts it, "wander restlessly and, as we should say, unmeaningly from place to place . . . until it ends in the creature finding some place of real or fancied security in which to undergo its change into a chrysalis"—the place of nativity. Had not the experimenter intervened, these caterpillars would have died instead of blossoming forth as butterflies in the following spring. Here is demonstrated the sequence of the two overmastering instincts in a butterfly's existence to which the author has constantly drawn attention—feeding (life-preservation); homing (for mating).
8. From these chrysalids—which had undergone not only two generations of transference from the place of nativity, but which had been latterly reared on a foreign food-plant though starting their career on the proper *native* one—were hatched out, nevertheless, *apparently* perfect butterflies:
9. *But*, to the surprise and disappointment of this brilliant experimenter, all attempts to continue the broods of these unnaturally and therefore disorderly reared butterflies failed.

Those who have carefully read the first part of this book, written before the author had come across this interesting experiment with Swallow-tails reared in captivity away from their birthplaces *on an alien food-plant*, will, he believes, be struck by the confirmation which this experiment affords of some, at least, of his conclusions in Part I of this book. It is for this reason that several references have been made in the first part of this book to this experiment, the record of which, as already said, had not been found when that part of the book was written. See particularly experiments in the naturalisation of the extinct Large Copper.

It is also of interest to note that the one chrysalis which failed to hatch out in 1841 did so in 1842, after nearly two years in its 'coffin' instead of the normal nine months or so—a fact which not only illuminates the marvel of butterfly existence, but which reveals a departure from normal life-habit which finds a counterpart in the egg and caterpillar stages of other species.

BLACK-VEINED WHITE

Aporia crataegi

(State of Hibernation—Caterpillar)

Egg

Size—0·94 mm. high
Incubation period—10 to 24 days
No. of Broods—1
Food-plants—Hawthorn, blackthorn, cultivated plum

Chrysalis

Size—25·4 mm.
Pupation period—about 1 month

Caterpillar

Size—1·4 to 35 mm.
Larval period—about 9 months
No. of Moults—4

Butterfly

Wing-span—$2\frac{1}{4}$ to 3 in.
On the wing—June–July

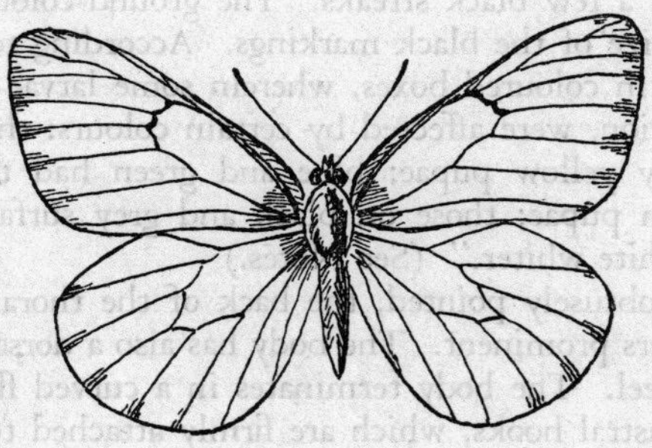

MALE

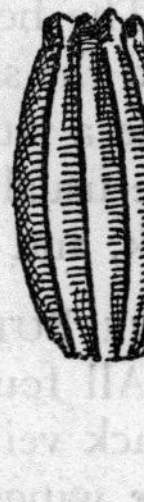

THE EGG

Laid in July on the food-plant in batches varying from 100 to 200. They are deposited in rows, closely packed and standing erect. The colour, when first laid, is a bright rich primrose yellow, changing to olive with a dark crown shortly before hatching.

In shape they resemble elongated acorns and have fifteen to sixteen longitudinal keels, seven running from near the base to the summit, where each terminates in a glassy globe enveloping an opaque white knob; the remaining keels are simple at the ends, disappearing into the surface by the base of the globes. The spaces between the keels are angular and very faintly ribbed transversely.

THE CATERPILLAR

On emergence it is pale yellow, the legs dusky, and the head black. After the second moult in September it hibernates. Before pupating in April or May, after the fourth moult, it becomes thickly covered with white hairs, and on the sides and underneath is of a dark grey colour with two longitudinal stripes of red or yellow. They hibernate in batches in separate compartments formed of a dense silken web spun between the leaves. On a bright day in March they emerge. They feed till May when, at a caterpillar age of about 280 days, they pupate. Frohawk records that "before hibernation several of a nest of these caterpillars had fed upon a laurel leaf which had come in contact with the plum branch upon which they were; they ate a large part of the upper cuticle of the leaf. Therefore a few larvae were supplied with laurel when in the last stage, and although they fed on some of the young leaves it caused them to vomit and one died in consequence." (See Notes.)

THE CHRYSALIS

Greenish white, with two streaks of yellow on the sides, a number of black dots, and a few black streaks. The ground-colour is liable to vary as well as the size of the black markings. According to Frohawk, "those which pupated in coloured boxes, wherein some larvae were placed when ready for pupation, were affected by certain colours: those in yellow produced decidedly yellow pupae; blue and green had the same effect of producing green pupae; those on black and grey surfaces became greyer and those on white whiter." (See Notes.)

The head is obtusely pointed, the back of the thorax sharply pointed, and the shoulders prominent. The body has also a dorsal keel and on each side a lateral keel. The body terminates in a curved flattened horn with the usual cremastral hooks, which are firmly attached to an ample pad of silk, and a silken girdle passes round the body at the waist.

THE BUTTERFLY

All four wings are of a dull milk white colour streaked over with the black veins from which the insect derives its name. They show through, the wings being semi-transparent, so that the markings on the underside resemble those on the upper. In the female the veins of the fore-wings are generally of a brownish hue.

Distribution

For many years past this butterfly is said to have disappeared from places in the Southern and Midland counties of England where, fifty years ago, it was abundant. It was last found in Kent, and even there in only one locality. There is no record of this butterfly ever having occurred north of Northampton. "It began to die off towards the end of the 'sixties and in a comparatively very brief period had quite vanished." In its very restricted locality it usually appeared towards the end of June. It frequents clover, lucerne and cornfields. It is common on the Continent and ranges to Japan, but is now said to be altogether extinct in England.

Notes

It is interesting to note that the alien food—laurel—did not seemingly harm the caterpillars in their early state and before hibernating. After hibernating, however, the alien food killed one, and would have killed all but for the life-saving operation of vomiting. A similar account has been given to the author by Mr. Russwurm in the case of White Admiral caterpillars fed on an inappropriate food. Vomiting saved their lives.

The strange phenomenon of the chrysalids assuming the colour of that upon which they *pupated* should be contrasted with the similar effect on caterpillars of that upon which they *feed* (see Chapter VI). Both are examples of 'mimicry,' but in the case of the chrysalids the phenomenon is more of the chameleon nature—an effect of light rather than of food.

For the explanation of the disappearance of the Black-veined White from former native haunts and its failure to re-establish itself in old or new haunts, see Chapter XI.

LARGE WHITE

Pieris brassicae

(State of Hibernation—Chrysalid)

Egg	*Chrysalis*
Size—1·2 mm.	Size—25·4 mm.
Incubation period—4 to 17 days	Pupation period—14 days to 6 months
No. of Broods—2; occasionally 3	
Food-plants—Cabbage, mustard, turnips, radish, cress	

Caterpillar	*Butterfly*
Size—2·12 to 41·3 mm.	Wing-span—2½ to 3 in.
Larval period—about 25 days	On the wing—May–October
No. of Moults—4	

THE EGG

The first brood of eggs of the Large White is laid in May or June, standing erect in groups of about forty on both sides of the food-plant, and hatches out after periods varying from four to seventeen days or more, according to the temperature (see Notes). There are normally two egg broods, but in exceptionally warm summers three broods occur, the different stages being accelerated. When first laid the colour is a rich cream yellow. Before hatching they become opaque with a leaden-coloured crown.

Elliptical in shape, with an elongated apex, they have from seventeen to nineteen fine longitudinal keels running from the crown to the base, the intervening spaces being concave and transversely fluted by about forty-five ribs.

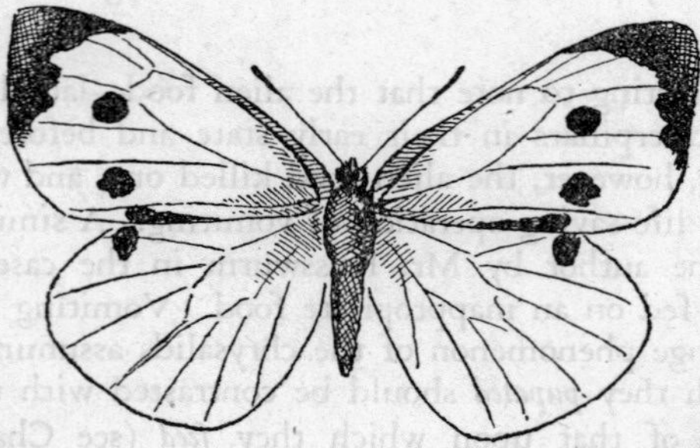

FEMALE

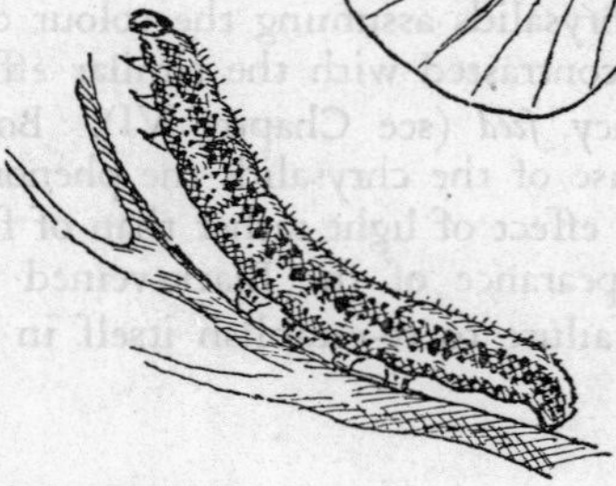

THE CATERPILLAR

The caterpillar feeds at the spot where it was born. On emergence it is pale greenish ochreous with a black head. After the fourth moult, before pupating, the body is grey-green, with three yellow longitudinal stripes, and the claspers are amber. The segments are almost covered with black tubercles of different size, from each side of which arise white hairs, three of the larger ones forming a triangle. The head, forelegs and hind segment are also black. There is a line of green down each side and one along the back.

THE CHRYSALIS

"The colouring varies considerably, as it greatly depends upon the surrounding colour of the object upon which it is attached." (See Note to Black-veined White and Chapter VII.)

The normal ground-colour is ivory white, the whole surface being speckled, blotched and reticulated with black: the point of the beak and dorsal keel is variegated with yellow, as also are the spiracles.

The head is beaked in front, the thorax angulated by a central dorsal keel which is continued along the abdomen, recommencing on the fourth abdominal segment.

The last brood of the Large White hibernate as chrysalids from September or October to the end of April or May. Those of the first, and sometimes the second, brood of eggs remain as chrysalids for about fourteen days, again according to the temperature. (See Notes.)

THE BUTTERFLY

The upper surface of all the wings is white, the fore ones having a broad black patch following the angle of the outside corner and indented on its lower inner edge. There is a pale blackish-grey margin at the front of the wings extending nearly to the patch at the corner: the whole front edge has a line of black along it. Occasionally, but very rarely, the male has a black spot on the fore-wings; the hind-wings have a black spot on the middle of their front edge.

Underside: there are two black spots on the fore-wings. The hind-wings are dull yellow, minutely dotted with black specks. The female has the outside patch larger than in the male. The hind-wings are of a dull greenish colour, dotted all over with very minute black spots and showing the black triangular patch rather obscurely through.

Distribution

Although it occurs annually throughout Britain in varying numbers, and is generally abundant, it is occasionally scarce over the whole of the British Isles.

Notes

The great variation of the times required to hatch out the eggs—four to seventeen days, according to the temperature—confirms the approximation of butterfly eggs to vegetable seeds rather than to birds' eggs. Indeed, the butterfly may be said to 'run to seed' as does an annual or a biennial, the butterfly like the plant dying as its seeds mature and are shed. In one case recounted to the author, a moth, set and to all seeming dead, shed a full clutch of eggs.

Frohawk speaks of the *migratory habits* of the Large White, and he recounts how vast swarms have frequently been observed at sea and arriving on our coasts in multitudes resembling a snowstorm. He attributes the occasionally great profusion of these butterflies to these *invasions*.

It should be noted that this butterfly hibernates as a chrysalis and is not therefore a 'migrant.' The true explanation of plentifulness and of the *invasions* of this butterfly is the same as in the case of the migrant Painted Ladies and Clouded Yellows examined in Chapter XI. But in the case of the latter the winter was spent on the wing in a warm southern climate. The Large Whites, as hardy natives, wintered at home as chrysalids. It will be found that in all cases in which certain species have a very late brood, that is to say in propitious autumns, there is the phenomenon of exceptional plentifulness in the succeeding year. (See Chapters XI and XII.) Mr. Lorne Campbell confirms that in the Hebrides great plentifulness of butterflies is coincident with two consecutively agreeable seasons.

SMALL WHITE

Pieris rapae

(State of Hibernation—Chrysalid)

Egg

Size—
Incubation period—3 to 14 days
No. of Broods—3
Food-plants—Cabbage and garden plants, especially mignonette

Chrysalis

Size—19 mm.
Pupation period—about 14 days to 6 months

Caterpillar

Size—1·2 to 25 mm.
Larval period—about 19 days
No. of Moults—4

Butterfly

Wing-span—$1\frac{3}{4}$ to $2\frac{1}{2}$ in.
On the wing—March-October

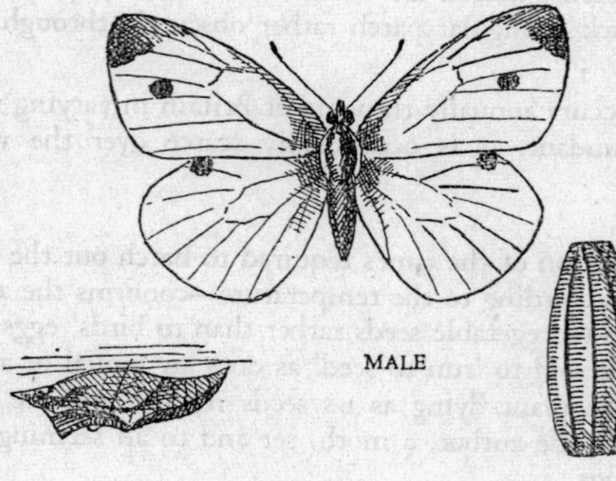

MALE

THE EGG

The egg, which stands erect, is deposited singly on the under-surface of the food-plant. When first laid it is a very delicate pale yellow-green white; in twenty-four hours it assumes a slightly deeper tone.

It is of elongated conical form, a little convex just below the summit, and fullest about the middle. The extreme summit is flat. There are twelve longitudinal keels; the spaces between the keels are delicately ribbed transversely by about thirty-five ribs.

Frohawk records how a captured female was placed on sprays of mignonette enclosed with gauze and exposed to sunshine in a shade temperature of 86°. She immediately started laying; thirty eggs were laid and she died almost immediately afterwards. The eggs hatched in three days.

THE CATERPILLAR

On emergence it is light ochreous yellow. After the fourth moult, before pupating, it is pale green with a narrow line of orange-yellow along the back and an interrupted line of yellow on the lower part of each side. The head, feet and tail are entirely green. The body is slightly striated across with the segments.

Frohawk records how a caterpillar that was watched started, when full-fed, to *roam* before pupating. (See Notes to Swallow-tail.)

THE CHRYSALIS

The colour varies greatly in different specimens, usually harmonising with its surroundings and being highly sensitive to backgrounds. The chrysalids of spring are generally attached to the leaves of the food-plants when they are *invariably* green. The later ones are under the copings of walls, ledges of sheds and palings, and are darker in colour. (See Notes to Black-veined White and Large White.)

The head is beaked in front, the thorax strongly angulated by a central dorsal keel which rises acutely at the middle and declines to the abdomen.

THE BUTTERFLY

The ground-colour is milk white, the fore-wings having a dusky or black mark extending along part of the margin; there is a black spot near the middle of the wing and a second indistinctly visible. The hind-wings have a dull dusky black mark in a line with them, about the middle of the fore-edge. The hind-wings are yellowish, thickly dusted, principally near the base, with minute dots. The female has two black spots near the centre of the upper side of the fore-wings.

Underside: Very similar to the upper sides, but the hind-wings are more yellow.

These insects are extremely variable, Morris recording that out of a whole row in his cabinet no two are exactly alike. (See Notes.)

Distribution

Universally throughout Great Britain. According to Newman this butterfly appeared in Canada in 1863, up to which time it had been included in no work on American entomology. It was, as Newman shows, an unusual vagrant from east to west, and must therefore have been carried west in an exceptional wind or been transported by ship on its food-plant in the egg or chrysalis state.

Notes

This butterfly, like the Large White, is sometimes seen in myriads over the South and East Coasts. (See Chapter XI.) In hot summers three broods occur, in cold and wet ones only two. (See Notes to Large White.)

The great variability in the colour and markings of this butterfly in all its stages has its counterpart in other species with varied food-plants. The fact that the later broods are darker and more pronounced in their colourings is attributable to the strength of the sunrays which, as many authorities emphasise, have a great influence on variation. (In this connection see also experiments in the artificial breeding of *Drosophila melanogaster*, page 88.)

GREEN-VEINED WHITE

Pieris napi

(State of Hibernation—Chrysalid)

Egg

Size—1 mm. high
Incubation period—4 to 10 days
No. of Broods—2
Food-plants—Various cruciferous plants: charlock, cuckoo flower, hedge-mustard, yellow rocket, etc.

Chrysalis

Size—19 mm.
Pupation period—about 6 months

Caterpillar

Size—25·4 mm.
Larval period—about 16 days
No. of Moults—4

Butterfly

Wing-span—$1\frac{1}{2}$ to 2 in.
On the wing—May–July

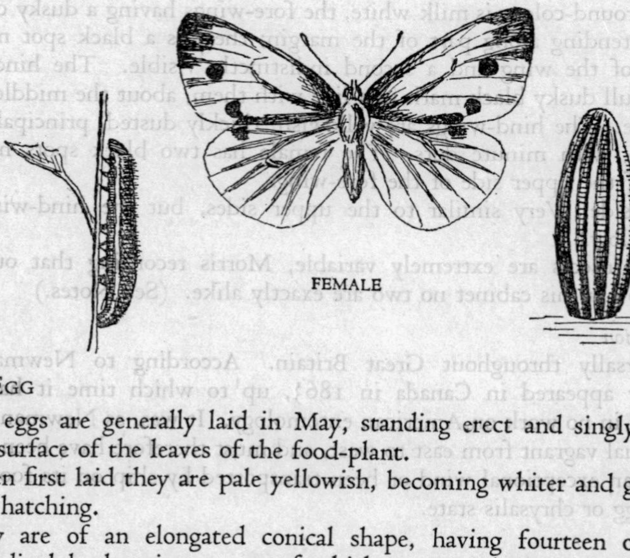

FEMALE

THE EGG

The eggs are generally laid in May, standing erect and singly, on the under-surface of the leaves of the food-plant.

When first laid they are pale yellowish, becoming whiter and glistening before hatching.

They are of an elongated conical shape, having fourteen or fifteen longitudinal keels, nine or ten of which run mostly in pairs the entire length; the remainder start a little below the summit and run to the base. The intervening spaces have about forty-five transverse ribs.

THE CATERPILLAR

On emergence the entire colouring is a light ochreous yellow. After the fourth moult, before pupating, it is dull green on the back, the sides being of a lighter shade with red dots placed on yellow spots on each segment. The colour varies. (See Notes.)

THE CHRYSALIS

It closely resembles that of the Small White. In colouring it is very variable both in ground-colour and markings—being green, ochreous, straw yellow, and pale buff; some are almost spotless, others speckled and marked with black, while every intermediate variation occurs. The colour variety is largely governed by the surrounding colouring of the site on which pupation takes place (see Notes). Though occasionally attached to palings and walls it is usually attached to the stems of the food-plant.

THE BUTTERFLY

The Green-veined White varies greatly in its colouring and markings (see Notes). Normally the wings are white, dusky black at the tips and the base, and generally with a black spot not far from the outside edge of the fore-wings. Some, however, have no spot. There are some small irregularly shaped triangular marks at the end of the nerves at the outside edge of the wing: the hind-wings are white.

Underside: The fore-wings have two spots, as in the female, on the upper surface. The hind-wings are pale yellowish with the nerves broadly margined on each side with dusky green.

Distribution

Though generally distributed and common throughout the British Isles, except in the extreme north, it is more restricted in its haunts than the Large or Small Whites. It chiefly frequents open country and is not destructive to garden crops.

Notes

The Green-veined White well illustrates all that has previously been said on the matter of variation and mimicry, and their causes. The caterpillar and chrysalis assume the general colouring of the food-plant and the pupation site. The variety of food-plant is also reflected in the variety of colouring and markings of the butterfly. Frohawk emphasises that caterpillars fed on garlic mustard produce butterflies of a richer yellow colouring on the underside, or what he calls mustard yellow. The Swallowtail, it will be remembered, smells of fennel—its food-plant. The effect of temperature on this butterfly's colour and marking is equally noticeable, the imagines which emerge in the height of summer being much darker and more boldly marked. The one invariable stage is *the egg* (see Chapter I, and remarks on classification). A careful study of the life-history of the Green-veined White, as given by Frohawk, Newman or Morris, seems to justify the author's contention that butterflies should be regarded mainly as a branch of botanical study.

ORANGE TIP

Euchloë cardamines

(State of Hibernation—Chrysalid)

Egg

Size—1·21 mm.
Incubation period—about 7 days
No. of Broods—1; occasionally 2
Food-plants—garlic mustard, hedge mustard, yellow rocket and garden honesty

Chrysalis

Size—23 mm.
Pupation period—about 11 months, occasionally 22 months

Caterpillar

Size—31 mm.
Larval period—about 21 days
No. of Moults—4

Butterfly

Wing-span—$1\frac{3}{4}$ to 2 in.
On the wing—April or May–September

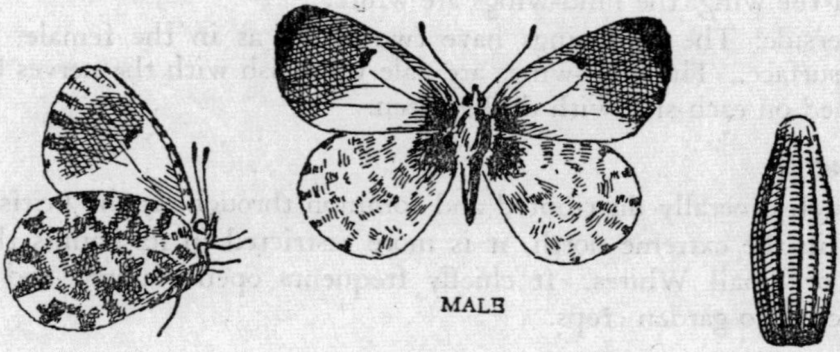

MALE

THE EGG

The egg is laid singly, standing erect, late in May on the food-plant.

When first laid the egg is a pale greenish-yellowish white which deepens into yellow at the base and blends into orange at the middle. It afterwards changes to orange all over, and finally, before hatching, to pale ochreous brown.

It is of an elongated pyriform shape, widest about the middle. There are about eighteen longitudinal keels, twelve running the entire length; the remaining six commence a little below the summit and run to the base. The intervening spaces have each about forty transverse ribs.

THE CATERPILLAR

On emergence it is entirely of an ochreous yellow. After the fourth moult, before pupating, it is green, finely dotted with black and with a white stripe along the side. After becoming full-fed it attaches itself to the stem of the food-plant by a silken thread and takes as much as nine days to pupate. After becoming full-fed, a specimen carefully watched by Frohawk *roamed about for thirty hours before pupating*. The caterpillar is hardly distinguishable from the seed-pod upon which it feeds. Orange-tip caterpillars sometimes feed on one another. (See Notes.)

THE CHRYSALIS

It so strongly resembles the seed-pod of the food-plant upon which the caterpillar feeds that it almost defies detection. In this state of resemblance to its food it remains attached to the stem of its food-plant for about eleven months, and sometimes twenty-two months. It is noticeable that the colour of the chrysalis changes from green to a dark purplish hue as the days pass, just as does the fresh seed-pod as it dies off.

In shape it is elongated and attenuated at the ends, and strongly concave dorsally.

THE BUTTERFLY

The ground-colour is white, the upper wings are black at the base and have a black mark, varying in shape, near the centre. The space between is a lovely orange colour, bordered on the outside corner with brownish black with orange specks. The hind-wings are also black at the base.

Underside: The fore-wings resemble the upper, except for a dash of pale yellow near the base. The female is without the orange tip but in other respects resembles the male.

This butterfly, while at rest with closed wings on its food-plant during dull weather, or when 'roosting' for the night, becomes practically an invisible object. So closely does it resemble the small white clustered flowers that its disguise is perfect. Though generally an early butterfly it is sometimes to be seen on the wing as late as September. (See Notes.)

Distribution

Universal throughout Britain; on the Continent it is always double-brooded.

Notes

The Orange Tip, whether as a caterpillar, a chrysalis, or a butterfly, is a remarkable example of 'mimicry.' The fact that the caterpillars feed on one another—as do the Hairstreaks and other species—and have apparently no other enemies, is a striking demonstration of the fallacy of the *objective* and *protective* nature of 'mimicry,' and an equally striking demonstration that mimicry is the chemical reproduction in the parasite of the chemistry of the food-plant with its variations. That, in fact, it is subjective and not objective. (See Chapter VI.)

In this connection Frohawk refers to the *protective* theory, and he explodes it by pointing out that a large proportion of the stems of the food-plants are destroyed during the winter months when the pupae would also perish. He therefore concludes, surprisingly, that "in all probability it is but seldom that this species pupates on its food-plant." This conclusion is at variance with his earlier account of how, after roaming for thirty hours, caterpillars attach themselves for pupating to their food-plant. Thus can an incorrect theory, such as the objective protectiveness of mimicry, confuse an otherwise plain issue.

The exceptional appearance of Orange Tips late in the year indicates that in exceptionally warm late summers chrysalids emerge as butterflies, and that in such years they are, like the Continental variety, double-brooded. There is, in fact, a second crop—as in other species there is occasionally a third crop with its repercussions on the next year's plentifulness.

WOOD WHITE

Leucophasia sinapis

(State of Hibernation—Chrysalid)

Egg

Size—1·3 mm. high
Incubation period—about 11 days
No. of Broods—1; occasionally 2
Food-plants—Tuberous pea, sweet and cultivated pea

Chrysalis

Size—16 mm.
Pupation period—8 days, 10 months

Caterpillar

Size—19 mm.
Larval period—about 30 days
No. of Moults—4

Butterfly

Wing-span—$1\frac{1}{2}$ to 2 in.
On the wing—July

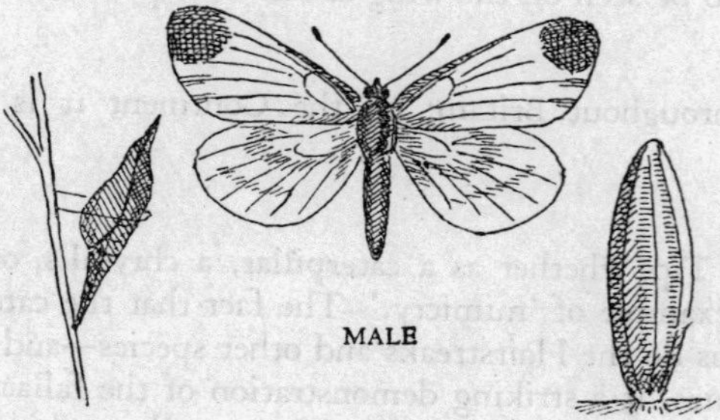

MALE

THE EGG

The eggs are normally laid in June, singly and standing erect, generally on the under-surface of the tuberous pea. They are first of a clear pale lemon yellow colour and so remain until just before hatching, when they become tinged with ochreous.

They are of an elongated conical form, indented about the middle, attenuated at each end and terminating in a point. The base of the egg is rounded and firmly attached to the leaf by a short pedestal of glutinous substance. It has eleven longitudinal keels, nine of which generally run the entire length while two start a little below the summit. The spaces between the keels are delicately and finely ribbed transversely, each space having about forty-two ribs.

THE CATERPILLAR

On emergence it is pale primrose yellow. After the fourth moult, before pupating, it is green in colour, darker near the end, and with a yellow stripe along the sides above the feet. It feeds along the edges of the leaves of the food-plant and rests in a straight attitude.

THE CHRYSALIS

At first it is greenish but afterwards becomes whitish grey, with red dots upon the sides and upon the wing-cases. The general colouring and shape then closely resemble a withered and partly eaten leaf of the food-plant.

The head terminates in a rather long, pointed, and slightly upturned beak; the thorax is swollen and slightly sunken at the middle segments.

The latest chrysalids, hibernating as such, remain in the pupal state for about ten months. The chrysalis is firmly attached to a pad of silk spun on the stem of the food-plant.

THE BUTTERFLY

This fragile-looking butterfly is of a delicate white colour with a rounded dull black spot at the tip of the fore-wings. In the female, however, this spot is nearly, and sometimes quite, obliterated.

Underside: Very similar. It is a denizen of woods, down the glades of which it can be seen floating lightly in a slow and undulating manner.

Distribution

The Wood White has disappeared from many of its former haunts in the past sixty years. It still occurs in many isolated localities from Cornwall to Cumberland and is widely distributed in the south and west of Ireland. It is said to be unknown in any part of Scotland. Single specimens have from time to time been taken in localities where the species has not been known to occur before or after. (See Notes.)

Notes

The Wood White, as will be noticed, follows the almost invariable rule of closely resembling, in two of its stages, the food-plant. (See Chapter VI.)

The disappearance of the species from former haunts and the failure to re-establish itself in such former localities is a phenomenon common to other species. It may be described as local extinction. The specimens taken in localities where this butterfly had not been observed before, or subsequently, were *vagrants*. (See Chapter XI.)

SILVER-WASHED FRITILLARY

Argynnis paphia

(State of Hibernation—Caterpillar)

Egg

Size—1 mm. high
Incubation period—about 15 days
No. of Broods—1, occasionally 2
Food-plant—Dog-violet

Chrysalis

Size—22 mm.
Pupation period—about 18 days

Caterpillar

Size—38 mm.
Larval period—about 8 months
No. of Moults—4

Butterfly

Wing-span—$2\frac{3}{4}$ to 3 in.
On the wing—July–September

MALE

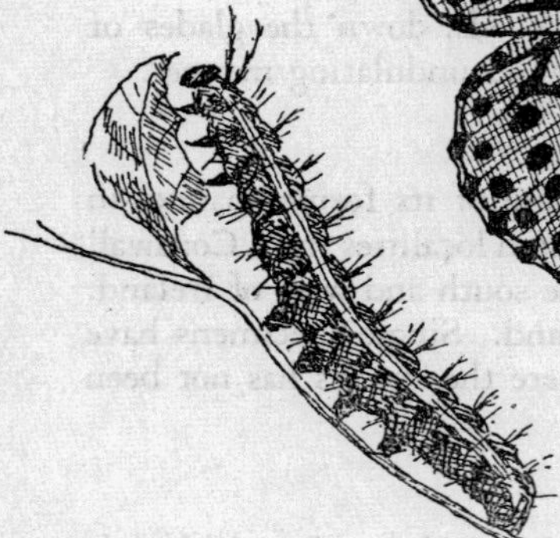

The Egg

The eggs of this butterfly are laid (according to Frohawk) several feet above the ground in the chinks of the bark of tree-trunks growing among violets, the food-plant of the caterpillar. The female, when about to lay, flies low over the ground and, having found violet plants, flies upward, settles on a tree-trunk and deposits. (See Notes.)

The colour of the egg is a light ochreous yellow tinged with green.

The eggs are usually laid in July and are small in proportion to the butterfly, conical in shape and with rounded base. There are twenty-five longitudinal keels, about twelve of which rise above the crown and run to the base. The spaces between the keels are transversely ribbed.

THE CATERPILLAR

On emergence it is light yellow. After hibernation, before pupating, it is light brown with a row of yellow spots on the back. It is covered with long spines, the two next the head being longer than the rest.

Immediately after emerging it enters into hibernation and rests close to the empty egg-shell in a crevice in the bark. The larva exists without food from August to the end of March, except for the crown of the egg-shell. If disturbed during hibernation it falls to the ground and rolls into a ring, so remaining for a minute or two. It then crawls away to regain its birth-place. In the spring it wakes and betakes itself, by crawling or dropping, to its food-plant beneath. It then becomes full-fed in about forty-five days.

THE CHRYSALIS

The ground-colour is normally a pale buff, finely reticulated with dark brown.

The head has two lateral horns and is itself beaked. The thorax is keeled and angular, sunken at the base of the abdomen which is furnished with hooks by which the pupa is attached to a silk pad. It closely resembles a withered brown curled-up leaf.

THE BUTTERFLY

The fore-wings are rich fulvous with numerous blackish spots and bars, the latter horizontal, and of the former there are three rows following the outside edge of the wing. The hind-wings are of the like ground-colour, with also three rows of larger spots.

Underside: The fore-wings are paler in colour, the outer corner being dashed with metallic green. The hind-wings are pale metallic green with two short waves of silver near the base, a third tinged with purple running across the wing, and another still more tinged with purple following the margin. Between these two last is a row of darker green spots with lighter centres, and another of green half-moons, the latter outermost.

The female is larger than the male, without streaks, the spots larger, the fulvous colour less bright and tinged with green.

A remarkable variation of this butterfly, named *Valezina*, is a subject of much speculation among entomologists, ancient and modern. In this variety the fulvous ground-colour is replaced by smoky-green bronze. All the normal markings, however, show through the general ground-colour. This beautiful *mutation* from the normal is confined to the female, and between these two extreme forms a gradation of intermediate variations occur. (See Notes.)

Specimens have been taken in which the distinctive characteristics of the male and female appear, the right wings being characteristic of the male and the left wings of the female. According to Frohawk and Newman, this butterfly, like other members of *paphia*, is gynandromorphic.

Distribution

The Silver-washed Fritillary occurs in most of the larger woods of the southern and south-western counties of England and Wales, becoming rarer northwards and being scarce in Scotland. In Ireland it is abundant.

Notes

A whole book might be written on this butterfly which presents such remarkable examples of variation and gynandromorphism. Its life-history as given by Newman differs widely from that by Frohawk. For example: According to Newman the caterpillar hibernates on the stems of the dog-violet on which the eggs are laid—and not on the bark of the trees above. In the matter of variation Frohawk, discussing the well-known variety *Valezina*, writes: "From what we know of the earliest existing lepidoptera, they then lacked the brilliancy of colouring now prevailing in so many species, and that in the world's earlier ages only white, black, and brown forms existed, therefore very probably *Valezina* still represents the ancestral form of *paphia*. And it is also probable that the recurrent white-spotted forms so prevalent in the males may be instances of the reversion to a primitive type." But according to Eltringham in *Butterfly Lore*, there is no record of these 'primitive types,' and the existence of such is purely evolutionary speculation. What little evidence there is indicates that the very earliest butterflies of which any record exists were similar in form and colour to those of to-day. (See Preface, page ix.)

It is to be noted that Linnaeus classified this butterfly as *Papilio adippe*; Fabricius as *Argynnis adippe*, and Hubner as *Acidalia adippe*. In his life-history of this butterfly, Frohawk emphasises the immense influence the climate and surroundings exercise upon its appearance. For example: he records that in 1893 this species was well out in June, and that in that year there was an abnormal number of *Valezina*. "During that season," he writes, "a large proportion of these butterflies were considerably dwarfed, and most of the variation *Valezina* were very much paler in colour. These abnormal conditions were probably caused by the unusual heat and resultant drought of that year." Then why speculate about reversions to types existing in fabulous ages of the world's history? In this connection the reader is invited to re-examine the Painted Lady abnormality that occurred in the year 1903, as recorded in Chapter XI: 1903, it will be remembered, was one of the *wettest* on record, but the swarms of Painted Ladies in that wet year had their origin in the preceding autumn which must have had as great an influence on the breeding of these non-hardy migrants as did the hot and dry summer on the breeding and variation of the hardy Silver-washed Fritillaries. The heat of 1893 produced partial second broods or, again, second 'crops.' Surely the simple explanation of the phenomenon of variation and mutation, like that of varying plentifulness, is to be found in the facts revealed in the first part of this book, rather than in speculations about past ages of which we have no record.

And, as previously shown, there are almost as many classifications as classifiers.

The various records of unusual butterfly phenomena in the years 1893 and 1903 shed considerable light on problems which have perplexed entomologists.

HIGH BROWN FRITILLARY

Argynnis adippe

(State of Hibernation—Egg)

Egg

Size—0·8 mm. high
Incubation period—about 8 months
No. of Broods—1 (2 artificially) (see Notes)
Food-plant—Dog-violet

Chrysalis

Size—20 mm.
Pupation period—about 5 weeks

Caterpillar

Size—38 mm.
Larval period—about 9 weeks
No. of Moults—5

Butterfly

Wing-span—about 2½ in.
On the wing—July

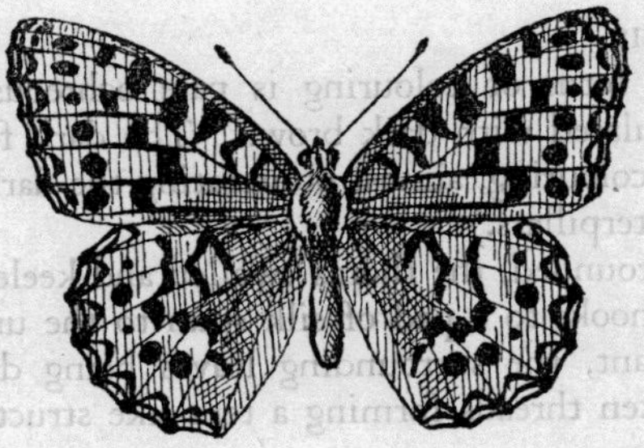

FEMALE

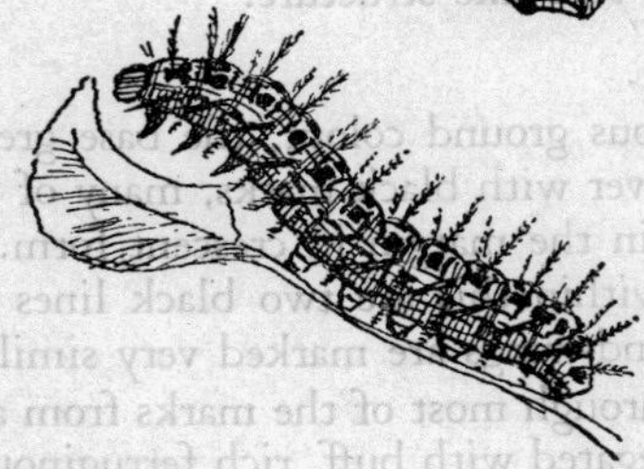

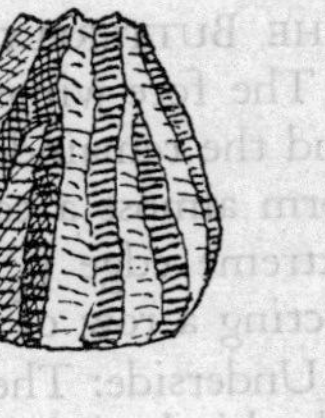

THE EGG

The eggs are laid singly in July near the base of the stems and stalks of the food-plant.

When first laid the eggs are a pale greenish ochreous, gradually deepening in colour: when a week old they are purplish buff, inclining to apricot colour. They gradually become duller in colour, changing to a pinkish grey. They so remain throughout the winter, darkening further before hatching in March. They are slightly pyriform in shape with from thirteen to fifteen longitudinal keels boldly sculptured. In most specimens only eight run the entire length, the remaining ones either branch off the main keels or else rise separately between them. They are all transversely ribbed, the ribs continuing across the intervening spaces. The keels resemble white glass. Though the High Brown Fritillary hibernates as an egg, remaining in this state about eight months, the caterpillar is perfectly formed inside the egg about a month after being laid.

The Caterpillar

There are two distinct colourings in these caterpillars, both equally common. The light form has the ground colour a light ochreous brown, variegated with black markings outlined with white and cream. The spines and bristles, as well as the legs and claspers, are light red; the head is bright tawny. The dark form has the entire colouring of a much deeper tone. (See corresponding difference of shade in males and females as chrysalids and butterflies.)

Eggs laid in July 1892 were observed to begin hatching in the middle of February 1893 (a very early warm spring), and others continued hatching till the end of March.

The Chrysalis

The normal form of colouring is pale ochreous brown, densely and minutely reticulated with dark brown. The dark form of chrysalis has a darker ground colouring, almost obliterating the darker reticulations. (See colouring of caterpillars.)

The head is rounded, the thorax swollen and keeled. It is suspended by the cremastral hooks to a pad of silk spun to the under-surface of a stem of the food-plant, the surrounding leaves being drawn together with a network of silken threads forming a tent-like structure.

The Butterfly

The fore-wings are of a rich fulvous ground colour, the base greenish, and the remainder thickly mottled over with black marks, many of which form almost a complete streak within the margin in crescent form. The extreme edge is pale fulvous, and within this are two black lines intersecting a row of black dots. The hind-wings are marked very similarly.

Underside: The fore-wings show through most of the marks from above. The hind-wings are beautifully variegated with buff, rich ferruginous and brown, the upper edge near the base being silver, outside which are from five to seven large silver spots. The female is similar in markings to the male but is much larger and the ground-colour is paler. (See colouring of caterpillars and chrysalids.)

This butterfly is essentially a woodland species. Its flight is rapid and powerful. The species is liable to considerable variation and sometimes tends to albinism. A rare and noticeable variation, known as *cleodoxa*, has the silver spots replaced by ochreous, but the sub-marginal red spots are sometimes centred with silver as in normal specimens.

Distribution

The butterfly occurs in most of the largest woods throughout the country, especially in the south. It does not occur north of Cumberland, and only a few specimens have been recorded in Ireland.

Notes

The variation between the colouring of the males and females seems to be constant in all stages after the egg. This distinction is thus *genetical*, whereas the variations to be found *in* each sex are environmental.

Frohawk records an interesting experiment carried out in the very hot and dry year, 1893. In this year the High Brown Fritillary was fully out during the latter half of June, and from eggs obtained at the end of that month a few abnormally hatched out in August resulting in one caterpillar pupating on October 13th, which produced a butterfly on November 21st. The chrysalis was in no way *forced* prior to November 10th, but from that date till November 21st it was subjected to an average temperature of 55°. There is no record of a second brood ever having occurred in a wild state in the British Isles. This striking experiment by which a butterfly 'bloom,' so to speak, was produced under heat (or glass) from 'seed' sown in June, is one among scores which seems to justify the treatment of butterfly life as vegetable rather than animal. (See Chapter VI.)

DARK GREEN FRITILLARY

Argynnis aglaia

(State of Hibernation—Caterpillar)

Egg	*Chrysalis*
Size—1 mm. high	Size—19 mm.
Incubation period—about 17 days	Pupation period—about 1 month
No. of Broods—1	
Food-plant—Dog-violet	

Caterpillar	*Butterfly*
Size—2·12 mm. to 38 mm. full-fed	Wing-span—2¼ to 2½ in.
Larval period—about 300 days	On the wing—June–August
No. of Moults—5	

THE EGG

The eggs are laid singly, generally in July, on various parts of the food-plant.

When first laid the colour is a pale primrose, gradually deepening and becoming purple on the top and more ochreous in the centre.

They are of conical form; the summit is sunken, the base rounded at the edge but otherwise flat. There are from nineteen to twenty-two longitudinal keels varying in length. Some commence at the summit and run to the base, others at different intervals from the summit, but all run to the base and disappear just before reaching it. The keels are prominent and stand out in bold relief; the spaces between the keels are transversely ribbed, about twenty in number, being most prominent near the summit.

The Caterpillar

When first hatched this caterpillar rolls into a ring when touched. At this stage it is pale ochreous with eight rows of black warts, and it immediately enters into hibernation. After the fifth moult, and before pupating

FEMALE

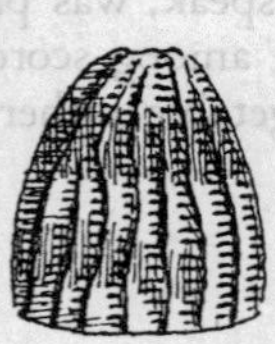

the following May, the ground colour is black, shading into purple-brown on the sides and ventral surface. It remains as a caterpillar for about two months after waking from hibernation in early April.

The Chrysalis

The ground-colour is ochreous, blotched with brown-black; the abdomen is tawny or orange ochreous.

The head is rounded, the thorax lobed and keeled dorsally. It is attached by the cremastral hooks to a pad of silk on the food-plant.

The Butterfly

The ground-colour is of a rather pale but fine fulvous, marked over with numerous black billets; the base is dusky.

Underside: The fore-wings are marked underneath as above, but the dark marks near the outside edge are much paler; the tips of the wings are paler than the rest, as are the front edges, and there are a few minute faint silver dots near the corner.

The hind-wings are dull green over all their inner and larger portion. The border is pale greenish yellow. There is an irregular row of seven silver spots on the outside edge.

Great variations of this species occur. This butterfly has an exceptionally powerful flight and is difficult to capture on the wing. It can best be caught when at rest on field thistles.

Distribution

Widely distributed over the British Isles, but in Scotland is confined generally to the mainland. It has, however, been recorded from the Isle of Skye. In Ireland it is commonly seen in various localities on the coast. (See Notes.)

Notes

The occurrence of this butterfly on islands and in coastal localities, though being native to wooded country on the mainland, is almost certainly attributable to *vagrancy*. This is to be expected in a butterfly constantly on the wing and, as Frohawk records, "frequently encountered over exposed and wind-swept country" in what he calls "its wild careering habit."

PEARL-BORDERED FRITILLARY

Argynnis euphrosyne

(State of Hibernation—Caterpillar)

Egg	*Chrysalis*
Size—0·8 mm. high	Size—14 mm.
Incubation period—15 days	Pupation period—9 days
No. of Broods—1; occasionally 2	
Food-plant—Dog-violet	

Caterpillar	*Butterfly*
Size—1·4 mm. to 25 mm.	Wing-span—$1\frac{1}{2}$ to $1\frac{3}{4}$ in.
Larve. period—330 days	On the wing—May–June
No. of Moults—4	

THE EGG

When first laid the colour is of a greenish ochreous yellow, becoming paler yellow and finally whitish ochreous with a dark crown before hatching.

The egg is conical, the micropyle sunken and finely pitted, and it is longitudinally keeled. The keels average twenty-five; some rise at the summit and run down the entire length, widening apart at various distances, where others start and run to the base. Round the crown the keels meet, forming a zigzag brim of triangular points. The spaces between the keels are very irregularly ribbed transversely.

The Caterpillar

Shortly before hibernation late in July, after the third moult, the colour is dark purplish speckled with greyish white forming a lateral stripe. At this stage it measures 10·5 mm. (see Notes). Before pupating in April the ground-colour of the dorsal surface is black and the central surface smoky brown, the whole freckled with greenish markings.

After becoming full-fed there was a lapse of forty-six days before pupating in a case carefully observed and recorded by Frohawk.

The Chrysalis

The ground-colour is light ashen grey and pinkish grey, finely reticulated with red-brown.

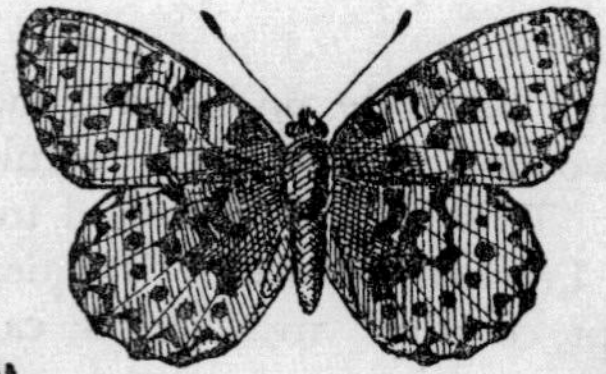

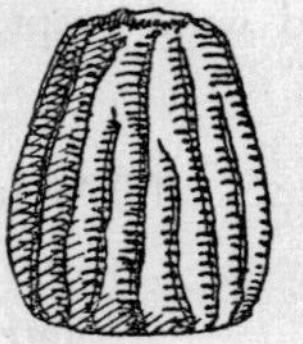

FEMALE

The head is slightly beaked in front, the thorax keeled and angular, deeply sunk at the waist. The abdomen is swollen across the middle, tapering to the extremity. It is suspended by the cremastral hooks to a pad of silk spun upon a leaf or stem.

The Butterfly

The ground-colour is rich fulvous, all the markings black, and the base of all the wings dusky and powdered with fulvous.

Underside: The fore-wings are light fulvous, inclining to amber at the apex, which is blotched with rust red. The hind-wings are similar, with an addition of a medium band of straw yellow markings which are conspicuously outlined with black. The central marking of the band is a large elongated silver pearl patch; a smaller silver triangular mark at the base and a marginal row of seven silver spots constitutes the silver ornamentation of this species. The female is larger and the ground-colour paler.

This butterfly is subject to great variation.

Distribution

Common in all the larger woods of England and Wales, less common in Scotland, and unknown in Ireland.

Notes

Frohawk records that a brood of larvae hatched from eggs in May passed through the third moult and stopped feeding in mid-June. Though subjected artificially to very high temperatures, rising as high as 100° for several days, they persistently hibernated.

On the other hand, in a state of nature, the remarkable year 1893 again produced a surprise for entomologists. First specimens appeared in mid-April and again in August. These latter were from caterpillars which, instead of going into hibernation in July, fed up, moulted for the fourth time, became chrysalids and emerged as butterflies in August. In this case the caterpillar stage lasted only a few weeks instead of the normal 330 days. From which we must conclude that nature has a way with it which eludes Man in many of his experiments. (See page 93.)

SMALL PEARL-BORDERED FRITILLARY

Argynnis selene

(State of Hibernation—Caterpillar)

Egg	*Chrysalis*
Size—0.6 mm.	Size—14·5 mm.
Incubation period—11 days	Pupation period—? about a month
No. of Broods—1; occasionally 2	
Food-plant—Dog-violet	

Caterpillar	*Butterfly*
Size—1·4 to 12·2 mm.	Wing-span—1¾ in.
Larval period—320 days	On the wing—June–July
No. of Moults—4	

The Egg

The eggs are laid singly on the under-surface of the food-plant. When first laid they are of a greenish orange colour, soon becoming paler and finally becoming pale ochreous with the crown dull grey.

They are conical in shape, the micropyle being sunken and the base slightly rounded. There are from eighteen to twenty longitudinal keels, irregularly formed and varying in length: about half run from crown to base, others originate at different distances from the crown. The spaces between the keels have about twenty transverse ribs.

The Caterpillar

When a week old the body is greenish. After the third moult, when it hibernates, the ground-colour is pale ochreous checkered with chocolate brown, the dorsal stripe being primrose yellow spotted with brown. After the fourth moult, before pupating, the ground-colour is sienna brown freckled with minute cream-white spots, each bearing a minute black bristle. About fifteen days elapses between becoming full-fed and pupating.

THE CHRYSALIS

The ground-colour is lilac-buff, reticulated with dark brown and blotched with black. The head is blunt and rounded and the thorax swollen, the waist deeply sunken.

The pupa is suspended by the cremastral hooks to a pad of silk spun on the stem of the food-plant.

THE BUTTERFLY

The ground-colour of the fore-wings is fulvous, the base black, with a series of waved lines of irregular black dots. The hind-wings are similar in colouring.

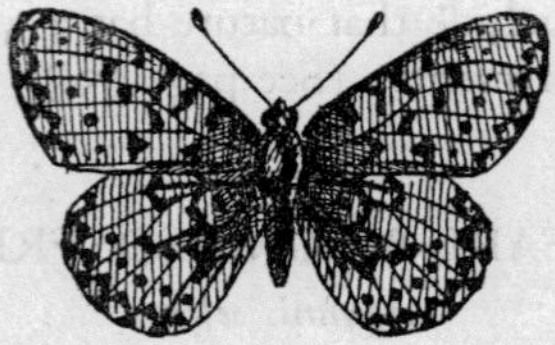

MALE

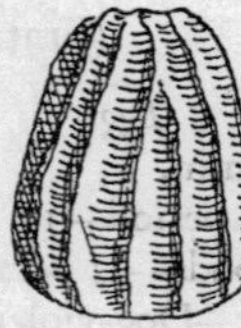

Underside: The fore-wings are much the same as on the upper side except that they are duller. The hind-wings are delicately marked with reddish ferruginous, buff- and straw-coloured bars. The central pale bar has one large spot of silver diagonally across it. The female is rather larger but otherwise marked and coloured much as the male.

Variations are marked and correspond generally to those of *euphrosyne*.

Distribution

It is more local in its distribution than *euphrosyne*, but is much more plentiful in Scotland. Only one specimen is recorded in Ireland, which was undoubtedly a vagrant.

Notes

The same remarks with regard to variation are applicable as in the case of other species. An exceptional variation is one in which almost the entire upper sides are deep purple-brown, almost black. In these cases the undersides have a pattern of various colours. In this connection see the association of purple and brown in the case of the Purple Emperor and Purple Hairstreak. Here again *selene*, though normally single-brooded, occasionally appears on the wing in late summer, and the remarks on *euphrosyne* are again applicable.

HEATH FRITILLARY

Melitaea aethalia

(State of Hibernation—Caterpillar)

Egg

Size—0·5 mm.
Incubation period—16 days
No. of Broods—1
Food-plants—Cow wheat, plantain, wood sage, ragged robin

Chrysalis

Size—12·7 mm.
Pupation period—15 days

Caterpillar

Size—1·3 to 25 mm.
Larval period—300 days
No. of Moults—6

Butterfly

Wing-span—$1\frac{1}{2}$ in.
On the wing—June–July

MALE

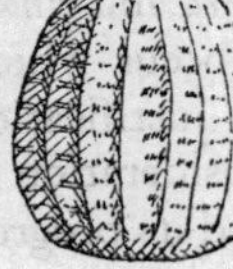

THE EGG

Laid in batches on the underside of the leaves of the food-plant, sometimes as many as 300 in all. When laid they are pale greenish white. Before hatching they turn to opaque creamy yellow, the dark head of the larva filling the crown.

The egg is ovate in form with a slightly flattened base. The crown is slightly pitted and the base smooth: there are about twenty-six shallow longitudinal ribs and it is finely striated transversely.

THE CATERPILLAR

When hatched the whole colouring is pale greenish ochreous white. After the third moult, and before hibernating, it becomes covered with black bristles. After the sixth moult, and before pupating in the spring, the ground-colour is velvety black, the legs and claspers green and black, and the head shining bronze-black.

About fifteen days elapses between being full-fed and pupation.

THE CHRYSALIS

The ground-colour is pearl white, the head, thorax, wing-cases, and legs being checkered with black.

The head is bilobed; it is slightly concave at the waist and bulging at the middle of the abdomen, tapering to the anal segment.

THE BUTTERFLY

The ground-colour varies from a deep rich fulvous to pale tawny ochreous. The fore-wings have their bases dusky with three transverse black bands crossing the wings. The hind-wings are dusky over the basal half with a rounded central fulvous spot. The fringes are whitish with black spots.

Underside: The fore-wings are orange tawny, the apex and outer margins straw yellow. The hind-wings are white shot with mother-of-pearl.

The female is larger than the male.

Variations are considerable.

Distribution

It is said to be extremely local, occurring chiefly in Kent, Devonshire, and Cornwall. In Sussex and Kent it is becoming scarcer each year. It is unknown in the northern counties and Scotland.

Notes

This butterfly varies very much as do the other Fritillaries, and particularly as *aurinea* and *cinxia*. Occasionally striking recurrent aberrations from the normal occur which have sometimes been claimed as distinct species, but without justification. (See mutations, page 93.)

For a consideration of the causes of the increasing scarceness of this butterfly, and its progressive confinement to a few localities, see Chapter XI.

GLANVILLE FRITILLARY

Melitaea cinxia

(State of Hibernation—Caterpillar)

Egg

Size—0·5 mm.
Incubation period—26 days
No. of Broods—1; occasionally 2
Food-plant—Plantain

Chrysalis

Size—12·7 to 14·8 mm.
Pupation period—14—20 days

Caterpillar

Size—1·25 to 25·4 mm.
Larval period—8 to 9 months
No. of Moults—6

Butterfly

Wing-span—$1\frac{3}{4}$ in.
On the wing—May–July

THE EGG

Laid in batches of 200 to 300 on the underside of a leaf of the food-plant.

When first laid it is primrose yellow turning to an ochreous white, with a dull leaden crown before hatching. It is of a truncated pyriform shape with a flattened base. Twenty longitudinal keels run from the crown to about half-way down the side, where they branch off in different directions.

The Caterpillar

After the first moult the body is pale ochreous white, mottled with dark olive and covered with black points. After the *fourth* moult, and before hibernating, the body is black, speckled with white, and covered with black spinelets. The head is rust red. After the sixth moult, in the spring, before pupating, the ground-colour is velvety black, very slightly spotted with white, and the head fulvous.

In the autumn the caterpillars live in societies under a kind of tent formed by drawing together the tips of the leaves on which they feed, and covering them with a silken web.

FEMALE

The Chrysalis

Brownish, with rows of raised fulvous marks on the back.

The head is square in front, convex across the middle, the abdomen gradually tapering and rounded.

The chrysalids are generally found adhering, just above the ground, to the stems of plantains. They are generally to be found in pairs.

The Butterfly

The fore-wings are of a rich fulvous ground-colour, tessellated with black-brown markings. The margin is a yellowish cream colour. The hind-wings are very similar in colouring.

Underside: The fore-wings are lighter fulvous, the whole of the tip being broadly washed with pale yellow, with a waved black line and a row of black dots skirting the outside of the wings. The hind-wings have three broad straw-coloured bars across them, the inner one at the base and the outer one on the outside with a waved line of black edging.

Variations are considerable.

Distribution

Very restricted in range. One hundred years ago Newman confined it to Hampshire, Kent, and the Isle of Wight, the latter being the most fruitful locality. To-day, according to Frohawk, its habitat is confined to the Isle of Wight.

Notes

The most interesting feature of this species is the narrow limits of its distribution and its apparent *extinction* in adjacent localities where, 100 years ago, it was resident and plentiful. This confinement to a few localities, and its extinction in others where formerly it was found, is considered generally in Chapter XI and specifically in many of the Notes to Part II of this book.

So also the variations of this insect which are common among all the Fritillaries.

This butterfly, though normally single-brooded, occasionally has a partial second brood in exceptional weather conditions.

MARSH FRITILLARY

Melitaea aurinia

(State of Hibernation—Caterpillar)

Egg

Size—0·8 mm.
Incubation period—14 to 20 days
No. of Broods—1
Food-plants—Devil's bit, scabious, greater and ribwort plantains

Chrysalis

Size—12·7 to 14·8 mm.
Pupation period—15 days

Caterpillar

Size—1·2 to 30 mm.
Larval period—300 days
No. of Moults—5

Butterfly

Wing-span—1½ to 2 in.
On the wing—May–June

The Egg

Laid in heaps of 400 to 500 on the underside of the leaves of the food-plant. When first laid it is a clear lemon colour, gradually turning to an ochreous-yellow and to brownish-drab before hatching. It is ovate in form, broadest below the middle; the base is rounded, the crown slightly sunken. About twenty bold but irregular ribs run from the crown down to nearly half the length, where they branch off in wavy curves. The ribs are smooth and triangular.

The Caterpillar

When first hatched the head is bilobed, black and shining. The colour of the whole body is pale yellow. After the *third* moult, and before hibernating, there are two distinct colourings of the body, one being wholly black above and ochreous brown below, the other dusky above and ochreous below. (See Notes.)

After the fifth moult in the spring, and before pupating, the caterpillar is black and covered with black bristles. Like the Glanville Fritillary the caterpillars make tents in which several live prior to hibernating. Before hibernating, the groups congregate at the foot of the food-plant and spin a common tent.

THE CHRYSALIS

The ground-colour of the head and thorax is grey, the wing-cases are whitish, the abdomen pale yellow, and orange knobs replace the caterpillar's tubercles. Before emergence the chrysalis becomes grey and the wing-cases red-brown and black.

The head is rounded, the thorax slightly sunken, and the abdomen convex.

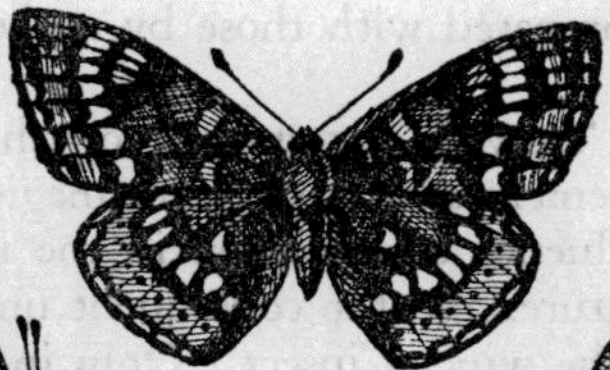

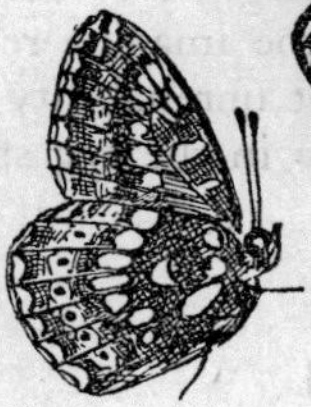

MALE

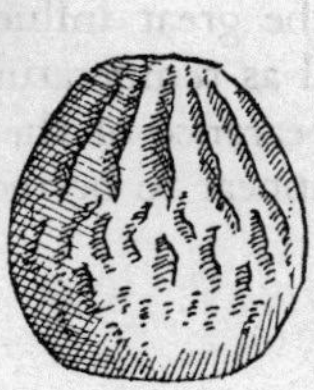

THE BUTTERFLY

The fore-wings are of a dark reddish orange colour, barred crosswise with straw-coloured bars or spots. The base of the wings is blackish brown. The hind-wings are similar with red ground-colour, their base and inner side blackish brown with an orange spot near the former. They are also barred with a bar of dark brown and in it a row of light orange spots.

Underside: The fore-wings are more obscure and dull, the markings from the upper side showing through. The hind-wings, of a slightly brighter ground-colour, have three yellowish curved bands margined with thin black lines.

The female resembles the male.

The markings of this butterfly vary considerably and some curious aberrations occur.

Distribution

It is widely distributed throughout the British Isles, but very local, being rare in Scotland. In the bogs of Ireland it is very highly coloured. It is to be found in marshy meadows and in marshy places in woods, and in some localities on heaths. The localities in which it is found are said to be diminishing, probably due to drainage. (See Notes.)

Notes

The two distinct colourings of the caterpillar should be compared with the same curiosity in the High Brown Fritillary. (See page 93.)

The habit of straying independently while feeding, and congregating again before pupating on the same food-plant, confirms the sequence of the two strong instincts of the butterfly in all its stages—first, feeding for self-preservation, involving straying; and second, for ultimate reproduction, homing to the birthplace.

The tendency for the localities of natives to diminish, and the failure to re-establish new localities where they are native, seems to be universal wherever the local environment is liable to be changed by drainage or by other wholesale interference with natural conditions by Man. This phenomenon becomes very clear when distributions recorded by authorities of 100 years ago are compared with those by authorities of to-day. (See Chapter XI.)

It is recorded that 'starved' caterpillars of this butterfly reared in captivity produced extremely small and pale imagines—a fact which well illustrates the great influence on variation in the imagine resulting from food as well as temperature, and the consequent unreliability of classification by appearance of the winged insect. Only in the egg stage do these influences appear to be inoperative.

WHITE ADMIRAL

Limenitis sibylla

(State of Hibernation—Caterpillar)

Egg

Size—0·91 mm.
Incubation period—6 to 7 days
No. of Broods—1 (rarely 2)
Food-plant—Honeysuckle

Chrysalis

Size—22 mm.
Pupation period—13 days

Caterpillar

Size—2·1 to 28·6 mm.
Larval period—8 months
No. of Moults—?

Butterfly

Wing-span—$2\frac{1}{4}$ to $2\frac{1}{2}$ in.
On the wing—June–July; rarely in September

The Egg

Laid singly on the edge of the upper surface of a leaf of the food-plant. When one has been laid the female flutters from leaf to leaf, laying on each.

The colour is olive green, semi-transparent, and very glassy. Before hatching it becomes paler, the dark head showing through the shell.

In shape it is spherical, beautifully adorned with hexagonal cells, exactly resembling honeycomb. From the angle of each cell rises a sharp transparent spine. (See Notes.)

The Caterpillar

On hatching, the colour is ochreous with pale warts. After the *second* oult, and before hibernating, the dorsal surface is tawny with a white lateral stripe, the under-surface being of a rich dark brown closely matching the withered leaves of the honeysuckle in which it is about to hibernate. After the fourth moult in the following May, and before pupating, the ground-colour is green with a white dilated lateral stripe commencing on the fourth segment. When full-fed the tubercles are pale ochreous and the whole colouring becomes paler. They attach themselves by their hind claspers to a pad of silk spun on the stems of honeysuckle, and hang suspended for pupation.

FEMALE

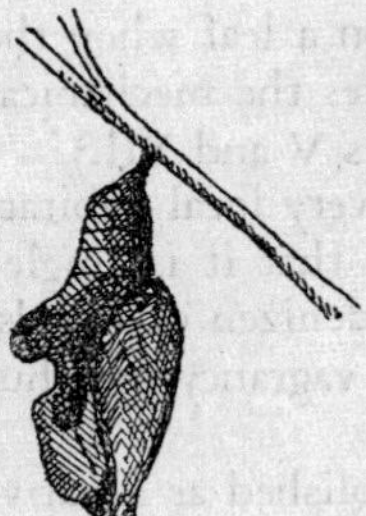

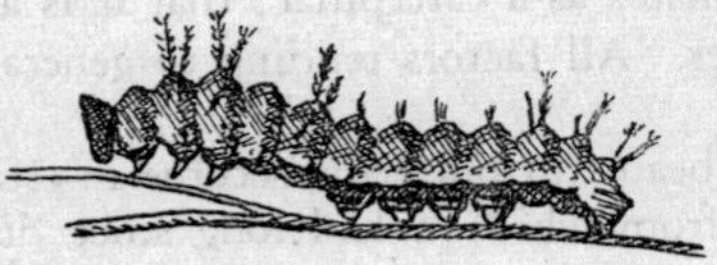

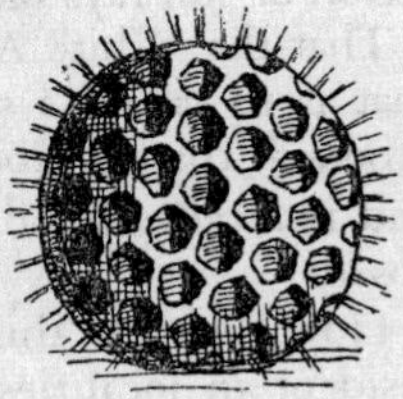

THE CHRYSALIS

The ground-colour is light green, the whole of the dorsal keel olive brown; an olive line crosses the wing-cases and a few olive streaks spread over the head and thorax which are adorned with burnished silver-gilt.

THE BUTTERFLY

The upper surface of the fore-wings is dull brownish black with a curved band of interrupted large white spots. Near the corners there are two small white spots. The hind-wings have the same white band continued through their centre, narrowing to the end. Near the lower inner corners there is a faint red spot. Inside the fringe is a band of darker colour than the ground-colour.

Underside: the general ground-colour of the fore-wings is fulvous red and all the white marks from above show through. The hind-wings have two rows of blackish brown dots between the white bar and the margin. An extraordinary variation, or mutation, occurs in which no trace of the markings on the upper side occur.

This butterfly has a swift and gliding flight, and frequents woods and forests. Though reared on the honeysuckle it is often a foul feeder like the Purple Emperor which feasts on dung. When the sun goes in, or down, it rests on the underside of a leaf. (See Notes.)

Distribution

Once common only in the New Forest (Hants.) it has in recent years spread to all the larger woods in Southern England, including the London area, where it is now abundant. It is exclusively a woodland butterfly. (See Notes.)

Notes

Though it is not suggested that there is any significance in the matter, it is philologically interesting to note that the egg of a butterfly suckled on honeysuckle shows the exact hexagonal markings of a honeycomb. Its fall from grace in subsequently feeding on filth, like the Purple Emperor, seems almost to be a natural parable!

The habit of immediately resting with closed wings on a leaf when the sun goes in or down, as do most butterflies, demonstrates the mechanical action of sun rays on the flight machinery. (See Chapters V and XII.)

That the White Admiral is never seen away from its very local habitat, that is to say in a state of vagrancy, is due to the fact that it is single-brooded, that it hibernates as a caterpillar; that it is a denizen of woods, and is a powerful flyer. All factors tending to general vagrancy are thus absent.

How then has this beautiful butterfly become re-established as a native resident in localities from which it had long since disappeared? Almost certainly under the exceptional circumstances carefully considered in Chapter XI, pages 86-7. It is noteworthy that very rarely this normally single-hooded butterfly has a second hood which appears on the wing in *September*, a stormy month. Its food-plant is widely and profusely distributed. It may therefore be assumed with confidence that the year of the appearance of the White Admiral in new localities followed an exceptional year when it was double-hooded, and thus vagrant in the autumn, which in summer it seldom, if ever, is.

For the effect on these caterpillars of an unsuitable food, see Notes to Black-veined White.

PURPLE EMPEROR

Apatura iris

(State of Hibernation—Caterpillar)

Egg

Size—1 mm.
Incubation period—14 days
No. of Broods—1
Food-plant—Sallow

Chrysalis

Size—30 mm.
Pupation period—28 days

Caterpillar

Size—44 mm.
Larval period—about 300 days
No. of Moults—4

Butterfly

Wing-span—$2\frac{3}{4}$ to $3\frac{1}{4}$ in.
On the wing—July–August

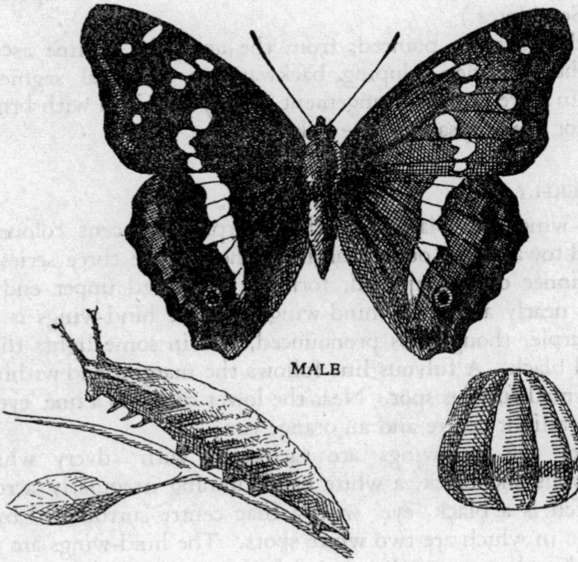

MALE

THE EGG

Laid singly on the upper surface of a leaf of the food-plant. When first laid it is uniformly of an ochreous green, growing darker and becoming blackish before hatching.

It is of a blunt conical shape, indent at the base, which is rounded and embedded in glutin. The micropyle is finely reticulated, from which run fourteen longitudinal keels down to the base. The spaces between are concave and are developed into fine transverse ribs towards the base. The keels are curiously constructed, each being formed of three very fine ridges, the outer two being united at each end.

THE CATERPILLAR

On hatching, the surface is covered with raised reticulations forming an ochreous yellow network. The remainder of the surface is shining black. After the second moult (fifty days), and before hibernating, the surface becomes pinkish, and white below. After the fourth moult, before pupating, the general shape becomes slug-like and is furnished with a pair of horns 6·3 mm. long. Fine white hairs sprout from both head and horns, which are of a light greenish-blue. (For method of hibernation, see Notes.)

THE CHRYSALIS

The whole colouring is a pale whitish green. The dorsal keel is yellow on the abdomen, blending into the white on the head. The whole is indistinguishable from the underside of the sallow leaf upon which it pupates. (See Notes.)

The head is sharply pointed; from the apex the outline ascends in a curve to the abdomen, sloping backward to the anal segment which terminates in a cremastral arrangement, amply provided with brown hooks which anchor the chrysalis to the silk pad.

THE BUTTERFLY

The fore-wings are blackish with a purple iridescent colour. In the middle, and towards the outer margin at the top, are three series of white spots, the inner ones conjoined, forming the waved upper end of a bar which runs nearly across the hind-wings. In the hind-wings is the same splendid purple, though less pronounced, and in some lights they appear to be a dull black. A fulvous line follows the margin, and within its outer corner is a small fulvous spot. Near the lower corner is a fine 'eye,' a black pupil, with a light centre and an orange rim.

Underside: the fore-wings are variegated with silvery white, grey, orange, fulvous and black, a white band running irregularly across them, behind which is a black 'eye' with a lilac centre surrounded by a broad orange circle in which are two white spots. The hind-wings are grey with a greyish white bar across them. In the corner is a black 'eyelet' with a lilac pupil and orange centre.

The female is larger than the male but less brilliantly coloured, the purple sheen being entirely absent.

Variation is confined to the white markings, and in some extreme cases all the markings are obliterated on the upper side.

This butterfly is one of the collectors' great prizes. It has a powerful flight and is generally seen flying above the tops of oak trees on which, between flights, it 'perches.' The males are often seen chasing one another high in the air. This butterfly, most difficult to net, is generally taken by hanging up rotting animal matter, on which it feasts, as a bait.

Distribution

It occurs in the larger oak woods in most of the counties of the southern half of England. In Scotland and Ireland it is unknown. It varies in plentifulness, and in recent years it has tended to diminish.

Notes

The hibernation of this butterfly is so remarkable as to deserve further remark, and Newman's account cannot be bettered.

"With the first change of skin the caterpillar loses every tinge of brown, and becomes exactly of the same hue as the sallow leaf on which it feeds: a portion of the leaf is consumed every day, but the midrip is left intact, and the little creature, when resting from its alimentary labours, climbs to the devoured bristle-like tip of this midrip and there remains perfectly motionless with the anterior raised as we see it in the caterpillars of the hawk-moth and the puss-moth. Dr. Maclean's caterpillar continued this mode of life until the 15th of November, when it descended from the leaf and, covering with silk the rind of the twig immediately below the attachment of the leaf, grasped this web with its claspers, stretched itself out at full length with its horns projected before it, and thus settled down to endure the winter's cold and the winter's storms. This is always the case; its *modus operandi* is the same whether in a state of nature or in the vivarium of an entomologist. Instinct, that infallible and inscrutable guide, tells the *unreasoning* caterpillar that dehiscence of the leaf-stalk will take place after the first frost and that the leaf will fall to the ground: the leaf does fall, but not until its falling is a matter of indifference to the caterpillar; not until the caterpillar has attached itself so firmly to the twig that neither wind nor rain can remove it. In the ensuing spring the same influences which impel the sallow to throw out new twigs and new leaves also resuscitate the torpid or dormant caterpillar, and its eating propensities are aroused and it feeds greedily until the period of its first metamorphosis has arrived." (See Chapters VI and XII.)

And here it may be of interest to draw attention to the fact that the purple sheen on the upper membrane of the wing of the male Purple Emperor is associated with brown on the underside, and heavy 'dusting' on the upper side. The same association of colouring and 'dusting' is to be found in the Purple Hairstreak, Holly Blue, Long-tailed Blue, Mazarine Blue and Camberwell Beauty, and in the *chrysalis* of the latter. (See page 236.) It is pointed out by authorities that with the disappearance of the infinitely delicate 'dust' the purple shade disappears.

MARBLED WHITE

Melanargia galathea

(State of Hibernation—Caterpillar)

Egg	*Chrysalis*
Size—1 mm.	Size—12 to 15 mm.
Incubation period—20 days	Pupation period—15–25 days
No. of Broods—1	
Food-plants—various grasses	

Caterpillar	*Butterfly*
Size—3·12 to 28 mm.	Wing-span—2 to $2\frac{1}{4}$ in.
Larval period—340 days	On the wing—June–July
No. of Moults—3	

MALE

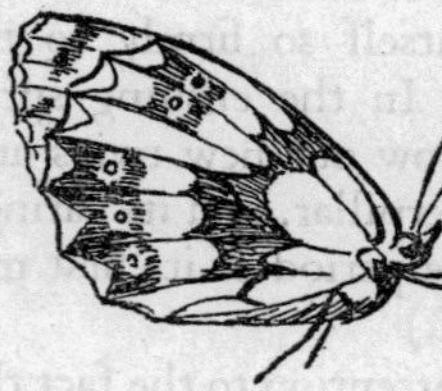

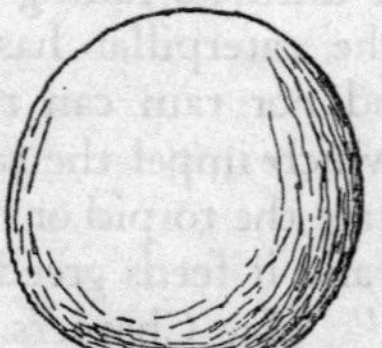

THE EGG

Laid at random on the ground among the stems of grasses. Directly it is extruded, and before it drops, it is a greenish white, but it almost immediately turns white and is then dropped. Before hatching some assume a pinkish hue and others become greyish ashen colour.

In shape it is almost spherical, narrower near the apex; the base is flattened and sunken in the middle. The apex to one-fourth down is covered with extremely fine reticulations of a network pattern: these diverge into longitudinal ridges, numbering between thirty and forty, which are very slightly raised and chiefly formed of tiny projections; the entire surface is finely granulated.

"In colouring and structure it resembles a miniature ostrich egg." (See Notes.)

THE CATERPILLAR

On hatching, the head is large with a granulated surface of pale ochreous, beset with white tubercles each bearing a cream-coloured hair. The ground-colour is pale straw yellow with rust-coloured stripes running the entire length.

After eating the empty egg-shell they at once enter into hibernation and take up their position without attempting to feed, resting on the dead, withered, buff-coloured grass stems and blades, which they closely resemble in colouring, the stripes of the larvae harmonising with the ribs on the grass-blades and the fine hair-like blades of fescue grass. "It is a remarkable fact," writes Frohawk, "that I have not seen one out of a very large number of larvae resting on any of the green stems or blades but only on the buff or ochreous ones, although both the dead and living are intermingled. The larvae *have obviously some sense enabling them to select only the grass similar to their own colouring as a protective resemblance*. Shortly before the first moult, 210 days old, it measures 4·20 mm. The ground-colour is similar to when first hatched, but the longitudinal lines are darker drab colour and the dorsal surface is more or less tinged with green, '*caused by the food consumed.*'" (See Notes.)

After the third moult in the following June, and before pupating, the ground-colour is variable, varying from pale yellow to pale green and sometimes to a full green with a whitish longitudinal band above and a darker band below.

Unlike that of other butterflies, the caterpillar of the Marbled White makes no preparation for pupation beyond crawling to the base of the grass stems where it lies, and after a few days pupates.

THE CHRYSALIS

The female is 3 mm. longer than the male. The ground-colour is yellow ochre, head and thorax flesh-tinted, wing-cases cream-coloured. Colouring is very variable; in some specimens there are minute brown rings dotted over the surface. (See Notes.)

The head is projecting and rounded, meso-thorax swollen, meta-thorax sunken, and the abdomen full and rounded. In place of cremastral hooks it is furnished with a bunch of clubbed spines. (See Notes.)

THE BUTTERFLY

In both sexes the colour varies from white to primrose yellow marbled with deep black. The chief markings consist of a broad, oblique band crossing the fore-wings. There are also narrow bands on both fore- and hind-wings, more or less broken up by a series of marginal spots of the ground-colour in the shape of a crescent on the hind-wings; the black band of the latter encloses a series of ocellated spots which are intensely black with pale blue centres.

Underside: similar in pattern to the upper sides, but always paler, being only outlined with black.

Variation in the ground-colour of the *underside* is remarkable, ranging from pure white to primrose yellow in the fore-wings of the females, while the hind-wings of the latter vary from white to yellow and the markings from pale olive through various shades of ochreous olive and brown, exhibiting a great variety of hues in different specimens. (See Notes.)

Distribution

Locally abundant, occurring in profusion in certain favourable localities, and in some districts has entirely disappeared. Most common in Southern England and unknown in Scotland and Ireland. (See Notes.)

Notes

No British butterfly better demonstrates the author's arguments in Part I of this book than does this unique insect in every one of the four stages of its life-history. Let us take the points seriatim.

1. The egg is designed not for sticking to a leaf of a particular food-plant but for dropping and lying undamaged on the ground. In this unusual design Frohawk stresses that it closely resembles the ostrich egg, as do the reproductive habits of the creature itself. (See Chapter I, page 5.)
2. The caterpillar closely resembles whatever leaf it is feeding upon, and as Frohawk again stresses, the *dorsal* surface becomes tinged with green "caused by the food it consumes." Here is a natural and spontaneous admission of the common-sense explanation of the cause of variable 'mimicry,' just as is the smell of fennel exuded by the fennel-feeding Swallow-tail the plain and obvious cause of scent 'mimicry.' What need is there to search for fantastic causes that are required to accommodate the theory of evolution? (See Chapter VI.)

   Frohawk also says that "the larvae have obviously some *sense* enabling them to select only the grass similar to their own colouring." (See Chapters VI and XII.)
3. Variation in the colouring and markings of the chrysalis conform to the caterpillar, but the most noteworthy feature is the absence of cremastral hooks for which it has no need.
4. It should be noted that the Marbled White is immensely variable on the *underside* of the wings which vary as do the caterpillars whose colour and markings are derived from their food, as Frohawk stresses. This confirms, as mentioned in Chapter VI, that the *undersides* of a butterfly's wing derive their appearance from the chemistry of the food plant, being thus in some way in contact from the outset with the caterpillar's digestive organs. If the upper sides of the wing (which until a few moments after emergence from the chrysalis are entirely separate from the underside—see Chapter IV, page 20) are not connected with the digestive organs in the developing and

growing stages, their colouring and markings might be expected to be the result of reflected light acting upon the undersides. In this connection it is well to remember that colour is not a material thing but an optical illusion. (See Chapter IV, page 21.) This explanation of the colouring of the upper membrane is a question for an expert in colour photography, as suggested elsewhere.

In all these remarkable phenomena of colour and marking variations in the three states of caterpillar, chrysalis and butterfly, it is significant that the one unvariable *constant* is the egg, which assures every student that what emerges from it will be 'after its kind,' no matter what the strange variations of the 'kind' may be.

The increasing number of localities in which this butterfly has become extinct is attributable to the ploughing up of old grasslands or the reclamation of ancient waste land. It will be noted that it does not occur as a *native* where the reverse process has taken place, though in such localities it may occur as a *vagrant*. (See Chapter XI.) Contrast this invariably single-brooded butterfly with the very rarely double-brooded White Admiral.

It should also be noted that whatever variations of colour and form occur, the extraordinary stability of its life-habit remains, like the egg, inviolate—e.g. the immediate hibernation before moulting, and the absence of any pupating craft or contrivance.

SMALL MOUNTAIN RINGLET

Erebia epiphron

(State of Hibernation—Caterpillar)

Egg	*Chrysalis*
Size—1 mm.	Size—10 to 11 mm.
Incubation period—18 days	Pupation period—21 days
No. of Broods—1	
Food-plant—Mat grass	
Caterpillar	*Butterfly*
Size—2 to 19 mm.	Wing-span—$1\frac{1}{4}$ to $1\frac{1}{2}$ in.
Larval period—290 days	On the wing—June–July
No. of Moults—3	

The Egg

The egg is laid singly, standing erect on mat grass which is the only food-plant in a state of nature, although in captivity the larva will readily eat other grasses. (See Notes.) When first laid it is clear bright yellow. On the fourth day it is speckled with pale reddish brown, deepening gradually into rust red; and finally before hatching becoming drab.

In shape it is oblong, fullest below the middle, with a flattened crown and rounded base. There are from eighteen to twenty longitudinal keels, some rising just below the crown. The surface between the keels is very finely ribbed transversely. The whole structure is irregular.

The Caterpillar

When first hatched the colour of the body is pale yellowish buff with seven horizontal orange lines. The head is pale ochreous. Short white bristles emerge from twenty-four brown warts scattered over the body. After the *second* moult, and before hibernating, the head becomes light

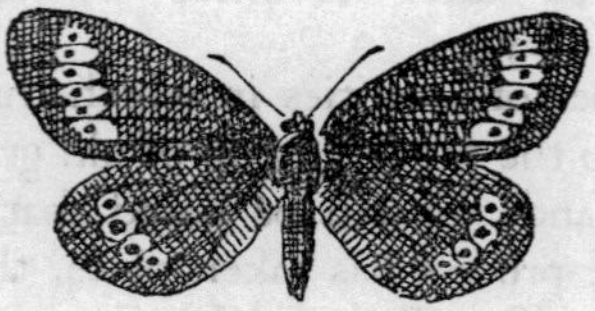

green. After the third moult, and before pupating, the head is green and sprinkled with white hairs, the colours have become richer and more clearly defined, the ground-colour is grass-green and two conspicuous white stripes run the length of the body.

The Chrysalis

The ground-colour varies from light yellow-green to cream. It is streaked similarly to the caterpillar, each stripe corresponding in form and colour.

The head is square in front, the thorax rounded, and the abdomen swollen at the middle, conical and tapering. It is without cremastral hooks, the pupa merely resting low down among the grass stems which are lightly spun together in the form of a tent.

The Butterfly

The upper sides of the fore- and hind-wings are rounded and of a deep sepia brown with a broad but indistinct ferruginous transverse band parallel with the hind margin of the wings. This band is divided into compartments in each of which there is usually a circular black spot.

Underside: these are very similar to the upper, but the colours are more suffused. In the hind-wings the ferruginous spots are very small. This butterfly varies greatly in the disposition of the fulvous bands and often tends towards albinism. (See Notes.)

Distribution

In England it is confined to the Lake District; in Scotland it is found at Rannoch and in certain localities in the Trossachs. In Ireland it has been found in County Mayo.

This butterfly is always to be found at considerable altitudes, sometimes as high as 4,000 feet.

Notes

The most noteworthy feature of this butterfly is the variety of classification which it has undergone. It has been named *Papilio melampos* by Esper; specifically as *Epiphron* by Knosch. To Fabricius it was *Cassiope*, and to Haworth *Mnemon*. Frohawk and Newman are at one in naming it *Erebia epiphron*. According to Frohawk "the normal form found in Britain is var. *cassiope*, while true *epiphron*, if it exists, is exceedingly rare."

This confusion of classification is common to all other butterflies, but the Small Mountain Ringlet is a good example of the widespread confusion. It is significant that in all these controversies little, if any, reference is ever made to the egg which, as previously shown, seems to be the factor round which classification should primarily centre.

SCOTCH ARGUS

Erebia aethiops (blandina)

(State of Hibernation—Caterpillar)

Egg

Size—1·3 mm.
Incubation period—16 days
No. of Broods—1
Food-plant—Blue moor grass (see Notes)

Chrysalis

Size—12·7 mm.
Pupation period—16 days

Caterpillar

Size—2·5 to 22·2 mm.
Larval period—290 days
No. of Moults—3

Butterfly

Wing-span—$1\frac{1}{2}$ to 2 in.
On the wing—August

THE EGG

Laid in groups in August on the food-plant. It is pale primrose when first laid, deepening to ochreous or straw yellow when two days old, with the crown slightly darker and spots appearing. On the seventh day the spots turn to dark purple. The extent and depth of the markings vary and are in the form of blotches fairly evenly distributed over the egg. Each blotch is composed of a number of minute speckles and streaks of purple-red. When ten days old the blotches fade and the ground-colour assumes a lilac-grey. (See Notes.)

The egg is large in proportion to the butterfly and of an ovate globular form. The base is rounded and there are about twenty longitudinal triangular keels, which are finely ribbed transversely.

The Caterpillar

On emergence it is pale ochreous, sprinkled with about sixteen short ochreous hairs, striped longitudinally with rust colour.

After the first moult the longitudinal stripes are chocolate brown, and the head and body are densely covered with short claw-like spines. Some of these caterpillars hibernate before moulting, some after the first moult (see Notes). After the *third* moult in the spring, and before pupating, the ground-colour is the same but the longitudinal stripes change to olive brown.

When ready for pupating the caterpillar forms a slight hollow in the ground at the base of its food-plant and spins a loose open network over itself. (See Notes.)

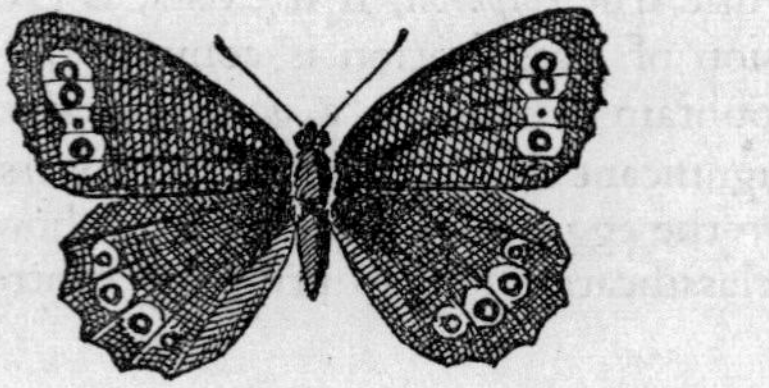

MALE

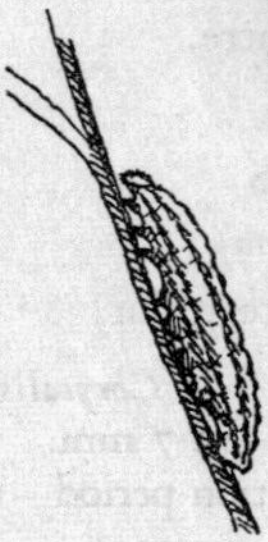

The Chrysalis

At first the colour is pale ochreous and semi-transparent. As it matures the colour deepens and becomes more opaque with three amber brown stripes.

In shape it is rounded and stout in proportion. The surface is finely granulated and, except for the wing-cases, is sprinkled with minute bristles.

The Butterfly

The upper sides are of a uniform dark bronze, the fore-wings having a dark orange-red patch near the tips. In the upper part of these patches are two black 'eyes,' each with a white speck in its centre. In some specimens there are as many as five 'eyes.'

Underside: the fore-wings are of the same ground-colour as the upper, the patch showing through as above but of a more yellow tinge. The hind-wings have a tint of grey with the brown at the base.

The colour of the patches varies between the sexes and also according to the locality in which it occurs.

Distribution

In England only in the northern counties. In Scotland it is widely distributed, occurring as far north as Forres. Unknown in Ireland. Though found at considerable elevations it mostly haunts sheltered valleys.

Notes

The most noteworthy characteristic of the Scotch Argus is the unusual and changing colour of the egg and the *variable* habit of hibernating before or after the first moult. Equally to be noted is the stability of this variable habit, or mutation, and its confinement to this species. The shape and form of the egg do not vary.

The variation in colour of the butterfly is again due to environmental conditions.

Some authorities assert that the Scotch Argus feeds on various grasses, but Frohawk disputes that this is so in a state of nature, though it is true of specimens reared in captivity. (See notes to Swallow-tail.)

This butterfly has been known to lay its eggs when enclosed in a box within a box, wrapped up in paper and sent by post. In fact, when mature it will 'seed' fruitfully though the parent is without light or air. Here seems to be another pointer to its vegetable nature. (See also the curious case of 'egg-shedding,' or 'seeding,' in the case of a set and seemingly dead moth recorded under Large White.)

GRAYLING

Satyrus semele

(State of Hibernation—Caterpillar)

Egg	*Chrysalis*
Size—0·8 mm.	Size—15 to 17 mm.
Incubation period—17 days	Pupation period—1 month
No. of Broods—1	
Food-plant—Various grasses	

Caterpillar	*Butterfly*
Size—1·6 to 31 mm.	Wing-span—2 to 2½ in.
Larval period—?	On the wing—July–September
No. of Moults—4	

THE EGG

Laid singly in August on the blades of various grasses. The colour is milk white turning to a pale lilac before hatching.

In shape it is of an ovate spheroid form with the apex flattened. There are about twenty-eight longitudinal ribs, joined and reticulated on the crown; the base is finely granulated and rounded. The ribs are irregularly formed and become broken near the summit.

THE CATERPILLAR

When hatched, the ground-colour is pale primrose, and there are eight rows of small black warts. After the *second* moult, and before hibernating, there are two dorsal stripes of light olive outlined with brown. After the fourth moult in the following spring the surface of the body is covered with minute points and sprinkled with tiny brown spine-like hairs.

THE CHRYSALIS

The colour is a rich rust-red and without markings.

The head is rounded and prominent, the thorax full and rounded dorsally, and the abdomen largest at the third segment.

FEMALE

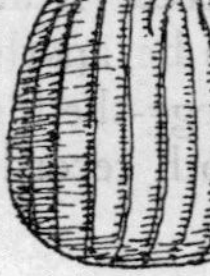

THE BUTTERFLY

The fore-wings of the female are dull brown with an irregular lighter brown band occupying nearly half of the outer part of the wing, on which are two white-pupilled black spots. The hind-wings have one such spot. In the male the light brown band is dusted over with brown scales, giving the butterfly a darker and duller appearance.

Underside: the fore-wings are fulvous with two very distinct white-pupilled black spots; the hind-wings are marked with various tints of grey and brown.

Distribution

Locally but widely distributed throughout the British Isles with the exception, apparently, of the Scottish islands.

Notes

The most noteworthy feature of the Grayling is its perfect obliterative colouring made more complete by its invariable habit of resting with closed wings. In chalky country it is lighter than on darker soils. Apart from this resemblance to the local soils it is not subject to great variation, but it has the occasional abnormality, very marked, of combining the colouring of both sexes in a single individual.

SPECKLED WOOD

Pararge aegeria

(State of Hibernation—partial as a Caterpillar)

Egg

Size—0·8 mm.
Incubation period—10 days
No. of Broods—2; occasionally 3
Food-plant—various grasses

Chrysalis

Size—12·7 mm.
Pupation period—27 days

Caterpillar

Size—2·5 to 28 mm.
Larval period—up to 200 days
No. of Moults—3

Butterfly

Wing-span—1½ to 2 in.
On the wing—April–August

FEMALE

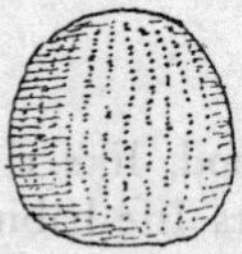

THE EGG

Laid singly on blades of grass.

The colour is of a translucent greenish yellow and has the singularity of not altering owing to the exactly similar colouring of the larva.

The whole surface is finely reticulated, forming a fine honeycomb pattern over the crown and base, and delicately keeled down the middle. The keels are irregular and connected by transverse ribs which gradually form into shallow hexagonal cells near the summit and base.

THE CATERPILLAR

When hatched it is a clear yellowish green. After the third moult, before pupation, the ground-colour is clear grass green with a darker longitudinal stripe bordered by a light greenish yellow line.

This caterpillar only undergoes partial hibernation and usually after the second moult. It feeds during the winter when the weather is sufficiently mild.

The Chrysalis

The colour varies at first from dull to brilliant green, gradually becoming opaque; the normal colour is attained when twenty-four hours old, and there are two distinct varieties. The dull variety is pale, finely streaked and speckled with brown. The light green variety varies in intensity, some being grass green and some pure green. In both forms the markings are of different shades of green.

The pupa is attached by the cremastral hooks to a pad of silk on the grass-stem, the cast larval skin usually adhering to the silken pad.

The Butterfly

The ground-colour is smoky-brown, the fore-wings having eight or nine creamy white spots and one black spot with a white pupil. The hind-wings have six or seven pale spots, three of which generally contain a black spot with a white pupil.

Underside: the fore-wings resemble the upper, but the hind-wings are suffused and marbled with various shades of fulvous.

This species varies considerably in the spots both in size and colouring.

Distribution

Though this butterfly has vanished from many localities it is still abundant and widely distributed over England and Wales. In Scotland it is uncommon, but in Ireland it is abundant all over the country. Mr. Lorne Campbell records two specimens in Canna this July (1945). (See Notes.)

Notes

The Speckled Wood, like the Scotch Argus, is chiefly remarkable for the variability of its life-habit, particularly in its caterpillar stage. (See page 6.) Not only does it de-hibernate in the winter as a caterpillar when the weather is warm, as do Brimstones as butterflies, but according to Frohawk it occasionally hibernates as a chrysalis. It is recorded "that of caterpillars resulting from pairing *induced* in captivity in August, eighty per cent hibernated as pupae and twenty per cent as half-fed larvae."

It should be noted that the pairing was *induced*, and this exceptional aberration in life-habit does not, according to Newman, occur in a state of nature. (See page 93.) The variability of life-habit, brought about by temperature, is invariable in this species and leads to a succession of butterflies in all four states throughout the season. It will be noted that in exceptional summers there are three crops. In his letter recording the two specimens taken this summer in Canna, Mr. Campbell writes: "I do not believe this butterfly has ever been found in the Hebrides before, except in Skye (when it might very well exist in the woods around Annandale in Sleat). It occurs in Morar and at Irvine. I don't think the butterfly can possibly be a native, as I am often in and out of the woods and never saw it before. This year there has been a lot of hot thundery weather and strong south winds, so I really expected something like this might turn up. As the woods are now, it might easily establish itself, so I've kept my specimens alive in the hope of getting some eggs. It could not have done so before the woods were planted." (See experiments with Large Copper, Chapter XI, page 85.)

WALL

Pararge megera

(State of Hibernation—partial as a Caterpillar)

Egg

Size—0·9 mm.
Incubation period—11 days
No. of Broods—2 to 3
Food-plant—various grasses

Caterpillar

Size—2·5 to 24 mm.
Larval period—33 days
No. of Moults—3

Chrysalis

Size—15·9 mm.
Pupation period—12 days

Butterfly

Wing-span—$1\frac{1}{2}$ to 2 in.
On the wing—July–August

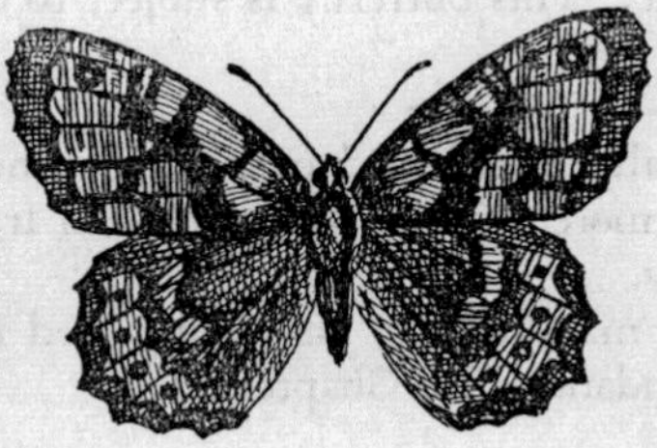

MALE

The Egg

When first laid it is a yellowish green-white, becoming semi-opaque before hatching and encircled with grey and blackish streaks.

It is spheroid in shape, and finely reticulated with a network pattern which runs into parallel longitudinal rows round the middle, giving it a slightly fluted appearance with transverse ribs. To the naked eye the surface appears smooth.

The Caterpillar

On emergence the ground-colour is pale ochreous yellow, becoming white below the spiracles. After the *third* moult, before pupating, the head and body are a rich green with a slight bluish tinge. Both are covered with minute white warts, each emitting a fine hair.

When pupating, which takes forty-eight hours, it hangs suspended in the form of a hook (see Notes). This butterfly, like the Speckled Wood, is a partial hibernator. (See Chapter I, page 6.)

The Chrysalis

The surface is sprinkled with creamy white granulations. The dorsal creamy white points are very conspicuous on the black pupa.

The head is broad and angulated in front; the dorsal outline of the abdomen forms a curve, and the ventral outline is nearly straight. The pupa varies extremely from grass green to deep black.

The Butterfly

The ground-colour is pale yellowish brown, marked irregularly across with several waved brown bars. Near the tip is a large blackish-brown eye with a white dot. The base of the hind-wings is brown with a row of three or four eyes varying in size.

Underside: the markings of the fore-wings nearly correspond to those of the upper side, but the brown bars are not so wide.

The hind-wings are freckled with brown and ash-grey with many waved marks of a darker shade. This butterfly is subject to only slight variation.

Distribution

Common and generally distributed over the southern half of England and Wales, becoming more local in the north. In Ireland it is abundant throughout the country.

This species, like so many others, has disappeared from many localities where it was once abundant. (See Chapter XI.)

Notes

The same remarks on the variability of the life-habit of the Speckled Wood apply to the Wall, though the variations in the habits of each are not identical. For example, the method of pupating differs. In one case a female produced a third brood in captivity in the very hot summer of 1893. All but one of the eggs produced imagines. The exception remained as a pupa until the following April when it produced a perfect male butterfly. (For another example of a phenomenal period for *one* chrysalis out of a brood, see Notes to Swallow-tail.)

MEADOW BROWN (LARGE)

Epinephele ianira

(State of Hibernation—partial as a Caterpillar)

Egg

Size—0·5 mm.
Incubation period—14 to 30 days
No. of Broods—1; occasionally 2
Food-plant—various grasses

Chrysalis

Size—15·9 mm.
Pupation period—25 to 30 days

Caterpillar

Size—1·4 to 25·4 mm.
Larval period—250 to 260 days
No. of Moults—5

Butterfly

Wing-span—1½ to 2 in.
On the wing—June–October

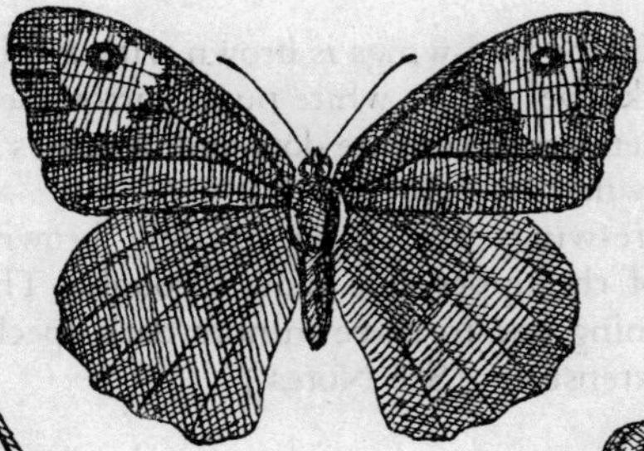

FEMALE

THE EGG

Laid singly on blades of grass and is very small in proportion to the butterfly.

When first laid the colour is a clear primrose yellow, deepening when a few days old and gradually becoming mottled with bright rust red. No two specimens agree in the arrangement of the pattern. (See Notes.)

The summit and base are flat; there are from twenty to twenty-four longitudinal keels, all originating from a ridge encircling the micropyle. The intervening spaces are deeply concave, giving the egg a strongly fluted appearance. Each furrow is delicately ribbed transversely by about twenty-four ribs.

THE CATERPILLAR

On emergence the body, like the head, is pale ochreous yellow, having a longitudinal orange-tawny line. After feeding it assumes a green ground-colour. After the *fifth* moult, before pupating, it is entirely of a bright green colour with a fine white line running the length of the body.

During the last stage it feeds only at night. If disturbed, it falls from the stem and rolls in a ring, then uncoils itself and crawls up the stem to the point at which it will hang suspended for two days before pupating (another example of 'homing'). Like the Speckled Wood and the Wall, this butterfly feeds during the winter in mild weather. (See Chapter I, page 6.)

The Chrysalis

The ground-colour of the whole surface is bright green sprinkled with speckles of primrose-yellow. The pupae vary in the markings, but in all specimens the combination of colour and marking has a variegated appearance (see Notes). The head is bi-angular and forms almost a straight line with the thorax, which is swollen, with a central dorsal keel.

The Butterfly

The upper surface of the fore-wings is brown with a fulvous tinge. Near the tip is a small black 'eye' with a white pupil surrounded by orange-buff. In some specimens there are two white dots and in others more. The hind-wings are wholly brown.

Underside: the fore-wings are orange yellow brown, with a darker border. The 'eyes' of the upper side show through. The hind-wings are darker brown, containing one to three minute dark specks.

Variation is very extensive. (See Notes.)

Distribution

General and abundant throughout the British Isles.

Notes

The colour and markings of this butterfly in all its stages, including that of the egg, are extremely variable, as is the food-plant, and are certainly interconnected. It is to be noted, however, that the *form* of the egg is constant, as is its life-habit which differs from that of the Speckled Wood and Wall in that it pupates after the *fifth* moult instead of the *third*. When it is considered how drastic is the metamorphosis of moulting, a difference in the number of moults, apart from other differences, seems clearly to indicate species, or kind.

HEDGE BROWN

Epinephele tithonus (see Notes)

(State of Hibernation—Caterpillar)

Egg

Size—0·65 mm.
Incubation period—20 days
No. of Broods—1
Food-plant—Grass (poa annua)

Chrysalis

Size—11 to 12·7 mm.
Pupation period—22 days

Caterpillar

Size—1·6 to 23 mm.
Larval period—240 days
No. of Moults—4

Butterfly

Wing-span—1 to $1\frac{1}{2}$ in.
On the wing—July–September

MALE

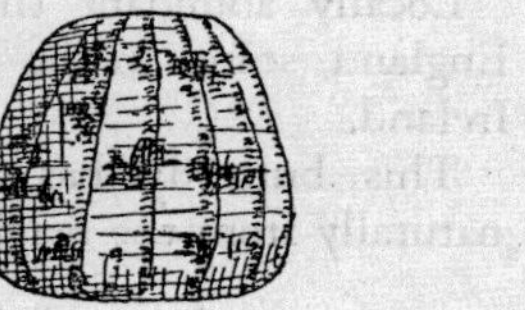

THE EGG

The egg is very small in proportion to the butterfly, but is considerably larger than that of the bigger Meadow Brown.

When first laid it is pale yellow, slowly turning to pearly white with rust-red markings.

The shape is a truncated cone, flattened at either end and indented at the base. Sixteen keels run from the crown to the base, the surface between them being concave and ribbed transversely by about fourteen ribs. On the flattened crown the keels and ribs form a network, making a series of 'steps' over the brim.

THE CATERPILLAR

When hatched the colour is pale cream with a sub-dorsal longitudinal rust-coloured stripe. After the fourth moult, before pupating, the ground-colour is pale greenish ochreous with an olive-black longitudinal stripe and an indistinct wavy stripe of claret colour, bordered below by the pale ground-colour. The body and head are covered with white serrated bristles.

This caterpillar is singular in that it does not shed its last skin but pushes it down like a rolled-down stocking. (See Chapter II.)

THE CHRYSALIS

The ground-colour is pale cream, the head and thorax in some specimens inclining to green. It is streaked and blotched with brown and black.

The head is slightly beaked and square, the meso-thorax swollen, the meta-thorax sunken, and the abdomen rising in a curve with the extremity embedded in the larval skin (see Caterpillar).

THE BUTTERFLY

The ground-colour is rich fulvous, the fore-wings being margined with brown. Near the apex is a large bi-pupilled black spot. The hind-wings are brown with a central fulvous blotch and a white-pupilled black spot near the anal angle. The male has an oblique band of dark brown across the centre of the fore-wings; this is absent in the female.

Underside: The fore-wings are similar to the upper sides but without the central cloud. The hind-wings are fulvous over the basal half and have a series of white spots on the outer margins.

This butterfly is subject to many variations.

Distribution

Locally abundant throughout the southern and western counties of England, scarce in the Midlands, and occurring in Southern Scotland and Ireland.

This butterfly has disappeared from former localities chiefly, and naturally from the neighbourhood of towns.

Notes

The most noteworthy fact about this butterfly, apart from its singular method of pupating, is the confusion in its classification. For example: though Frohawk and Newman name it *Epinephele tithonus*, the former calls it in the vernacular the Hedge Brown, while Newman calls it the Large Heath, which by Frohawk is named *Coenonympha tiphon*. In the case of Morris it is difficult, if not impossible, to sort out the Heaths and the Large and Small Meadow Browns. The point to note is that the eggs and life-habits of the Meadow Browns and Heaths are distinct, apart from some similarity in the case of the eggs of *ianira* and *tithonus*. (See general remarks on Classification in the Introduction to this part of the book; see also Large and Small Heaths.)

RINGLET

Epinephele hyperanthus

(State of Hibernation—partial as a Caterpillar)

Egg

Size 0·8 mm.
Incubation period—16 to 20 days
No. of Broods—1
Food-plant—various grasses

Chrysalis

Size—11 to 12·7 mm.
Pupation period—14 days

Caterpillar

Size—1·8 to 21·2 mm.
Larval period—300 days
No. of Moults—4

Butterfly

Wing-span—?
On the wing—July

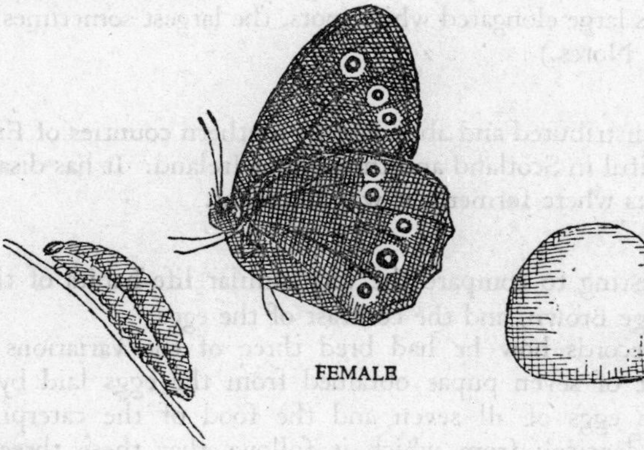

FEMALE

THE EGG

Laid singly at the foot of the food-plant.

When first laid it is a pale primrose yellow gradually deepening to a lilac-buff.

It is dome-shaped with a deeply concave base; the surface is glassy with a delicate honeycomb pattern running in rows from base to crown, where it forms a regular network.

THE CATERPILLAR

When hatched it is ochreous with dark eye spots and brown mouth parts.

After the second moult, before partially hibernating, the body is covered with hairs of varying length. After the *fourth* moult, before pupating, the body is covered with short longitudinal rose-coloured streaks, and with hairs, the longer of which are amber-coloured. When about to pupate it forms a slight silken cocoon at the roots of grasses without attaching itself in any way.

THE CHRYSALIS

The ground-colour is pale ochreous, tinged with pink; the entire surface is finely reticulated with amber brown. In shape it is stout with a short contracted abdomen. The head is blunt without angulation.

THE BUTTERFLY

The ground-colour is deep brown, inclining to black. In the middle of the outer half of all wings are from two to three ocellated spots. The fringes are whitish.

Underside: normally of fulvous brown, the fore-wings having two to three, and the hind-wings five, white-pupilled black spots, each encircled with straw yellow.

The female is rather lighter in colour and generally more strongly ocellated.

Great variation occurs in the size and number of the spots on the underside. Some specimens have no spots. A marked variety, known as *Lanceolata*, has large elongated white spots, the largest sometimes measuring 6 mm. (See Notes.)

Distribution

Generally distributed and abundant in southern counties of England and Wales, plentiful in Scotland and throughout Ireland. It has disappeared in some localities where formerly it was abundant.

Notes

It is interesting to compare the very similar life-habits of the Ringlet and the Hedge Brown, and the contrast of the eggs.

Frohawk records how he had bred three of the variations known as *Lanceolata* out of seven pupae obtained from the eggs laid by a normal female. The eggs of all seven and the food of the caterpillars were, apparently, identical; from which it follows that these three abnormal varieties were the result of interbreeding between a normal parent and a variety or mutation; and thus present a clear-cut case for the application of Mendel's Law. (See experiments with *Drosophila melanogaster*, Chapter XI, also Notes to Comma.)

LARGE HEATH

Coenonympha tullia

(State of Hibernation—Caterpillar)

Egg

Size—0·8 mm.
Incubation period—10 to 15 days
No. of Broods—1
Food-plant—various grasses

Chrysalis

Size—11 mm.
Pupation period—23 days

Caterpillar

Size—2·5 to 25·4 mm.
Larval period—about 9 months
No. of Moults—4

Butterfly

Wing-span—$1\frac{1}{2}$ to $1\frac{3}{4}$ in.
On the wing—June–August

THE EGG

Laid singly on the blade or stem of the food-plant.

When first laid it is whitish ochreous green turning gradually to straw yellow with pale brown spots under the shell. These become more pronounced, and finally the shell becomes opalescent with a bluish reflection in the high light.

It is of an elliptic-spheroid form with a swollen micropyle with a fine reticulated surface. These reticulations develop into about fifty longitudinal keels down the sides, which disappear on rounding the base.

THE CATERPILLAR

When first hatched, the surface is pale ochreous with five longitudinal amber-coloured lines. After the *second* moult, before partial hibernation,

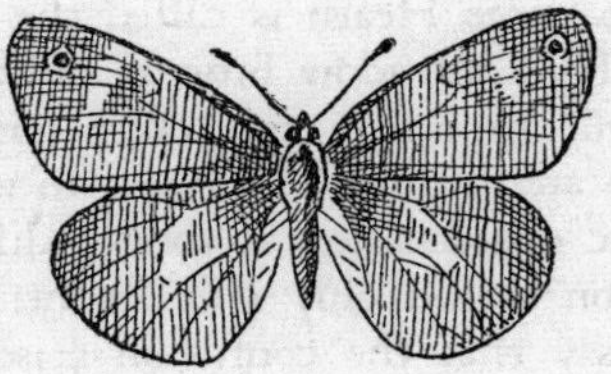

the stripes are bolder; after the *fourth* moult, and before pupating, the ground-colour is grass green, striped longitudinally with a very dark velvety green medio-dorsal band. The head, legs and claspers are green, mouth parts and eye spots brown.

THE CHRYSALIS

The colour at first is a vivid green, gradually darkening and developing white freckles. About two days before emerging it turns to a purplish brown.

In form it greatly resembles the Small Heath, as does the imago, but note the dissimilarity of the eggs.

THE BUTTERFLY

The fore-wings are fulvous brown, the fringe pale grey, near the outer corner of which are two dark 'eyes.' The hind-wings are darker.

Underside: the fore-wings are much the same colour as the upper sides, but near the outer corners are one or two dark eyes with white pupils. The hind-wings are greyish-brown at the base and, as far as the middle, edged by an irregular pale buff band.

The variations of this butterfly are so extreme and, according to Frohawk, "the variation *laidon* in all respects so closely resembles in colour and markings the Small Heath, that if it were not for the larger size of *laidon* the two species might be mistaken for the same butterfly." (See Notes.)

Distribution

The Midland and northern counties of England, and in Scotland to the Orkneys. Each district has its peculiar variety which, by earlier entomologists, was classified as a distinct species. (See Notes.)

Notes

The Large and Small Heaths present another remarkable case of confusion in classification, as do the Meadow Browns. For example, in some earlier authorities, the Large Heath is called the Small Meadow Brown, the Small Heath the Least Meadow Brown, and the Meadow Brown the Large Meadow Brown. In other cases older authors, while giving the same popular names as are given in this book, in which Frohawk has been followed, the scientific classification is totally different. To attempt to elucidate this confusion would only still further confound it. It must suffice, therefore, to say that the confusion arises from the practice of comparing the many varieties of the *imagines* of all these butterflies with one another instead of classifying them by the perfectly distinctive and invariable *eggs*, which clearly proclaim what some entomologists treat as varieties or mutations as distinct *species* or 'kinds.'

In this connection, Frohawk mentions the immense variations of the Large Heath in three distinct districts, and is finally persuaded to classify the Large and Small Heaths as distinct species (interbreeding communities) on the ground of *size*. But why on the ground of size when he himself shows in many other cases that size, like markings, is frequently the result of temperature and food? Frohawk seems to have overlooked the *significance* of eggs as a firm basis for classification, notwithstanding the immense new knowledge that his remarkable egg studies have opened up. Only in the case of the White Letter Hairstreak does he classify by reference to the egg. (See Black and White Letter Hairstreaks.)

The three distinct varieties of the Large Heath, all laying the same egg, are geographical races of the same species or 'kind.' The Large and Small Heaths are different species, as their eggs, caterpillars, chrysalids, and life-habits reveal. The similarity of the colour and markings of the Large and Small Tortoiseshells are comparable to those of the Large and Small Heaths, as are their complete dissimilarities in the eggs, caterpillars and life-habits. (See Chapters I and XI and Introduction to Part II.)

SMALL HEATH

Coenonympha pamphilus

(State of Hibernation—partial as a Caterpillar)

Egg

Size—0·7 mm.
Incubation period—14 days
No. of Broods—2
Food-plant—various grasses

Chrysalis

Size—8·5 mm.
Pupation period—26 days

Caterpillar

Size—1·7 to 19 mm.
Larval period—70 to 270 days
No. of Moults—4

Butterfly

Wing-span—1 to $1\frac{1}{2}$ in.
On the wing—June–October

MALE

The Egg

Laid singly on the food-plant.

When first laid it is clear light green, gradually changing to a more ochreous green with blotches of sienna brown. Finally it is transparent white, through which the larva is clearly visible.

It is of a truncated oblong shape, the sides convex, particularly near the base, which is slightly rounded. The crown is sunken but with a round convex centre. The whole surface is pitted, and there are about fifty irregular longitudinal keels, mostly running from base to brim. The spaces between are faintly ribbed transversely.

The Caterpillar

When first hatched it is pale green with olive green longitudinal stripes. After the *second* moult, and before partially hibernating, the colouring is more clearly defined. After the *fourth* moult, before pupating, the upper half is pale yellowish green and the lower half dark green, and there are two dark green longitudinal stripes bordered on each side by a whitish line.

The Chrysalis

At first it is brilliant green. When four days old it is pale whitish green finely irrorated with darker green.

It is suspended by the cremastral hooks, firmly anchored to the pad of silk spun on the grass blade or stalk.

The Butterfly

The colouring and markings are extremely variable and so closely resemble varieties of the Large Heath, except in size, that a description is unnecessary. In the case of the Small Heath, however, all types of variations occur in the same locality, whereas in the Large Heath the variations are more rigidly geographical.

Distribution

Common and generally distributed through the British Isles, excepting Orkney and Shetland.

Notes

See notes on Large Heath.

BROWN HAIRSTREAK

Thecla betulae

(State of Hibernation—Egg)

Egg

Size—0·65 mm.
Incubation period—7 months
No. of Broods—1
Food-plant—Blackthorn

Chrysalis

Size—12·7 mm.
Pupation period—20 days

Caterpillar

Size—1·3 to 19 mm.
Larval period—30 days
No. of Moults—3

Butterfly

Wing-span—$1\frac{1}{8}$ to $1\frac{1}{2}$ in.
On the wing—July–September

The Egg

Glued singly to the twigs of blackthorn (see Notes).

The colour is white and greenish grey at the bottom of the cells.

It is of a compressed conical shape, flattened one-third from the crown, then bulging to its greatest diameter near the base, which is flat. The whole surface consists of pentagonal cells which are large and deep, the walls of each cell being deeply toothed.

The Caterpillar

On hatching the colour is pale greenish ochreous thickly sprinkled with minute black points.

After the *third* moult, before pupating, it is light green with paler oblique lines on the sides and straight ones down the back.

Though blackthorn is its natural food, Frohawk records that in captivity "the larvae thrive best *and produce large imagines* when fed upon the succulent young shoots of any variety of cultivated plum." (See Notes.)

The Chrysalis

The ground-colour is ochreous brown, speckled with deep purplish brown.

The head is rounded and runs in a line with the swollen rounded thorax. The abdomen is swollen and rounded, curving to the anal segment which remains embedded in the larval skin. (See caterpillar and chrysalis of Hedge Brown.)

The Butterfly

The upper side of the female is of a rich glossy brown with an oblong mark of bright orange near the middle of the fore-wings. The hind-wings have a round orange dot at their lower inside corner and another at the base of the tail. The orange mark on the fore-wings is absent in the male.

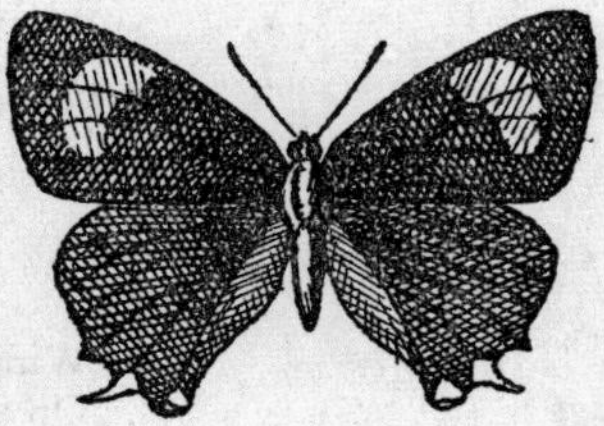

FEMALE

Underside: the ground-colour is fine orange yellow, the edges having a lighter border; the mark shows through from the upper side. The hind-wings are of a richer brown. The tail is bordered with a black edge to the inner corner.

Variation is chiefly confined to the oblong mark. It is seldom seen on the wing, and the moment the sun is obscured it immediately settles, remaining motionless until the sun reappears. (See Notes.)

Distribution

Widely but locally distributed and not common. It occurs in all the southern counties in England, Northern Wales and in the south and west of Ireland.

Notes

Here is a carefully recorded example of the effect of the food on the *size* of the butterfly. It is noteworthy that the more succulent, cultivated plum, which produced exceptionally large imagines, is not the food-plant in a state of nature. It is of interest to consider whether this richer artificial food, which produced exceptionally fine 'blooms' as do artificial foods in the case of plants, produced imagines which would have perpetuated their race. In this connection see Swallow-tails reared on *cultivated* carrot in captivity.

With regard to the immediate cessation of wing movement when the sun's rays are obscured, see Chapter V. In many species this phenomenon occurs.

PURPLE HAIRSTREAK

Thecla quercus

(State of Hibernation—Egg)

Egg
Size—0·8 mm.
Incubation period—8 months
No. of Broods—1
Food-plant—Oak

Chrysalis
Size—16·2 mm.
Pupation period—20 days

Caterpillar
Size—1·5 mm.
Larval period—45 days
No. of Moults—3

Butterfly
Wing-span—1 to $1\frac{1}{8}$in.
On the wing—June–July

FEMALE

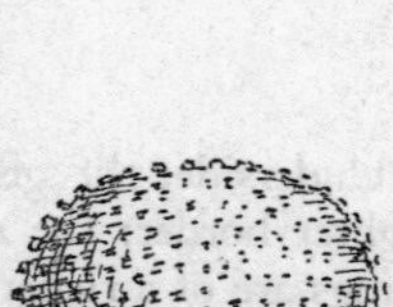

THE EGG

Laid singly at the base of oak buds.

To the naked eye the egg appears pearly white. When first laid it is of a slightly bluish tinge, gradually becoming white during the autumn.

In shape it is of a compressed spherical form, flattened at the base; the micropyle is sunken and finely pitted, and the whole surface beautifully reticulated with projecting points round the micropyle. On reaching the crown the pattern becomes more open and the points larger. All the points are connected by a fine network of elevated keels but the whole pattern is irregular. The ground-surface is finely granular.

THE CATERPILLAR

On hatching, the ground-colour is pale greenish ochreous; the head is shining olive-black, bearing a number of white hairs. After the *third* moult, and before pupating, the caterpillar is of a dull rust-red colour, covered with short hairs and with several rows of dark greenish lines or dots. According to Morris, it sometimes when full-fed goes underground. Frohawk confirms this habit in specimens bred in captivity. Normally it spins silk over the stems of the oak leaves and then eats its way into the centre of the expanded buds. The silken coils retain all the parts that would otherwise fall. The part that remains uncovered is so exactly similar to the ochreous and brown bracts that it becomes indistinguishable from its environment. (See Notes.)

THE CHRYSALIS

In colour it is of a shining rusty brown with three rows of brown spots on the back.

In shape it is stoutly proportioned, the thorax rounded and swollen, the abdomen curving to the anal segment which has no cremastral hooks.

The pupa lies on the ground under a slight silken network cocoon.

THE BUTTERFLY

The ground-colour of the fore-wings of the female is blackish brown all round, the outside edge white, the remainder being filled with iridescent purple. The hind-wings, which have a short tail, are blackish brown. The male is bluish-black, and bears no trace of the purple seen in the female.

Underside: the fore-wings are bronzed ash-colour with a slender white streak shadowed on the inside with brown. Near the lower corners are two orange fulvous marks. The hind-wings are very similar.

It is almost a miniature of the Purple Emperor, and the only other native species of a glowing purple colour. Its habit on the wing is also very similar, though in all other respects its life-habit is totally different. It haunts the upper parts of oaks and ashes. (See Notes.)

Distribution

One of the commonest of the British Hairstreaks; it is distributed throughout the British Isles except in the most northerly parts.

Notes

It is noteworthy that the Purple Hairstreak and Purple Emperor, whose food-plants are oak and sallow, are very similar in colouring on *both* sides of the wings as well as in their habit on the wing, though dissimilar in all other respects. Here again seems to be ground for thinking that the upper wing-membrane may act as a filter to the lower membrane which derives its colour and markings from the chemistry of the food-plant. (See Chapter IV and Notes to Purple Emperor.)

BLACK HAIRSTREAK

Fixsenia pruni

(State of Hibernation—Egg)

Egg

Size—0·8 mm.
Incubation period—9 months
No. of Broods—1
Food-plant—Blackthorn (see Notes)

Chrysalis

Size—9·5 mm.
Pupation period—18 days

Caterpillar

Size—1·3 to 15·9 mm.
Larval period—42 days
No. of Moults—3

Butterfly

Wing-span—1 to $1\frac{1}{4}$ in.
On the wing—June–July

FEMALE

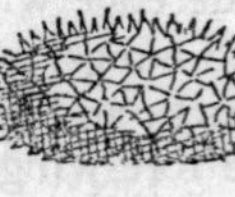

The Egg

Laid singly at the base of the forks of the smaller branches.

When laid the ground-colour is pale buff, reticulations rust brown, and the points dark brown. During the winter they become paler.

In shape they are of a compressed spherical form, the micropyle is sunken and finely pitted; the surface is covered with irregular raised reticulations forming a cellular pattern surrounding the micropyle, increasing in size over the rest of the surface into a network pattern, chiefly in the form of hexagons.

The Caterpillar

When hatched the whole colouring is lilac-brown and covered with minute shining points.

After the *third* moult, before pupating, the head is white, the mouth parts red-brown and white, and the eye spots black. The ground-colour is clear green with four oblique pale yellow-green stripes and a longitudinal lateral line of the same colour.

The Chrysalis

Pale green at first it gradually darkens, the ground-colour becoming brown-black with a varnished appearance.

In shape it is short, stout and humped, the head being pointed in front. The under-surface forms a straight line.

The Butterfly

The fore-wings are of a blackish brown with a light patch near the middle towards the front edge. The hind-wings have two or three pale orange semicircular spots near the hind margin.

Underside: ground-colour ash-grey, the fore-wings having a slender bluish line extending nearly across them. Outside this line there are several obscure fulvous patches, preceded by seven black and silver dots. The hind wings are very similar. There is little variation.

Distribution

Now confined to Huntingdonshire, Northamptonshire and Buckinghamshire. Monkswood is said to be the 'Headquarters' of this butterfly. (See Notes.)

Notes

Newman gives the food-plant as the *elm* and *wych-elm*. In England, 100 years ago, it was widely distributed. Its food-plant is still to be found everywhere, and its disappearance from many localities can only be attributed to the reasons given in Chapter XI.

The caterpillars of this species, like those of the Orange Tips, have been found devouring each other greedily. Frohawk records an instance in which a larva ate through the base of a leaf upon which a younger larva was fixed for moulting, and the larger one was devouring it greedily. When moved to an adjoining branch it crawled back, and again began eating the moulting larva in precisely the same manner through the hole in the leaf, and on the identical part of its victim. Here is a proof that the caterpillar is, as described in Chapters II and VII, 'a crawling leaf,' and as such only another form of the creature's food-plant—a vegetable!

But the most interesting feature in Frohawk's life-history of this butterfly is his footnote, in which he says: "As the egg of *pruni* greatly differs from that of *C. w-album* (White Letter Hairstreak), this species (*pruni*) must be generically separated, therefore the genus *Fixsenia*, Tutt, is adopted." Here Frohawk, for the first time, emphasises the need of classifying mainly, if not wholly, by the egg, and not by the similar appearance of the imagines.

On the other hand, the eggs of the Brown and Purple Hairstreaks are singularly alike, though the imagines are very different. In this case, however, Frohawk classifies the two butterflies as generically distinct on account of the unlikeness of the imagines, though the eggs correspond. (See notes to White Letter Hairstreak.)

WHITE LETTER HAIRSTREAK

Chattendenia w-album

(State of Hibernation—Egg)

Egg

Size—0·45 mm.
Incubation period—9 months
No. of Broods—1
Food-plant—Elm

Chrysalis

Size—9 mm.
Pupation period—10 days

Caterpillar

Size—1·3 to 15·9 mm.
Larval period—42 days
No. of Moults—?

Butterfly

Wing-span—?
On the wing—July–August

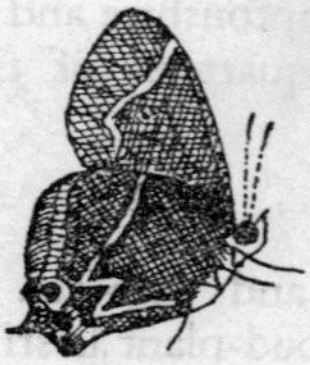

MALE

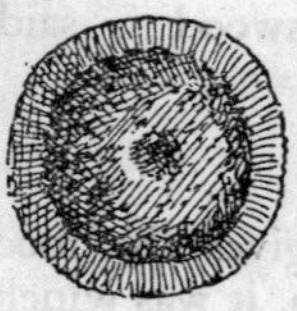

THE EGG

The eggs are laid singly at the forks of the branches. When first laid the egg is sea green with a cream-white rim, gradually deepening in colour and turning to a purplish drab before hatching.

In shape it is like a compressed button. The micropyle is sunken, the crown flattened, gradually sloping to a prominent projecting rim surrounding the base, which is slightly convex. The upper surface of the rim is covered with fine reticulations which develop into a dense series of white points encircling the egg. (See Notes.)

THE CATERPILLAR

When hatched it is olive ochreous, the entire surface being densely sprinkled with black points. After the *third* moult it turns duller and becomes of a dull brown-olive colour. The entire surface is covered with white hairs. The larva spins two or three of the small terminal leaves together with a thick layer of silk spun on the underside of one, and thereon pupates. (See Notes.)

THE CHRYSALIS

The ground-colour is a pale ochreous brown, lightest on the abdomen. The head is purplish-black. The head and thorax are rounded, the abdomen swollen at the middle and rounded at the anal extremity. The ventral surface forms a straight line. (See Notes.)

THE BUTTERFLY

Except that the orange semicircular spots on the hind-wings are absent, the colour and markings on the upper and lower sides so closely resemble those of the Black Hairstreak that it is hardly possible to distinguish the one from the other. (See Notes.)

Distribution

Widely but locally distributed in England and Wales. It is not known to occur in Scotland or Ireland.

Notes

Newman does not include this butterfly in his list, neither does he mention it as a variety of the Black Hairstreak. To him it didn't exist, except as the Black Hairstreak whose food-plant he gives as elm and wych-elm. (See Notes to Black Hairstreak.)

Morris, another old authority, gives the food-plant of the Black Hairstreak as elm *and* blackthorn. He includes the White Letter Hairstreak in his list, but he does not commit himself on the food-plant. Frohawk gives the blackthorn for the Black and elm for the White Letter Hairstreak.

Frohawk is clearly aware of the doubts about the White Letter Hairstreak as a separate species, because in its life-history he has this note: "This species must be separated generically owing to the remarkable shape of the egg, which differs entirely from that of any other British Hairstreak."

Here Frohawk confirms the author's claim that the egg, and to a less extent the life-habit (which is different as between the Black and White Letter Hairstreaks), should determine species and play the chief part in classification.

The long-standing difference on the true status of the Black and White Lettered Hairstreaks provides the only occasion on which he goes to the egg for his justification in the whole course of his *Natural History of British Butterflies.*

GREEN HAIRSTREAK

Callophrys rubi

(State of Hibernation—Chrysalis)

Egg

Size—0·65 mm.
Incubation period—8 days
No. of Broods—1
Food-plants—Broom, furze, dogwood rock rose and other plants

Chrysalis

Size—8 to 9·5 mm.
Pupation period—10 months

Caterpillar

Size—0·94 to 15·9 mm.
Larval period—25 days
No. of Moults—3

Butterfly

Wing-span—1 to 1¼ in.
On the wing—May–June

THE EGG

Laid singly on a variety of plants.

When laid it is clear green, gradually becoming paler and greyer. The surface is granular.

In shape it is of a compressed globular form, the micropyle sunken. It is covered with raised reticulations which are smallest, and form a pitted surface, over the micropyle. They become largest on the side, where they form an irregular pattern, studded with knobs connected by five to seven ridges, but usually six.

The eggs of this butterfly much resemble those of the Blues, and of the Brown and Purple Hairstreaks. (See Notes.)

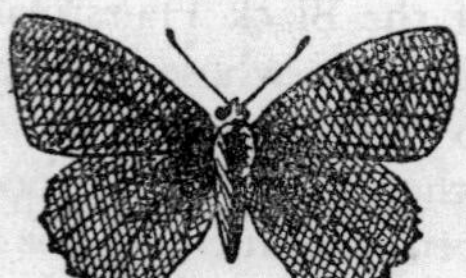

MALE

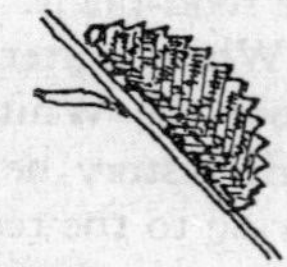

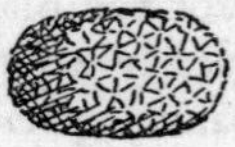

THE CATERPILLAR

When hatched, the ground-colour is pale olive-yellow studded with tiny black points.

After the third moult, before pupating, the ground-colour is pure green with a greenish-white lateral line. The head is black and shining and the body is covered with brown hairs of varying length.

THE CHRYSALIS

The ground-colour is amber brown speckled with black. The head is angular, the thorax rounded and slightly sunken at the waist, and the abdomen swollen. The ventral outline is almost straight. The pupa is not fixed but lies on the ground with a few silken threads spun over it.

THE BUTTERFLY

The ground-colour is a rich bronze brown; at the anal angle there is a short tail-like tuft of black scales and a small edging of dull orange scales. The fringe is white spotted with black.

Underside: green, except in the inner marginal area which is greyish fulvous. A transverse row of white spots extends across the wings, usually represented by dots, but sometimes forming almost a complete line across the hind-wing. Variation is chiefly in the white markings.

Distribution

It occurs throughout the British Isles except in the Isle of Man, Orkney and Shetland Isles.

Notes

Though the egg resembles the general characteristics of many of the Blues, and of the Hairstreaks previously mentioned, the butterfly itself is hardly distinguishable from the Brown Hairstreak on the upper sides. On the undersides, however, the Green and Brown Hairstreaks are in complete contrast.

SMALL COPPER

Chrysophanus phleas

(State of Hibernation—partial as a Caterpillar)

Egg

Size—0·6 mm.
Incubation period—6 days
No. of Broods—3
Food-plants—Sorrel and various species of dock

Chrysalis

Size—10·5 mm.
Pupation period—30 days

Caterpillar

Size—1·1 mm.
Larval period—70 days
No. of Moults—4

Butterfly

Wing-span—1 to 1¼ in.
On the wing—April–August

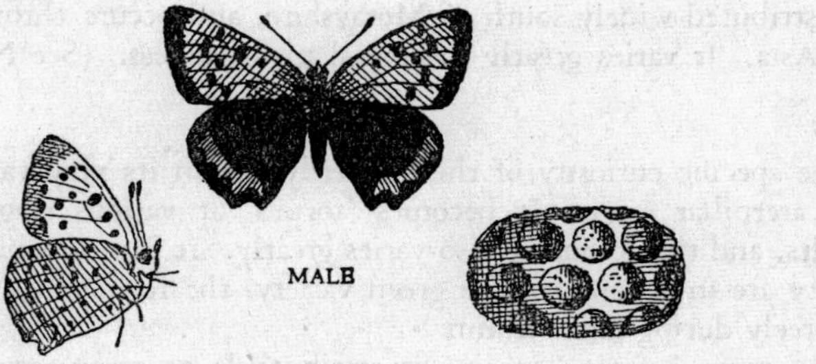

MALE

THE EGG

Laid singly and firmly glued to a leaf of the food-plant. The colour is a greenish-grey white tinged with ochreous, and remains unchanged.

In shape it is of a compressed circular form, the micropyle sunken, and the base flattened. It has a cellular surface resembling a honeycomb. The cells are deeply concave; those on the crown are mostly pentagonal and those on the sides hexagonal. The rims of the cells are undulating, otherwise the surface is finely granulated.

THE CATERPILLAR

On hatching the body is a clear pale ochreous yellow with black spiracles.

After the *second or third* moults, during which period it partially hibernates, some are uniformly clear green; others are striped with rose-pink.

After the fourth moult in the spring, and before pupating, the colour is a deep clear green; the surface is sprinkled with minute white warts (without hairs), and thickly covered with short stiff reddish-brown hairs. The head is pale olive marked with black. Some specimens are adorned with longitudinal pink stripes. (See Notes.)

THE CHRYSALIS

The ground-colour is light ochreous brown, finely speckled with dark amber-brown and spotted with black in longitudinal rows.

In shape it is long, stout, and dumpy; the head is blunt and rounded, the thorax slightly sunken round the middle, and the abdomen rounded.

THE BUTTERFLY

The fore-wings are resplendent copper with eight to ten black spots in the centre. The front edges are narrowly margined with brown. The hind-wings are dark blackish-brown with a copper bar at the lower side.

Underside: the fore-wings are orange, the black spots showing through. The outer margin is dull buff. The hind-wings are also buff with irregular rows of golden-brown specks. The wings have short 'tails.'

This species varies greatly in size—from 19 mm. to as much as 36 mm. (See Notes.)

Distribution

Distributed widely south of Morayshire, and occurs throughout Europe and Asia. It varies greatly in annual plentifulness. (See Notes.)

Notes

The specific curiosity of this butterfly lies in its very variable habit in the caterpillar stage. It becomes 'torpid' at various stages of its four moults, and the colouring also varies greatly. It is noticeable that the pink variety are in advance of the green variety, the former being those which fed freely during late autumn.

The great variation in size is attributable to temperature as in other species.

The great variation in plentifulness is also the direct consequence of climatic conditions, particularly at the time of the third brood which affects the plentifulness of the next season. In the year 1893, repeatedly appearing in all records, the year of great heat and drought, this butterfly abounded. Also in 1911, another phenomenal year.

SILVER-STUDDED BLUE

Lycaena argus

(State of Hibernation—Egg)

Egg	*Chrysalis*
Size—0·6 mm.	Size—8·5 mm.
Incubation period—9 months	Pupation period—18 days
No. of Broods—1	
Food-plants—Broom furze, and leguminous plants	

Caterpillar	*Butterfly*
Size—1·1 to 12·7 mm.	Wing-span—1 to $1\frac{1}{4}$ in.
Larval period—50 days	On the wing—July–August
No. of Moults—4	

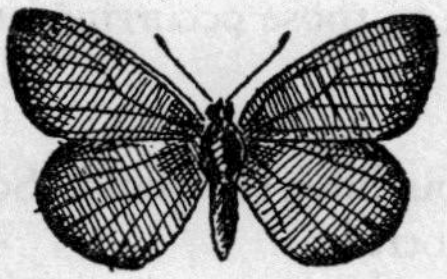

MALE

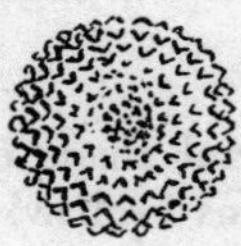

The Egg

Laid singly on a leaf of the food-plant.

The colour and texture resemble white porcelain, the depths producing a deep purplish grey shade.

In shape it is of a compressed spherical form. The base is slightly concave and the crown more so; the micropyle is deeply sunken and finely punctured, and on the sides form a pattern resembling lacework composed of prominences connected to one another by six keels, the interstices being deep.

The Caterpillar

After the first moult the colour of the body is pale ochreous with brown longitudinal lines each bordered with a whitish line. After the *fourth* moult, before pupating, the ground-colour is pale green, a purple stripe running the entire length; there are also sub-dorsal and sub-spiracular dark green stripes. Another form has these stripes lilac-red, and the whole caterpillar has a reddish hue.

The Chrysalis

The colour is at first pale ochreous green, deepening in colour, and shortly before emergence the wing-cases assume the colour of the imago.

The head is rounded; thorax swollen and nipped behind; the abdomen is swollen about the middle.

THE BUTTERFLY

The fore-wings of the male are very deep lilac blue with the front verging to white. There is a minute speck near the centre and the edge is black. The fringe is white. The hind-wings are very similar. The female is blackish brown with sometimes a dusting of blue scales. All the borders bear a row of orange spots.

Underside: the fore-wings are greyish lilac, the base blue with a waved row of black spots with white rims. The hind-wings are marked very similarly, but there are two additional small 'eyes' near the base and one at the front edge.

The most marked variation in this butterfly is in its size. In chalky districts, as is to be expected, and as is the case in other species, the ground-colour is paler than in those occurring on darker soils. (See Notes.)

Distribution

Widely distributed throughout England, Scotland and Wales, but in Ireland its existence is doubtful.

Notes

That the general shade of this butterfly is affected by the soil of its surroundings is, as Frohawk emphasises, in harmony with experience with other species. Presumably the effect is brought about by the chemical effects of the soil on the food-plant rather than directly by the soil itself.

The shape and colour of the egg should be compared with other species of the *Lycaena*, and of the Brown, Purple and Green Hairstreaks.

BROWN ARGUS

Lycaena agestis

(State of Hibernation—Caterpillar)

Egg	*Chrysalis*
Size—0·5 mm.	Size—8·5 to 9 mm.
Incubation period—5 days	Pupation period—13 days
No. of Broods—2	
Food-plant—Rock rose	

Caterpillar	*Butterfly*
Size—1 to 11 mm.	Wing-span—1 to 1¼ in.
Larval period—35 days to 10 months	On the wing—June–August
No. of Moults—4	

THE EGG

Laid singly on the under-surface of the food-plant.

When first laid the colour is greenish white, becoming opaque pearl white before hatching.

It is of a compressed globular form, sunken in the centre; the micropyle is finely pitted. The entire surface is covered with raised irregular reticulations of a network pattern. The juncture of each rib is raised to a prominent point.

THE CATERPILLAR

On hatching the colour is pale lemon yellow. After the first moult, when the second brood generally hibernate, it has become whitish green and is almost exactly the same colour as the under-surface of the leaves of the

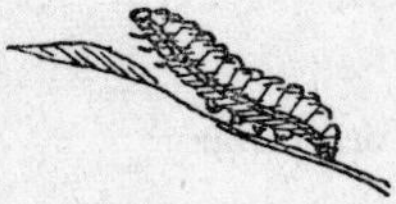

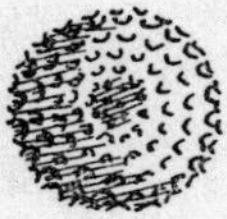

FEMALE

food-plant. (See Notes.) After the fourth moult, before pupating, the ground-colour is a clear delicate green with a purple longitudinal stripe. The entire surface is sprinkled with whitish hairs and the head is shining black.

THE CHRYSALIS

At first it is pale greenish yellow, inclining to olive yellow, the entire surface being decorated with amber-brown reticulations. Shortly before emergence the colour changes to an opaque straw yellow, the colour of the imago finally showing through.

THE BUTTERFLY

The fore-wings are generally glossy brownish black, with a small black spot near the middle. The margin is narrow and pale whitish grey. The hind-wings are similar in ground-colour with a row of light orange spots, the largest on the inside.

Underside: the ground-colour of the fore-wings is grey, with a curved row of black spots. Outside this row is another of orange. The inside border of the fringe is white. The hind-wings are of the same ground-colour, tinted with blue about the base, near which are three white spots, followed by an irregular row of white spots, followed by another of orange ones. All are bounded by a black line which marks the inside of the fringe which is white.

There are three distinct geographical varieties of this species. (See Notes.)

Distribution

Widely distributed throughout England and Scotland, the three distinct varieties occurring in the southern counties, Midlands, and Scotland.

Notes

For a consideration of the three distinct geographical variations of the Brown Argus see Chapter XI. Compare, also, the egg with that of other Blues and Hairstreaks.

Here again emphasis is laid on the almost exact similarity between the colour and markings of the *underside* of the wings and the food-plant. In the caterpillar stage the young larva feeds exclusively on the outside of the underside of the leaf, the leaf itself being formed on the same principle as the butterfly's wing. It tunnels between the upper and under cuticles of the leaf, feeding on the interior substance which, as Frohawk emphasises, "produces yellowish patches on the upper surface." (See Chapters IV and VI.)

COMMON BLUE

Lycaena icarus

(State of Hibernation—Caterpillar)

Egg

Size—0·6 mm.
Incubation period—10 days
No. of Broods—2
Food-plants—Rest-harrow, bird's foot trefoil, and many other plants

Chrysalis

Size—9·5 mm.
Pupation period—15 days

Caterpillar

Size—1 to 12·7 mm.
Larval period—45 days to 6 months
No. of Moults—4

Butterfly

Wing-span—1 to 1¼ in.
On the wing—June and August

THE EGG

Laid singly on the upper side of a leaf of the food-plant.

The ground-colour is pale greenish grey, all the reticulations being white.

In shape it is of a compressed circular form; the crown is sunken and the micropyle more so. The whole of the upper surface is covered with raised reticulations of an irregular network pattern, which increase in size on rounding the side, developing into a fine lacework pattern: the reticulations rise into knobs at each angle. Near the base the pattern decreases, finally leaving the base smooth and rather concave.

THE CATERPILLAR

Six days after hatching the colour is pale ochreous with a slightly darker greenish longitudinal stripe. After the *second* moult, and before hibernating in the winter, the colour is much the same. After the *fourth* moult, before pupating, the colour varies, but is generally brilliant green with a darker green longitudinal line and a greenish white lateral stripe. Before pupating it spins a loose cocoon among the stems of the food-plant.

THE CHRYSALIS

The head is buff, thorax green, and the abdomen greenish. The whole surface is finely reticulated and sprinkled with minute whitish bristles.

The head is rounded, the thorax swollen and sunken at the waist, the abdomen curves to the anal extremity, which like that of the Hedge Brown is firmly embedded in the cast larval skin.

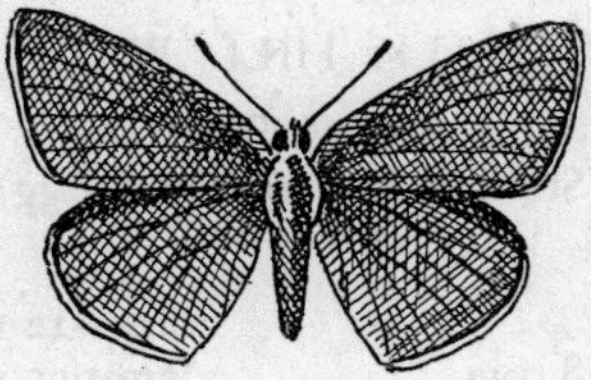

MALE

THE BUTTERFLY

The fore-wings of the male are lilac-blue, margined on the outer edge with a thin black line: the fringe is white. The hind-wings are very similar. The female is blackish brown with orange spots in borders, the whole often suffused with blue scales.

Underside: the front wings are ash-colour: towards the base is one ocellated spot, and beneath it a black line, then another spot, then a transverse row of six others and then two rows of fainter ones. The lower spots of each row have some orange marks between them. The hind-wings are irrorated about the base with silvery blue, and spotted much the same as the fore-wings.

This butterfly is subject to very wide and remarkable variations, not only in colour and marking but in size, specimens varying from 20 to 40 mm. in their wing-span. Gynandromorphic specimens are more common in this species than in any other British butterfly. Variation is not affected by locality, all forms appearing in any district. (See Notes.)

Distribution

Throughout the British Isles except in the Shetland Islands.

Notes

The immense variation in colour and marking of the Common Blue seems to be sufficiently accounted for by the great variety of the food-plants in all districts. The variation in size is to be expected in a double-brooded butterfly in which the two broods, in all their stages, may be subject to great differences in temperature. In artificial experiments, as well as under natural conditions, temperature has been proved to affect growth very considerably. (See page 93.)

Frohawk records that often two dozen or more Common Blues congregate at night on the same plant and often in company with other species. This is another example of the 'homing' instinct, and the fact that several species are found together is due to the variety of food-plants of the Blues. The single plant upon which different species 'roost' in company is undoubtedly one upon which they all originated as eggs.

CHALK HILL BLUE

Lycaena coridon

(State of Hibernation—Egg)

Egg

Size—0·5 mm.
Incubation period—228 days
No. of Broods—1
Food-plants—various chalk plants and grasses

Caterpillar

Size—1 to 16 mm.
Larval period—68 days
No. of Moults—4

Chrysalis

Size—12 mm.
Pupation period—30 days

Butterfly

Wing-span—$1\frac{1}{4}$ to $1\frac{1}{2}$ in.
On the wing—July–August

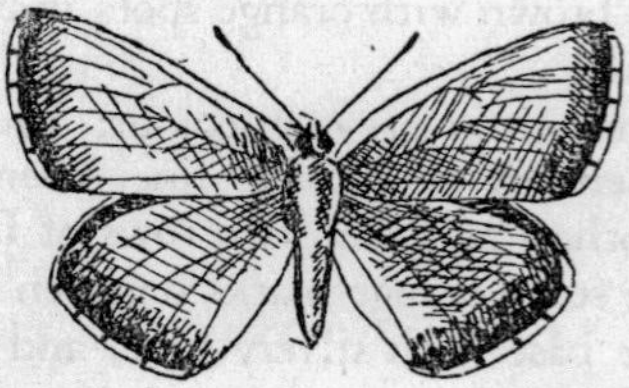

MALE

The Egg

Laid singly on the stems of various plants, sometimes as many as fifty on a single plant. (See Notes.)

When first laid it is almost white, gradually changing to a greenish-grey hue. Before hatching it assumes a lilac tinge.

The shape differs from that of all other British *Lycaenidae* (see Notes). Instead of the usual concave surface above, it is flat with merely the micropyle sunken; it is also higher in proportion and the sides are almost perpendicular. The base is flattened; the micropyle is very finely punctured; an irregular network pattern crosses the upper surface, increasing to the outer rim where it develops a beautiful lacework pattern which is considerably bolder than the other Blues' eggs. The reticulations are united by very large prominent projecting knobs and vary in number from five to seven.

The Caterpillar

On hatching the colour of the whole body is pale yellow. After the *fourth* moult, before pupating, the ground-colour is pure green studded with dark serrated spines with blackish bases. The whole surface is densely sprinkled with tiny white curved serrated hairs. The head is shining black. When first hatched it is of the usual *Lycaena* form. (See Notes.)

The Chrysalis

The general ground-colour is ochreous yellow, the whole surface being covered with rust-brown reticulation.

The Butterfly

The fore-wings are of a silvery blue colour, the front part verging to white; there is a minute speck near the centre and the edge is black, with sometimes a row of black dots at the edge. The hind-wings are of a similar colour but the dark edge is wider. The body above is clothed with silvery and blue down. The female is smoky brown with some orange spots along the border of the hind-wings.

Underside: The fore-wings are of a pale greyish lilac tint, the base saturated with blue; the spot shows through larger, and beyond it is a waved row of black spots with white rims. The hind-wings are very similarly marked and there is a band of clear orange with a row of white dots on their inner and outer edges.

The remarkable colour of this butterfly distinguishes it from all others.

Towards evening they roost for the night, packed together head downwards on the same head of grass. (See Notes.)

Distribution

Locally abundant in the chalky parts of England. Apparently unknown in Scotland or Ireland.

Notes

The packing of these butterflies on a single head of grass, where without doubt they were laid as eggs, is another interesting example of the 'homing' aspect of butterfly life.

It will be noticed that the Chalk Hill Blue egg is immediately distinguishable from those of the other 'Blues.' Furthermore its life-habit is totally different, as is its colour. Only in its early stage does the caterpillar resemble in shape that of the other *Lycaenae*. On what principle, then, is it classified as *Lycaena*? Hubner and six other famous authorities classify it as *Papilio;* five others as *Polyommatus;* and Fabricius as *Hesperia.* Here again a butterfly is treated as generically distinct from the other Blues and yet classified as being of the same family. How a creature can be generically distinct—a different species or interbreeding community—and yet be of the same family as another species in anything but general appearance is a matter which must perplex many besides the author.

ADONIS BLUE

Lycaena bellargus

(State of Hibernation—Caterpillar)

Egg

Size—0·5 mm.
Incubation period—2 to 6 weeks
No. of Broods—2
Food-plant—Horse-shoe vetch

Chrysalis

Size—11 mm.
Pupation period—18 days

Caterpillar

Size—1 to 15·9 mm.
Larval period—35 days to 8 months
No. of Moults—4

Butterfly

Wing-span—$1\frac{1}{4}$ to $1\frac{1}{2}$ in.
On the wing—May–October

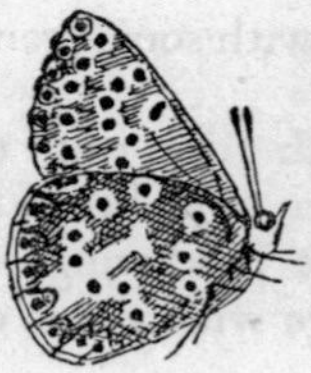

MALE

THE EGG

Laid singly on a leaf of the food-plant, generally the underside. The colour is of a green hue, closely resembling that of the Brown Argus. It differs in shape from the other Blues, excepting the Chalk Hill Blue. In the flatness of the upper surface it resembles the Chalk Hill, but it differs from that species and resembles the others in its compressed circular form. The drawing of this egg should be compared carefully with those of the other eggs of the Blues as the differences can be better appreciated by sight than by description. (See Notes.)

THE CATERPILLAR

When hatched the ground-colour is pale ochreous yellow covered with tiny black points.

After the *fourth* moult, before pupating, it so closely resembles the Chalk Hill Blue that it can readily be mistaken for it. (See Notes.)

THE CHRYSALIS

The chrysalis, like the caterpillar, so resembles that of the Chalk Hill Blue that the two should be compared visually. (See Notes.)

THE BUTTERFLY

This is the most brilliantly coloured of the British Blues, the male being pure cobalt blue and the female brownish black bordered with orange spots. Its resemblance to the Chalk Hill is in chalky districts. Alleged examples of hybrids between *bellargus* and *coridon* are recorded, but at that time no details of the egg of *coridon* were known as they now are, thanks to Frohawk's researches. (See Notes.)

Distribution

Very local and chiefly confined to the southern counties where it is abundant, more especially in chalk and lime country.

Notes

This butterfly, in all four stages, so closely resembles other Blues, and particularly the Chalk Hill, that it is not surprising to find it unmentioned in many lists, and in some difficult to trace under other names, whether scientific or popular. In this case Frohawk claims it as a species distinct from the Chalk Hill on the ground that it hibernates in the egg stage instead of in the caterpillar stage. Assuming that this butterfly is, in fact, always double-brooded, and the Chalk Hill always single-brooded, this great distinction in life-habit would seem to be decisive. But is it always a fact? The caterpillars of these two Blues are readily mistaken for one another, as Frohawk admits. The length of the egg-state varies very widely and is directly governed by temperature. After reading with great care the life-histories of these two butterflies, the balance of the evidence seems to make them variations of the same species.

HOLLY BLUE

Cyaniris argiolus

(State of Hibernation—? various)

Egg	*Chrysalis*
Size—0·6 mm.	Size 8·5 mm.
Incubation period—? various	Pupation period—? various
No. of Broods—? 1 to 3	
Food-plant—Various, but generally Holly	
Caterpillar	***Butterfly***
Size—0·9 to 14·8 mm.	Wing-span—1 to 1¼ in.
Larval period—? various	On the wing—sometimes 8 months, March–October
No. of Moults—3	

THE EGG

Laid usually on the base of the flower-buds of various trees and shrubs and very commonly on the holly when this is in flower.

Colour and shape very similar to other Blues (see Notes).

THE CATERPILLAR

Though the ground-colour is always green there are three distinct colour schemes of this caterpillar, each scheme being affected by the differing foods on which the various broods feed. Before pupating, however, the three forms tend to become similar and of a dull pinkish character. When fully fed, after the *third* moult, the caterpillar wanders for several days before pupating. (See Notes.)

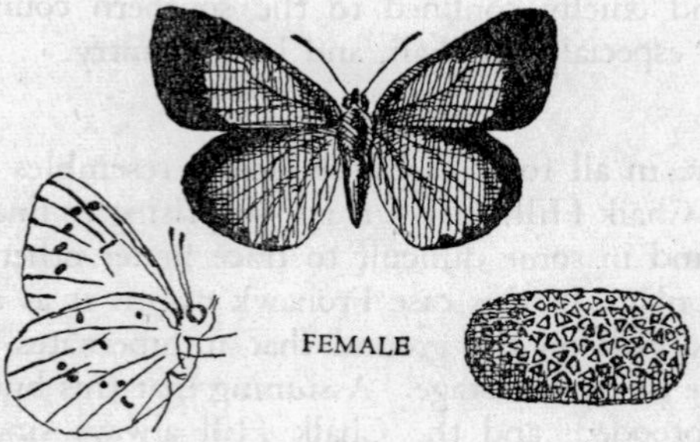

FEMALE

THE CHRYSALIS

The ground-colour is buff; the wing-cases, head, and legs are checkered with olive brown. The head is rounded, the thorax swollen, and the abdomen rounded and curving to the anal segment. The chrysalis should be compared with that of the Common Blue which, in form, is identical.

THE BUTTERFLY

The illustration shows a female of the summer brood, that of the spring brood is less heavily bordered with black, the males remaining uniform lilac-blue in both broods. Any form of variation extremely rare.

Distribution

Generally common, though variable in plentifulness, over southern England and Wales, becoming less abundant northwards and unknown in Scotland. (See Notes.)

Notes

This modest little butterfly remains an admitted puzzle to all the entomological authorities that have been studied. It undoubtedly exists simultaneously in all its four stages. The number of broods seems to be determined by weather conditions. Its food, the hearts of various berries and buds, must therefore be as various as are the times of new broods.

The caterpillars vary in colour according to their food and therefore according to the brood of eggs from which they emerge, though they become similar before pupating. The *shape* of the caterpillar is true to the normal *Lycaena*, and that of the chrysalis is identical with that of the Common Blue. In colouring it often corresponds to the Adonis Blue. The egg is very similar to the eggs of various Blues. From all of which facts, taken in conjunction, it certainly appears doubtful if the Holly Blue (called alternatively the Azure Blue) should be classified as a separate species. It is noteworthy in this connection that although its life-habit is so variable, according to the weather conditions, each variation of habit has a counterpart in one of the other Blues.

One remarkable observation by Frohawk on the colour and marking of the Holly Blue deserves special mention. He records that he observed one settle on a laurel leaf in the sunshine. "The sunlight on the glazed surface of the leaf (that is the *upper* side) produces a silvery whitish grey effect exactly resembling the colour of the *under*-side of the butterfly, making it very inconspicuous." Here again seems to be some confirmation of the author's suggestion of the causes of the colour appearance of both surfaces of a butterfly's wing, the construction of which seems to be identical with that of a leaf. Frohawk's *observation* is the author's *suggestion* in reverse. (See Notes to Purple Emperor.)

SMALL BLUE

Zizera minima

(State of Hibernation—Caterpillar)

Egg	*Chrysalis*
Size—0·4 mm.	Size—8 mm.
Incubation period—5 days	Pupation period—16 days
No. of Broods—1; occasionally 2	
Food-plant—Kidney vetch	

Caterpillar	*Butterfly*
Size—0·8 to 9·5 mm.	Wing-span—$\frac{3}{4}$ to 1 in.
Larval period—10 months	On the wing—June–September
No. of Moults—3	

THE EGG

Laid singly in calyces of the blossoms of kidney vetch. The ground-colour is a pale blue-green and the reticulations white.

The crown is flattened but not sunken; the micropyle has a dark central spot. The surface is covered with shallow reticulations which form an irregular network pattern over the crown, gradually developing over the side, forming a deep cellular pattern. In form it closely resembles that of the Adonis Blue, but in pattern the Large Blue.

THE CATERPILLAR

On hatching the body is pale bluish ochreous and yellowish vertically. After the *third* moult, before pupating, the colour varies from pale primrose yellow to pale greenish. All are more or less marked with pink, forming a longitudinal stripe. When in their long hibernation in a slight cocoon they assume a complete resemblance to the dead calyces, to two or three of which they are secured.

THE CHRYSALIS

The ground-colour is pale creamy buff, the head, thorax and wing-cases being speckled with brown. In colour and form it closely resembles the chrysalis of the Duke of Burgundy Fritillary.

MALE

THE BUTTERFLY

The fore- and hind-wings are dark brown glossed with blue, mainly at the base. They are fringed with white.

Underside: the fore-wings are silvery ash colour with a black dot near the front edge. There is also a transverse row of black spots with white rims. The hind-wings are similar in ground-colour and have three or four eyed spots irregularly placed. The female is duller than the male. This butterfly varies mainly in the spots on the underside of the wings.

Distribution

Widely distributed throughout the British Isles but very local. "It is generally found frequenting a very limited space of ground, where it occurs year after year in the same spot." (See Notes.)

Notes

In suitable weather the caterpillars of the first brood pupate and produce a second brood of imagines, the caterpillars of which hibernate.

The recorded very narrow restriction of its habitat, and its reappearance at the self-same spot year after year, are in harmony with Chapter XI.

Another striking example of the reappearance of a moth at the same spot was pointed out to the author by Mr. Russwurm. For five consecutive years he had taken the caterpillars of the Lime Hawk Moth from the self-same spot on a lime overhanging Kensington Park Road.

LARGE BLUE

Nomiades arion

(State of Hibernation—as Caterpillar in an ants' nest)

Egg
Size—0·5 mm.
Incubation period—7 to 10 days
No. of Broods—1
Food-plant—Wild thyme (and ant larvae)

Chrysalis
Size—12·7 mm.
Pupation period—20 days

Caterpillar
Size—0·8 to 14·8 mm.
Larval period—10 months
No. of Moults—3

Butterfly
Wing-span—$1\frac{1}{2}$ to $1\frac{3}{4}$ in.
On the wing—June–July

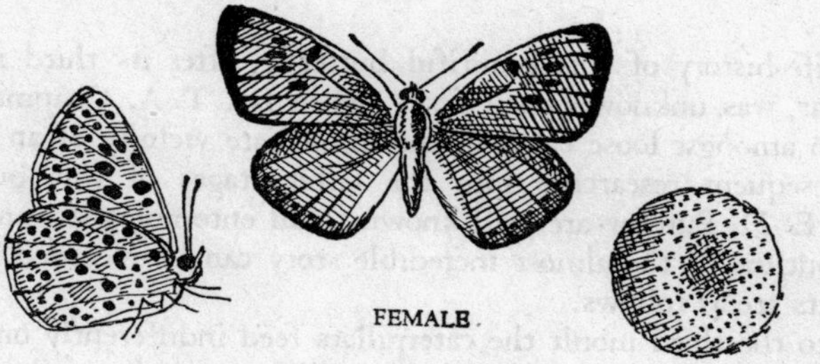

FEMALE

THE EGG

The egg is laid singly on leaves of wild thyme in the immediate vicinity of ants' nests. (See Notes.)

The ground-colour is a delicate greenish blue.

In form it is a compressed spheroid with the crown and micropyle sunken. The entire surface is covered with white raised reticulations which form an irregular network.

THE CATERPILLAR

On hatching, the colour of the body is pale ochreous tinged with green. After hibernation, when full-fed, the colour is pale ochreous with a pinky lilac tinge. The entire skin has a shining distended appearance. During its first three stages these caterpillars eat one another. Latterly they become full-fed on ant larvae. (See Notes.)

THE CHRYSALIS

At first the colour is pale apricot yellow, gradually deepening to dark amber.

The head is rounded and obtuse, the thorax convex, and the abdomen swollen, curving to the posterior segments.

THE BUTTERFLY

The fore-wings are deep blue with a large cluster of oblong black spots near the centre. The fringes are white. The hind-wings are of a like colour, bordered with blackish brown.

Underside: the ground-colour is dark grey; the black oblong spots are replaced by rounded ones. The hind-wings are much spotted; two irregular rows of black spots with white edges run across the middle, and there is a single one near the base.

The female is larger and the blue more lustrous than in the male. The lustre varies with the locality.

Distribution

Now found mainly on the North Cornish coast, where it is abundant, and in Devonshire and more rarely in Gloucestershire and Wiltshire.

Notes

The life-history of this beautiful butterfly, after its third moult as a caterpillar, was unknown until 1915, when Dr. T. A. Chapman found a specimen amongst loose earth in the immediate vicinity of an ants' nest. The subsequent researches into the latter stages of this butterfly by Captain E. D. Purefoy are well known to all entomologists, and only the merest outline of the almost incredible story can be recorded here. The main facts are as follows.

Prior to the third moult the caterpillars feed indifferently on the food-plant and on one another, a fact which well illustrates the synthesis between the larva and the food-plant to which it is parasitical. (See Notes on Orange Tip and Black Hairstreak.) At this stage, and when only about 3 mm. in length, they fall to the ground where they at once become an object of delight to the neighbouring ants which feed on the sweet fluid excreted by the caterpillar. After an hour or so, when it is 'milked' by the ants, the ant—and always the particular ant that first found it—picks it up, bag and baggage, and carries it into the bowels of the ants' nest where the caterpillar turns the tables by feeding on the larvae of the ants which previously had fed on it. For the next six weeks it feeds and trebles its size, but as winter approaches it settles down for hibernation in a cavity deep in the nest. Awaking in the spring it again feeds on ant larvae until early June when it becomes full-fed and measures 14·8 mm. As it does not moult again it is hardly surprising that its coat, which fitted it when 3 mm. long, has become a little tight and short at the knees and elbows, so to speak. When ready for pupation it attaches itself to the roof of the cavity in which it has been entombed for so many months. After a few days the chrysalis falls to the ground and after about twenty-one days the butterfly emerges, crawls through the ant-nest passages to the light of day, and immediately climbs some stem where its wings are dried and prepared for flight as described in Chapter IV.

Captain Purefoy, by his marvellous observation, resolved the century-old mystery of this butterfly's life-history. But what of the miracle of it? Apparently the caterpillars of several 'species' of the 'Blues' have been observed in intimate relationship with ants. Frohawk records that the Chalk Hill Blue and the Silver-studded Blue, for example, have both been observed being 'milked' by ants and being carried by them and deposited on their appropriate food-plants. This strengthens the author's suggestion that several of the Blues should be classified as geographical races of the same 'kind' rather than as distinct species.

DUKE OF BURGUNDY FRITILLARY

Nemeobius lucina

(State of Hibernation—Chrysalis)

Egg

Size—0·6 mm.
Incubation period—14 days
No. of Broods—1; 2 if forced
Food-plants—Primrose and cowslip (see Notes)

Chrysalis

Size—11 mm.
Pupation period—10 months

Caterpillar

Size—1·6 to 15·9 mm.
Larval period—43 days
No. of Moults—3

Butterfly

Wing-span—1 to $1\frac{1}{4}$ in.
On the wing—May–June (occasionally August)

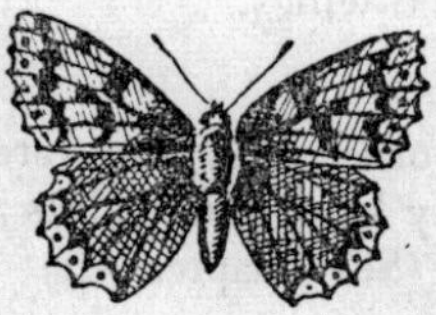

FEMALE

THE EGG

Laid singly, or in small clusters, on the underside of the leaves of the food-plant.

When first laid it is pale translucent greenish yellow pearly white. Before pupating it becomes more opaque.

In shape it is globular, the micropyle slightly sunken, and the base slightly flattened. Though apparently highly polished, under the microscope it is found to be covered with a delicate network of reddish reticulations, mostly hexagonal. Encircling the egg, near the base, are a number of fine perpendicular ribs with knobbed apices.

THE CATERPILLAR

When first hatched the colour of the body is pale primrose and is covered with long hairs.

After the *third* moult, before pupating, the body is pale buff. A dark purple line extends down the body enclosing a black spot in the centre of each segment.

(According to Hubner this butterfly has *five* moults.)

THE CHRYSALIS

The ground-colour is pale creamy ochreous with a tinge of flesh-colour. The thorax and abdomen are dotted with black.

The head is rounded, thorax swollen, and abdomen conical. The pupa is attached by a band of silk to the underside of primrose and cowslip leaves. Though the pupae remain normally in that state for ten months, if kept in a cool place they frequently produce imagines in the autumn and winter months. (See Notes.)

THE BUTTERFLY

The fore-wings are dark fulvous, crossed with three waved and indented bars of dark blackish brown. The extreme margins are yellowish. The hind-wings are almost entirely of the darker colour, the edge being formed by a row of whitish yellow marks.

Underside: the fore-wings are paler fulvous, the outside edge being cream indented with brown. The hind-wings are rather darker and richer, crossed with two bars of silvery white spots. Variation is chiefly confined to the markings on the hind-wings.

Distribution

Common throughout Southern England, rarer in the North. In Ireland it does not occur. It is very local in its habits and is said to be particularly attached to certain spots. (See Chapter XI.)

Notes

To a layman it is difficult to account for the classification of the popular name of this butterfly as a Fritillary, because its egg, its food-plant, and its life-habit are all quite distinct from those of the other Fritillaries. Only in colouring and marking does it resemble its larger namesakes, just as does the Small Tortoiseshell its large namesake which, in all other respects, is totally distinct. The two Tortoiseshells are, admittedly, not of the same 'kind.'

It is significant that the food-plant is primrose *or* cowslip, and that these two plants, so similar in some respects and different in others, have intermediates in form and colour in the polyanthus. To the author's surprise he found recently in his wood, covered with ordinary primroses and with a very few wild cowslip plants which he had introduced, a plant with *very pale* pink flowers of primrose form, with only one head on each stalk. In the cultivated garden in the middle of the wood are many polyanthuses of different shades. These facts are mentioned because they seem to show that it might be possible to hybridise any of the plants upon which multi-food-plant butterflies lay their eggs. In other words, butterflies are a branch of the vegetable world and might prove an aid to botanists in plant classification.

It is also to be noted that this butterfly, which normally hibernates like a bulb for a very long period under natural conditions, can be made to 'bloom' from the chrysalis in late autumn and winter if kept indoors. In suitable seasons this butterfly is double-brooded under natural conditions also, just as is its food-plant, primrose, apt to bloom in late autumn in exceptional weather conditions.

In this connection see Notes to Lulworth Skipper.

GRIZZLED SKIPPER

Hesperia malvae

(State of Hibernation—Chrysalis)

Egg

Size—0·6 mm.
Incubation period—8 days
No. of Broods—1; rarely 2 (see Notes)
Food-plants—Wild strawberry, raspberry, bramble and other plants

Chrysalis

Size—12·7 mm.
Pupation period—10 months

Caterpillar

Size—1·2 to 19 mm.
Larval period—65 days
No. of Moults—4

Butterfly

Wing-span—1 in.
On the wing—May–June

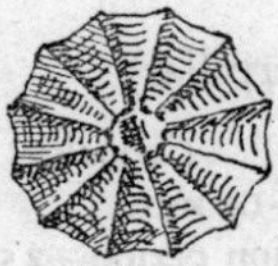

MALE

THE EGG

Laid singly near the margin of the leaves of the food-plants.

When laid it is a clear light green, turning paler and becoming more opaque before hatching.

In form it is dome-shaped; the micropyle is slightly sunken and finely reticulated with a network pattern. There are from eighteen to twenty very fine irregular white glassy keels from crown to base. Some start just below the summit and sometimes two or three near the base. The surface between the keels is very finely ribbed transversely.

THE CATERPILLAR

On hatching, it is pale greyish ochreous. After the *fourth* moult, before pupating, the ground-colour is pale green with an olive brown medio-dorsal stripe. It pupates in an open loose network cocoon spun among the basal stems of the food-plant.

THE CHRYSALIS

The ground-colour of the head and thorax is pale brown, the abdomen reddish, speckled with black. The head is bluntly conical, thorax slightly swollen, and the abdomen nearly straight.

THE BUTTERFLY

The fore-wings are dark brownish-black marked with about fourteen small white spots. The fringes are white crossed with the ground-colour. The hind-wings are very similar.

Underside: the fore-wings are paler and the spots larger. The hind-wings are mainly brown with larger spots. Variations consist mainly in the extent of the spots.

Distribution

Widely distributed and generally abundant throughout England and Wales, rare and local in Scotland. In Ireland it is said to be confined to Killarney.

Notes

Here again very unusual weather conditions will produce a later brood of imagines, or blooms, in August when normally it has settled down as a chrysalis for the winter: 1893 is again mentioned as a phenomenal year for this butterfly which appeared in that year earlier and later than usual.

DINGY SKIPPER

Nisoniades tages

(State of Hibernation—Caterpillar)

Egg

Size—0·5 mm.
Incubation period—10 days
No. of Broods—1; rarely 2 (see Notes)
Food-plant—Knapweed, thistle and grasses

Caterpillar

Size—1·2 to 17·5 mm.
Larval period—11 months, occasionally a few weeks
No. of Moults—4

Chrysalis

Size—14 mm.
Pupation period—25 days

Butterfly

Wing-span—1 to $1\frac{1}{4}$ in.
On the wing—May–June

THE EGG

Laid singly and generally on the upper surface of the leaf of the food-plant.

When first laid it is citrous yellow. On the seventh day it assumes a darker colour, the keels and ribs being a light lemon colour, producing a generally green effect to the naked eye.

It is spheroid in form with a flattened base; the micropyle is sunken. There are twelve to thirteen keels, less than half of which run the entire length. The others run only one-fifth over the crown and end abruptly. The spaces between the keels are concave and finely ribbed transversely.

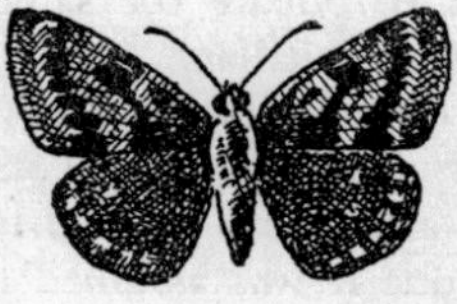

FEMALE

THE CATERPILLAR

On hatching its body is yellow ochre. After the *fourth* moult, before pupating, the whole colouring is green tinged with ochreous, the legs ochreous, claspers green, feet black.

For pupation purposes they spin together a few leaves forming a cocoon-like structure.

THE CHRYSALIS

At first the head, thorax and wing-cases are olive green, becoming later marbled with chestnut brown. The abdomen is then chestnut freckled with ochreous spots. About the twenty-fifth day the head, thorax and limbs turn to olive brown.

In form the head is rounded, thorax angular, and the abdomen tapers to the cremastral hooks.

THE BUTTERFLY

The fore-wings are blackish brown with three cross-waved bands of grey. The margins are grey, edged on the inside by a black line within which is a row of white dots. The hind-wings are of the same ground-colour with an indistinct row of paler dots and then of white dots.

Underside: the fore-wings are pale fulvous grey-brown with a small dot near the outer corner. The hind-wings are of a similar colour with a quadrant of dull white spots towards the front edge. Variations occur in the depth of the ground-colour and in the extent of the markings.

Distribution

Common and widely distributed over England and Wales. Very local in Scotland and Ireland.

Notes

The Dingy Skipper like so many other English species, though normally single-brooded, under exceptional circumstances is double-brooded. Frohawk again quotes the year 1893 as producing a phenomenal appearance of this species in August, when normally all the caterpillars of the first brood would have gone into their long winter torpor. In this case it was heat, not cold that caused the larva to pupate the same year and to produce late 'blooms.' (See Pearl-bordered Fritillary.)

The most significant fact about this butterfly, like other Skippers, if in fact it *is* a butterfly, is its habit of closing its fore-wings down over its hind-wings when resting—a fact first noticed in 1857 by Trimen. When first observed in this attitude it was assumed to be some noctuid *moth* at rest. "The wings were held in exactly the same position as a noctuid when resting. The fore-wings entirely covered the hind wings; the head bowed so as to touch the grass, *and the antennae bent back parallel to the central margins of the wing*." In this connection, Newman had previously emphasised the curiosity of this insect's antennae which, instead of being straight and clubbed at the extremities, are bent and gradually thickened. These organs seem to be half-way between those of a moth and a butterfly, a fact which should be noted in connection with the habit of covering its hind-wings with its fore ones.

In his Introduction to *British Butterflies*, Newman gives straightness of club-ended antennae, always stretched out in front or held quite upright, and the invariable habit of folding its wings *upwards* when resting, as the sure means of differentiating a butterfly from a moth. But he goes on to show that in some cases, especially in that of the Uranites, scientific opinion was at acute variance as to the classification of this species and others as moths or butterflies. There seems, therefore, to be justification for doubt as to whether the Dingy Skipper should be placed in the lists of British Butterflies or Moths.

SMALL SKIPPER

Adopaea thaumas

(State of Hibernation—Caterpillar)

Egg

Size—0·85 mm.
Incubation period—23 days
No. of Broods—1; ? 2 exceptionally
Food-plant—Cat's-tail grass

Chrysalis

Size—16 to 19 mm.
Pupation period—12 to 17 days

Caterpillar

Size—1·8 to 21 mm.
Larval period—310 days
No. of Moults—4

Butterfly

Wing-span—1 to $1\frac{1}{4}$ in.
On the wing—July–August

MALE

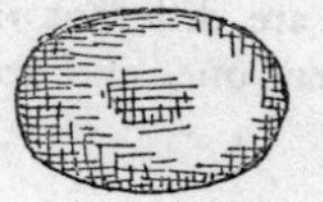

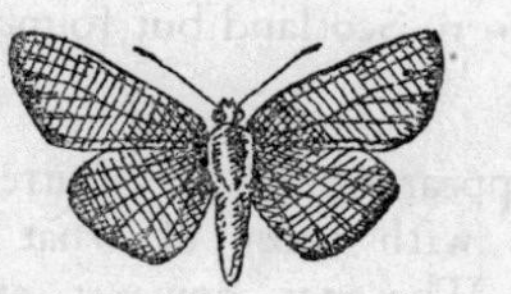
FEMALE

THE EGG

Laid in small clutches within a sheath of a plant of grass, very similarly to the method of the Lulworth Skipper. When first laid it is pearly white, tinged with primrose yellow, gradually becoming darker and then greyish pearl.

In shape it is a compressed oval, about half the width in height. The micropyle is sunken and finely reticulated, and the rest of the surface is covered with delicate reticulations of an irregular network pattern. Otherwise the shell appears to be smooth and glistening.

THE CATERPILLAR

When hatched the head is pale olive ochreous and covered with a few white hairs. After the *fourth* moult, before pupating, the ground-colour of the head is ochreous green with a darker band down the centre. The body is grass green with a darker green longitudinal band.

On emergence, the larva, after eating part of its egg-shell, immediately begins spinning itself over with silk until it is entirely covered in an oval white cocoon spun on the identical spot on which it was laid as an egg. In this cocoon it hibernates, waking in the spring to find its food sprouting freshly. In its method of hibernating the Small Skipper is unique, except in the case of what Frohawk calls its near 'ally'—the Lulworth Skipper. (See Notes.)

THE CHRYSALIS

At first the head and thorax are brilliant green, gradually growing duller and paler. It is striped longitudinally like the caterpillar.

The head is rounded, thorax rounded, and the abdomen tapers to the anal segment.

THE BUTTERFLY

The fore-wings are light bronzed fulvous; the hind-wings are of the same ground-colour, the upper edge bordered with black.

Underside: very similar to the upper sides with the outer corners greenish.

There is little variation in this butterfly.

Distribution

Common, and widely though locally distributed in England and Wales. Unknown in Scotland but found in Southern Ireland.

Notes

The appearance of this butterfly, and its caterpillar habit, are almost identical with those of what Frohawk calls its 'ally'—the Lulworth Skipper. The eggs, however, are different in shape though the colour is alike. The term 'ally' is a new one, and seems to indicate the dilemma that faces all classifiers.

ESSEX SKIPPER

Adopaea lineola

(State of Hibernation—Egg)

Egg

Size—0·8 mm.
Incubation period—8 to 9 months
No. of Broods—1
Food-plant—various grasses

Chrysalis

Size—15·9 mm.
Pupation period—20 days

Caterpillar

Size—1·6 to 22·2 mm.
Larval period—2 months
No. of Moults—4

Butterfly

Wing-span—1 to 1¼ in.
On the wing—July–August

THE EGG

Laid in a row in the sheath between the stem and blades of various grasses.

When first laid it is pale primrose yellow, gradually turning to an opaque white.

In shape it is oval and much flattened, the height being only one-third of the diameter—0·8 mm. The central part is slightly sunken; the micropyle is just discernible by the small reticulations which gradually develop in size and cover the surface with a fine network pattern.

THE CATERPILLAR

When hatched, the entire colouring of the body is clear straw yellow. After the *fourth* moult, before pupating, the ground-colour is green with darker longitudinal stripes. The entire surface is covered with fine short white bristles.

The larva spins a loose network of silk forming a slight cocoon.

THE CHRYSALIS

Light green with a darker green stripe bordered with a white line.

MALE

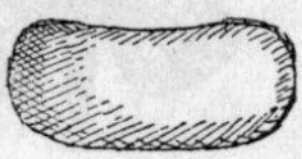

THE BUTTERFLY

The ground-colour of the upper surface is fulvous; the central margins of the forewings are edged with black, and are continued along the outer margins of the fore- and hind-wings.

Underside: very similar to the upper side.

Variation confined mainly to the shade of the ground-colour.

This butterfly is hardly distinguishable in appearance from the Lulworth Skipper.

Distribution

Confined to the south-eastern counties of England.

Notes

The Essex Skipper closely resembles the Small Skipper in its habits, and particularly in its flight, which is short, buzzing and rapid, and thus quite distinct from normal butterflies. When resting, its wings are lightly closed over its back, with only the apices of its fore-wings projecting beyond the hind ones. When settled in sunshine it depresses its hind-wings while the front pair are raised. See Notes to Small and Dingy Skippers.

LULWORTH SKIPPER

Adopaea actaeon

(State of Hibernation—Caterpillar)

Egg

Size—1·6 mm.
Incubation period—23 days
No. of Broods—1; rarely 2
Food-plants—Rest-harrow and various thistles and grasses

Chrysalis

Size—17 mm.
Pupation peroid—1 month

Caterpillar

Size—2·12 to 25 mm.
Larval period—8 months
No. of Moults—4

Butterfly

Wing-span—1 to $1\frac{1}{4}$ in.
On the wing—July–August

MALE

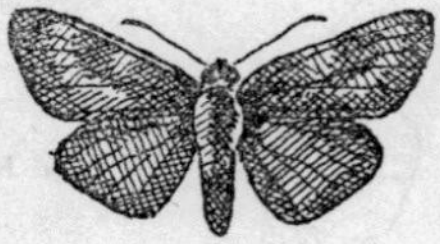

FEMALE

THE EGG

Laid in groups in the sheaths of the flower-stems of grasses.

When first laid it is pearly white with a yellowish tinge, gradually deepening to a dark purplish grey.

In shape it is an elongated oval, being half as long as it is broad. It is compressed and the base is concave. The surface is finely reticulated with an irregular network pattern.

THE CATERPILLAR

On hatching, the entire colouring of the body, legs and claspers is bright straw yellow. After the *fourth* moult, before pupating, the ground-colour varies from yellowish green to bluish whitish green. A darker green longitudinal stripe runs the entire length of the body. The whole surface is studded with small white bristles.

They mostly live in a tubular abode made of one or more blades of grass spun together.

THE CHRYSALIS

Similar to that of the Small Skipper except that the head horn is longer and the thorax less curved.

THE BUTTERFLY

The ground-colour of all the wings is golden olive; the margins are bordered with black and the fringes ochreous.

Underside: very similar to the upper sides but rather paler.

Variation chiefly occurs in the depth of the ground-colour.

Distribution

Very local and confined to the coasts of Dorset, Devon and Cornwall.

Notes

See Notes to Small Skipper, which it closely resembles in appearance and life-habit. Contrast shape and size of eggs, for herein seems to lie the only justification for classifying these two Skippers as distinct species.

This butterfly is normally on the wing in September, but in the memorably hot dry year of 1893 it appeared in May. The continually recorded eccentricities and abnormalities in the appearance, size, plentifulness and life-habits of many species of butterfly in this semi-tropical year seem to provide conclusive evidence of the domination alike of butterflies and plants by weather conditions. What affects one seems to affect identically the other. An example is the primrose, the food-plant of the Duke of Burgundy Fritillary. In a hot 'Indian summer' primroses can be picked in November, though normally dormant at that time. The Duke of Burgundy Fritillary chrysalis, when 'forced,' also appeared in November and December, though normally not 'blooming' till the spring.

LARGE SKIPPER

Augiades sylvanus

(State of Hibernation—Caterpillar)

Egg	*Chrysalis*
Size—0·8 mm.	Size—19 mm.
Incubation period—18 days	Pupation period—20 days
No. of Broods—1 (? 2)	
Food-plant—various grasses	
Caterpillar	*Butterfly*
Size—2·5 to 28 mm.	Wing-span—1¼ to 1½ in.
Larval period—8 months	On the wing—June–August
No. of Moults—6	

THE EGG

Laid singly on the under-surface of a grass blade and freely exposed.

The colour when first laid is pearl-white gradually changing to very pale yellow. In a week it becomes orange, changing to opaque pearl white before hatching.

In form it is dome-shaped, its greatest diameter being just above the base. The centre of the crown is slightly depressed. The surface is covered with a fine reticulated network pattern.

THE CATERPILLAR

On hatching, it is pale yellow. After the second moult it is greenish. After the third moult it develops a green line. After the *fourth* moult, before hibernating, the head is chestnut brown. After the fifth moult it is similar to the last stage. After the *sixth* moult, before pupating, the ground-colour is green with a darker green medio-dorsal stripe and a yellowish spiracular stripe. The surface is sprinkled with minute shining tubercles each emitting a white bristle. (See Notes.)

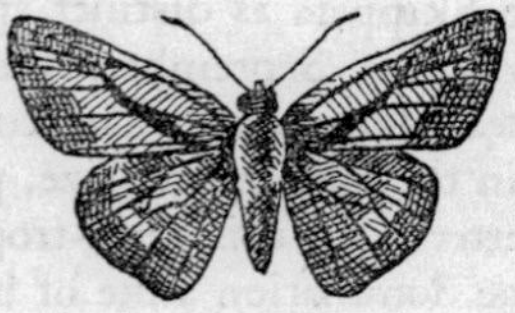

MALE

FEMALE

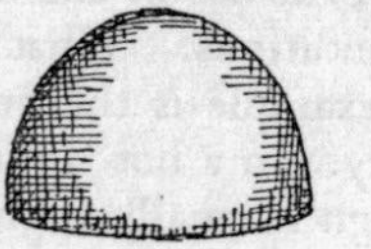

THE CHRYSALIS

The abdomen is green, and the remainder dull leaden black covered with a grey bloom.

The head is rounded, thorax only slightly swollen and almost in a continuous line with the abdomen.

THE BUTTERFLY

The fore-wings of the male are tawny orange with a large black vein following the front edge and an oblique bar near the middle. The hind-wings are of the same ground-colour with a waved bar of spots. In the female the oblique black bar on the fore-wings is absent.

Underside: the fore-wings are marked as above but are less distinct; the brown is tinged with green in some lights. The hind-wings are also of a greenish cast, the spots showing through, the lower corner and margin being orange.

Variation is very slight.

Distribution

Common throughout England and Wales. In Scotland it is confined to the extreme south. In Ireland it is recorded from Killarney and Wicklow.

Notes

The outstanding eccentricity of this butterfly is in its caterpillar stage. As it grows it increases the length of its 'tabernacle' by rolling up the grass blade. After the fourth moult, measuring 12·7 mm., it goes into total hibernation for six months, during which time it *shrinks*. In mid-March it begins feeding, and after about fourteen days it has recovered its size before hibernating. It continues to live and feed in its hibernating tabernacle, and when about to eject its excrement it protrudes its extremity beyond its dwelling and propels its excreta a considerable distance. After the *sixth* moult, when full grown, it pupates in its tabernacle by entangling its cremastral hooks in a network of silk cords.

All the butterfly caterpillars which pass their life in a tubular tabernacle are provided with comb-like apparatus for the forcible ejectment of their excreta, thus preventing the fouling of their habitation.

The Large Skipper, like the Lulworth Skipper, also figures in the 1893 eccentricities when it appeared on the wing phenomenally early. Indeed, it may confidently be said that the years 1893 and 1903 prove beyond possibility of doubt that temperature, and all that is associated with it in the vegetable kingdom, and in atmospheric movements, directly affects vegetable and aerial parasites—butterflies—in like manner.

Note the complete contrast between the egg of this species and those of other Skippers.

SILVER-SPOTTED SKIPPER

Augiades Comma

(State of Hibernation—Egg)

Egg

Size—0·9 mm.
Incubation period—7 to 8 months
No. of Broods -1
Food-plant—Various, chiefly sheep's fescue

Chrysalis

Size—19 mm.
Pupation period—?

Caterpillar

Size—2 to 28·6 mm.
Larval period—100 days
No. of Moults—4

Butterfly

Wing-span—1½ in.
On the wing—August–September

The Egg

Laid singly on blades or leaves of the food-plant. At first it is pearl white with a yellowish tinge gradually darkening to pale apricot yellow. In January it turns to opaque white with a yellowish tinge.

In shape it exactly resembles an inverted pudding-basin, having a sunken crown, rounded sides, and a well-developed basal rim. The base is flat, the surface finely granulated, forming reticulations near the base which run in ridges to the rim.

The Caterpillar

When hatched, the body is straw yellow. After the first moult the dorsal surface assumes a greenish hue. After the *fourth* moult, before pupating, the ground-colour is the same, the head shining black. The whole surface is sprinkled with minute shining black warts, each emitting an amber-coloured spine.

Immediately on emergence from the egg these caterpillars start spinning the grass blades together, and in this compact 'tabernacle' three or four may live together. They are nocturnal in their habits. (See Notes.)

THE CHRYSALIS

The head and thorax are pale olive mottled with blackish, the abdomen olive and spotted with a darker shade. The head is rounded, the thorax slightly swollen, the abdomen cylindrical, furnished at the extremity with a bunch of cremastral hooks with which it anchors itself to a pad of silk spun at the end of the cocoon.

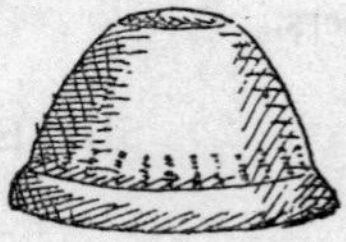

MALE

THE BUTTERFLY

The fore-wings, hollowed on their front edge, are tawny orange on the inside, the remainder being greenish brown with light orange spots near the tip. The margins are pale yellowish fulvous bordered by the ground-colour. The hind-wings are very similar. Sexual difference is similar to the Large Skipper.

Underside: the fore-wings are marbled with dark greenish at the tips, yellowish brown, orange and black from the base, with silvery spots. The hind-wings are brassy green with a waved row of six silvery spots.

Variation lies chiefly in the depth of the darker markings.

Distribution

Confined to the chalk and limestone hills and down of Southern England.

Notes

All the stages of this 'butterfly' much more resemble those of a moth than a butterfly. See the Large Skipper with regard to the caterpillar stage, and the Dingy Skipper with regard to its moth-like features. Note also the eccentricity of the egg which differs from all the other Skippers. It may be added that the very rapid 'buzzing' flight of the Skippers is unlike that of normal butterflies.

CHECKERED SKIPPER

Carterocephalus palaemon

(State of Hibernation—Caterpillar)

Egg

Size—0·6 mm.
Incubation period—10 days
No. of Broods—1
Food-plant—various grasses

Chrysalis

Size—15·9 mm.
Pupation period—42 days

Caterpillar

Size—2·1 to 23·8 mm.
Larval period—290 days
No. of Moults—4

Butterfly

Wing-span—1 to $1\frac{1}{4}$ in.
On the wing—May–June

MALE

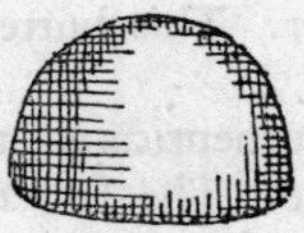

The Egg

Laid singly and firmly attached to grass blades. When laid it is whitish or yellowish white, gradually becoming more opaque as it germinates.

It is of a compressed conical form; the micropyle sunken. Starting from the centre of the micropyle is a fine network of raised white reticulations forming hexagonal cells, extending over the whole of the crown. The spaces between are ribbed.

The Caterpillar

On hatching, the ground-colour varies from straw yellow to pale primrose. After the *fourth* moult, before pupating, the ground-colour is whitish green with a darker green longitudinal line. The legs are dark grey with whitish extremities. The head has changed to a whitish green with a central black line separating the lobes of the crown.

The hibernating habits of this caterpillar are, with variations, much the same as those of the Large Skipper. The outstanding difference is that the Checkered Skipper hibernates in its full-grown state, slightly shrinking in length before pupating.

The Chrysalis

The head and thorax are pale olive mottled with black, the abdomen olive and spotted with a darker shade. The head is rounded, the thorax slightly swollen, the abdomen cylindrical and tapering to the extremity which, like that of the Silver-spotted Skipper, is furnished with a bunch of cremastral hooks for anchoring it to a pad of silk spun at the end of the cocoon. (See Silver-spotted Skipper.)

THE BUTTERFLY

Apart from its more clearly defined markings this butterfly resembles the Silver-spotted Skipper in general colouring. It also varies chiefly in the shade of the markings.

Distribution

Said to be very local and now confined chiefly to the Eastern Midlands.

Notes

This butterfly has proved a puzzle, like others of the smaller species such as Blues and Heaths, to the classifiers. Some do not mention it; others give it a variety of scientific names. It is noteworthy that the chrysalids of this and the Silver-spotted Skipper are identical in form, though differing in size. The imagines are very alike, the eggs not very dissimilar, but the life-habits differ. This butterfly shares the moth-like method of folding its wings.

The quite authenticated times of appearance on the wing deserve particular notice. The fact that the Silver-spotted hibernates as an egg and the Checkered as a caterpillar, seems to indicate that they are varieties of the same species which, *under suitable weather conditions*, is double-brooded and thus hibernates indifferently as an egg or larva. In this connection, see Notes to Grizzled Skipper which under certain weather conditions will 'bloom' again in August, when normally it will have settled down to hibernate as a *chrysalis*.

These remarkable divergences from normality under unusual temperature conditions of all kinds of butterflies are considered generally under the heading of 'Classification' in the Introduction to this part of the book, and in the experiments with *Drosophila melanogaster* on pages 91-3.

HARDY NATIVE VAGRANTS

Brimstone (Sulphur)	*Gonepteryx rhamni*
Comma	*Polygonia c-album*
Large Tortoiseshell	*Euvanessa polychlorus*
Peacock	*Vanessa io*
Small Tortoiseshell	*Vanessa urticae*
Red Admiral	*Pyrameis atalanta*

BRIMSTONE (SULPHUR)

Gonepteryx rhamni

(State of Hibernation—Butterfly)

Egg

Size—1·3 mm.
Incubation period—about 10 days
No. of Broods—1
Food-plant—Buckthorn

Chrysalis

Size—22·2 to 23·8 mm. in length; 9·5 mm. across the middle
Pupation period—14–20 days

Caterpillar

Size—31·8 mm. to 34·9 mm.
Larval period—about 21 days
No. of Moults—4

Butterfly

Wing-span—2 to 3½ in.
On the wing—April–September

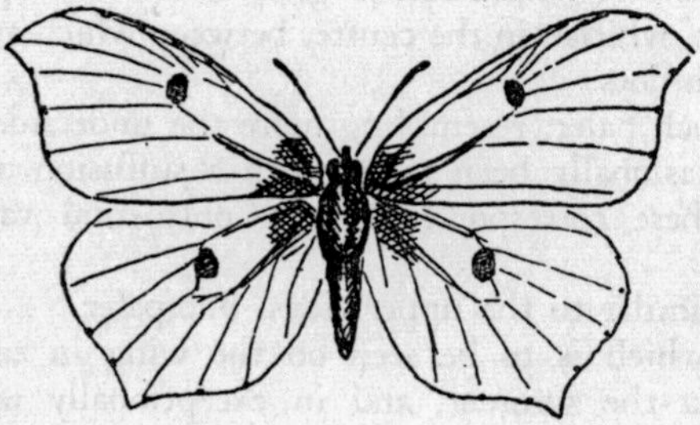

The Egg

The egg is laid singly, standing erect, on the undersides of the leaves of both species cf buckthorn, *Rhamnus catharticus*, and less frequently *R. frangula*. Deposition generally takes place at the end of May or in early June, but sometimes as late as July or as early as mid-April. The colour, when first laid, is a whitish blue-green, gradually turning to a citrous yellow and afterwards to a deeper yellow. Shortly before hatching it becomes drab grey.

The egg is slender, resembling a champagne bottle in shape, thickest about the middle sloping to the base. The extreme summit is rounded, and the base flattened and firmly adhering to the leaf. There are ten longitudinal keels running from the summit to the base and about forty-five very fine transverse ribs.

The Caterpillar

On emergence it is uniformly citrous yellow. After the fourth moult, before pupating, it is green, dotted on the back with black. There is a pale green or whitish line on each side, shading off on the upper edge into the green of the rest of the body.

The Chrysalis

The surface is wholly smooth, and in colour is green with several reddish dots. The head is strongly beaked in front and slopes to the centre of the thorax, which is angular and projecting at the base of the wings. It is suspended to the stem of its food-plant by the tail in an upright position, and retained by a silken thread round the middle of the body.

The Butterfly

In the male the whole of the upper wings is a splendid sulphur yellow with an orange spot above the centre of the fore-wings and a larger one similarly on the hind-wings. A line of the same colour, enlarged here and there into a small dot, borders the upper corners of the fore-wings. Underneath the colour is fainter with a cast of green in it. The spot is replaced by a ferruginous dot, whitish in the centre, between which and the margin is a row of brownish dots.

The female is much paler, resembling more the underside of the male. Specimens have occasionally been taken with a suffusion of orange over the fore-wings. These correspond to the Continental variety and are undoubtedly *vagrants.*

Underside: very similar to the upper sides, but paler.

The Brimstone, which is to be seen on the wing in early spring, is plentiful throughout the summer, and in exceptionally warm days has been seen during every month of the year. The authorities differ as to whether this butterfly is double- or single-brooded. According to Newman the sexes mate in April, and thereafter take no notice of one another until the following spring. According to Morris, they are definitely double-brooded. The life of the Brimstone sometimes lasts a whole year, the faded specimens of one year actually surviving until those of the ensuing year are on the wing.

Distribution

The Brimstone abounds wherever buckthorn, its only food-plant, is found. Most common in Southern England and Wales, it becomes rarer in the North and is apparently absent from Scotland. This butterfly is, however, often seen many miles from its food-plant. It is common in Cornwall, though the common buckthorn is not found in that county. Newman refers to this curiosity of the Brimstone because, he says, "it is anomalous for a butterfly to occur plentifully where its food-plant is absent or extremely rare." Frohawk confirms this when he says that "this butterfly undoubtedly travels for a considerable distance from its birth-place." (See Notes.)

Notes

The Brimstone, when at rest or hibernating on a leaf, is so indistinguishable from its surroundings as to be barely perceptible to the closest scrutiny. One such Brimstone was detected by lamplight on an ivy leaf in September 1911, remaining motionless until the following February. Six persons were taken to the spot at the same time to try and detect it; and although the patch of ivy surrounding the Rhamni (the food-plant) was pointed out to them, they all had to give up the search. (See Chapter VI.)

The fact that this butterfly has been constantly recorded far from its food-plant, and thus, as Frohawk emphasises, from its *birthplace*, is due to the *vagrancy* to be expected in a butterfly that is on the wing for most of the year, including those autumn and spring months when strong winds frequently occur. All butterflies that hibernate in the winged state are liable to extensive vagrancy. (See Chapters IX, X, and XI.)

The mating of the Brimstone is remarkable. This species usually remains paired for many hours, and in dull weather for much longer periods. An extreme case was noted by Captain E. A. Purefoy in the spring of 1910. A male had hibernated in his garden in Kent, pairing on April 28th. The couple remained in coition till May 12th, a period of fifteen days. Most of the period was cold and cheerless. When they finally separated both were perfectly strong.

The vagrancy of the Brimstone should be compared with that of the Red Admiral which also hibernates in the winged state. Both, unlike the Painted Ladies and Clouded Yellows, are hardy, the Red Admiral abounding in Iceland.

COMMA

Polygonia c-album

(State of Hibernation—Butterfly)

Egg

Size—0·8 mm.
Incubation period—17 days
No. of Broods—2
Food-plant—Stinging nettle

Chrysalis

Size—21·2 mm.
Pupation period—10 to 15 days

Caterpillar

Size—2·12 to 35 mm.
Larval period—45 days
No. of Moults—4

Butterfly

Wing-span—$1\frac{1}{2}$ to $1\frac{3}{4}$ in.
On the wing—June to October.

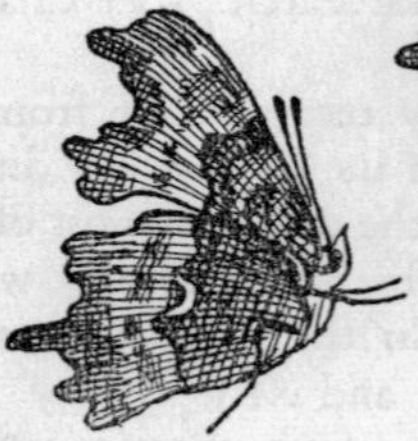

MALE

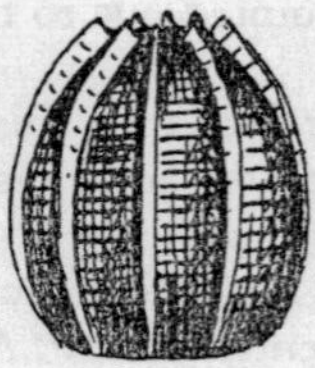

The Egg

Laid singly on the upper surface of the leaves of the food-plant. One Comma observed in captivity laid 275 eggs between April 17th and June 1st. She died on June 3rd. The colour is a clear green with whitish granulations, giving the appearance of a fine cellular pattern. Before hatching it turns to dark green grey, the crown turning to black.

The egg is of an elongated spheroid form, smallest at the crown; ten or eleven (generally eleven) glassy white longitudinal keels run from the crown to the base, all of which start at the edge of the micropyle, leaving the central part of the summit bare. They have the appearance of fluted glass and are of glistening whiteness. The spaces between the keels are slightly concave and very slightly ribbed transversely.

The Caterpillar

When hatched, the body, legs and claspers are of a pale ochreous tinged with green. After the fourth moult, before pupating, it is of a brownish-red colour, the back reddish, and the hinder part white. The sides of the head have two projections, which are bristled, as also are the spines on the body. When full-fed it spins a little mound of silk on one of the leaves or on the stem of the food-plant and, attaching itself thereto by its claspers, hangs head down and is transformed into a chrysalis.

The Chrysalis

The ground-colour of normal specimens is pinkish buff delicately reticulated with black. Two dark olive green bands cross the wing-cases. Some specimens are more uniform in colour, having the markings less clearly defined; these have the appearance of being washed over with bronze-gold and in some cases the ground-colour is a deep pink.

The pupa state, though normally lasting from ten to fifteen days, is entirely regulated by temperature.

The Butterfly

The fore-wings are a beautiful rich fulvous orange colour, the outer margins being of dark orange-brown. There are three black patches on the front edge. The hind-wings are dusky at the base and at the outer corner, their ground-colour being also fulvous orange, the border darker and edged with cream.

Underside: The fore-wings are beautifully variegated with transverse marks of rich brown, grey and metallic green, in the latter of which are small black specks. The hind-wings are similarly marked with a white C in the middle, from which the insect derives both its popular and scientific name. This butterfly varies greatly in colour and marking, in some specimens the C being replaced by a mark resembling the letter F. The most singular characteristic of this most interesting butterfly is the different colouring of the spring and autumnal broods. The former, in both sexes, has the jagged edges of the fore-wings much less hollowed out, and the projections of all the wings are shorter. The ground-colour of the upper sides is orange ochreous and the spots are more clearly defined. This regular early summer variety is sufficiently regular to have the special name of *hutchinsoni*. (See Notes.)

This butterfly, unlike most other species that hibernate as such, does not go into sheltered retreats but attaches itself to branches or tree-trunks on which it becomes almost invisible, so perfect is the ***mimicry***. (See Chapter VI.)

Distribution

Once scarce and local, this butterfly is now abundant over the whole of southern half of England and is rapidly extending its range northwards. Single specimens are frequently observed in unexpected localities, and these are almost certainly *vagrant*. The Comma does not occur, apparently, in Scotland or Ireland.

Writing on the vagaries of this butterfly, Frohawk says: "It is difficult to form any conjecture why this butterfly should have disappeared from so many of its former haunts, as the places it frequented—lanes, gardens, and wooded valleys—remain practically unaltered throughout the country. . . . Therefore we must look for the cause to be due to some climatic condition being unsuitable to some stage of the creature's existence, which is probably that of the imago during its hibernating period." (See Notes.)

Notes

Space is not available to do full justice to this remarkable butterfly which particularly interests all lepidopterists. A long chapter would not suffice to cover the curiosities of its life-history. The following, however, are points deserving of emphasis.

Newman denied that the Comma was double-brooded, but evidence has accumulated which seems to justify Frohawk's assurance that it is. His account of its breeding habit is as follows: "Pairing takes place after hibernation. The females begin to deposit their eggs early in April and continue till June. Of the total number of eggs laid by one of these hibernated females, between thirty and forty per cent (always the first eggs laid) produce butterflies of the form known as *Hutchinsoni*, while the rest are of the normal type. The *Hutchinsoni* examples pair at once and produce the second brood, which starts emerging in August and continues till October; all of the ordinary type hibernate and pair in the spring with the hibernated examples of the second brood. It will be seen that after hibernation copulation takes place between uncles, aunts, nephews and nieces." Here Frohawk claims for this particular species that close *inbreeding* which, according to the argument in Chapter XI and elsewhere in this book, is the habit of *all* butterflies, whether resident or migrant. The carefully observed mating of this curious species provides an interesting study for experts in Mendelism into which there is not space to enter here. Two points, however, deserve attention. The first is the bearing *of breeding*, as opposed to feeding and temperature, on the phenomenon of variation, and the second is that the *original* manifestation of the existence of the butterfly—the egg—does not vary except in a percentage which have one additional longitudinal keel. (See Chapter I.) It is this fixity of the colour and detailed markings of butterfly eggs, so remarkably confirmed in Frohawk's invaluable work, which justifies earlier entomologists in regarding the egg as the proper medium for classification. The fertility between *mutated* and normal specimens of the Comma are noteworthy and significant. (See page 93.)

With regard to the curiosities of the distribution of the Comma, Frohawk confirms the often-repeated argument of this book that butterflies reproduce themselves where they themselves were born. He emphasises the immense influence of temperature on this hibernating butterfly, and it is reasonable, therefore, to assume that plentifulness, or the reverse, is attributable to this cause at one of the stages of this butterfly's life-cycle. If *all* the specimens met with disaster in a given locality in some particular year they would not be expected to reappear in that locality except as vagrants. A partial disaster, on the other hand, would lead to rarity for some years.

The Comma provides another example of the constantly noted vagrancy, or migrancy, of butterflies which hibernate as such. As stated above, the vagrant Comma, like the normally resident White Admiral, has lately become abundant again in localities from which it had disappeared for some years, though whether as a *native* of the new locality, or as a *vagrant*, is not clear. If the former, the explanation must be the same as in the abnormal case of the resident White Admiral. If the latter, the unusual plentifulness over a wide area was due to a combination of plentifulness in the localities where they were born, and unusual wind conditions during this period of local plentifulness.

LARGE TORTOISESHELL

Euvanessa polychlorus

(State of Hibernation—Butterfly)

Egg

Size—0·8 mm.
Incubation period—18 days
No. of Broods—1
Food-plants—Common and wych elms; more rarely sallow and willow, cherry and pear

Chrysalis

Size—25·4 mm.
Pupation period—15 days

Caterpillar

Size—2·12 to 41·3 mm.
Larval period—30 days
No. of Moults—4

Butterfly

Wing-span—$2\frac{1}{2}$ to 3 in.
On the wing—April–May, sometimes late autumn

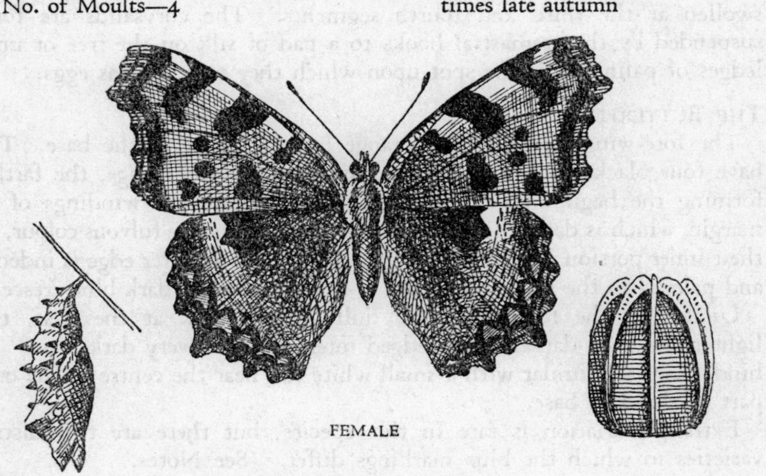

FEMALE

THE EGG

Laid in a cluster or necklace of about 200 to 400 at the tops of elms and other trees, surrounding or partly surrounding a twig or branch. They are closely packed and glued together and to the twig, though each egg is quite separate except for the point of contact. When first laid the colour is pure yellow ochre, changing to apricot yellow when twenty-four hours old. Before hatching the ground-colour becomes pale ochreous, which combined with the white keels gives the egg a dull purplish appearance.

It is dome-shaped, the micropyle being flattened and very finely reticulated. There are from seven to nine longitudinal keels which rise on the crown, where they are much elevated but rapidly decrease in height on traversing the side. They are fluted and resemble white frosted glass frills. The spaces between the keels are delicately ribbed transversely, each space having about forty ribs. (See Notes.)

The Caterpillar

When hatched the colouring of the body, including the legs and claspers, is a light olive yellow. After the fourth moult, before pupating, the ground-colour is velvety black; the surface is sprinkled with white warts from each of which protrudes a fine white hair. A yellow line runs along the side.

The whole brood is gregarious, being associated together until pupation. Single specimens are rarely found.

The Chrysalis

The colour varies from coppery ochreous to dull bronze, checkered with dull pink and black in the black form, to golden-bronze variegated with rust-red, pinkish and greenish olive in the light form.

The head is beaked in front, the meta-thorax sunken, and the abdomen swollen at the third and fourth segments. The chrysalids are found suspended by the cremastral hooks to a pad of silk on the tree or under ledges of palings near the spot upon which they were laid as eggs.

The Butterfly

The fore-wings are fine rich orange brown, dusky at the base. They have four black patches of different sizes on the front edge, the farthest forming the beginnings of a streak which follows the windings of the margin, which is dark. The hind-wings are of the same fulvous colour, but their inner portion is more extensively dusky. Their outer edge is indented and paler than the rest, and within it is a furbelow of dark blue crescents.

Underside: the fore-wings are dull brown, dark at the base, then lighter and then darker again, edged interiorly with very dark blue. The hind-wings are similar with a small white dot near the centre in the outer part of the dark base.

Extreme variation is rare in this species, but there are two distinct varieties in which the blue markings differ. (See Notes.)

It hibernates among dead leaves, which it closely resembles, in hollow trees and in faggots. They pair shortly after hibernating.

Distribution

Widely distributed throughout England and Wales, sometimes being abundant and sometimes scarce. In the North of England and Scotland it is always rare, and in Ireland it is unknown. In 1893 it was abundant, then diminished in numbers till it seemed almost extinguished in 1912, after which it again increased. (See Notes.)

Notes

Owing to a similarity in the colouring and markings of the Large Tortoiseshell and Camberwell Beauty, and of the bristles on their wings, Frohawk concludes that "it is obvious they are very closely related and generically distinct from the other Vanessids." But is it so 'obvious'? The eggs, though they have distinct resemblances in marking and colour, are different in shape as a study of Frohawk's beautiful illustrations will reveal. And the eggs remain constant and in no way confused. 'Closely related' and 'generically distinct' are terms which used in conjunction have little if any meaning, as a study of the various scientific classifications will reveal. Linnaeus, Haworth, and Lewin, for example, classified this butterfly as *Papilio*, Hubner as *Eugonia*. Furthermore, its life-history is different. (See Camberwell Beauty.)

In its distribution, periodicity and *hardiness* this butterfly resembles the Red Admiral and the Comma.

Once again 1893 was a year famed for the great plentifulness of this species, as it was of many others.

An interesting fact recorded about the Large Tortoiseshell is that the two distinct varieties were produced *from the same batch of eggs*, thereby revealing the genetic aspect of interbreeding between varieties of the same species. (See page 93, also Notes to the Ringlet, Small Tortoiseshell and Comma.)

PEACOCK

Vanessa io

(State of Hibernation—Butterfly)

Egg

Size—0·8 mm.
Incubation period—14 days
No. of Broods—1; rarely 2
Food-plant—Stinging nettle

Chrysalis

Size—25·4 mm.
Pupation period—12 to 14 days

Caterpillar

Size—1·6 to 44 mm.
Larval period—27 days
No. of Moults—4

Butterfly

Wing-span—2½ to 3 in.
On the wing—July -October; but occasionally in more months of the year

The Egg

Laid in a dense pile of 400 to 500 on the underside of a leaf of the food-plant.

When first laid it is a clear greenish yellow. Before hatching it turns to an opaque green with darker green blotches. The crown becomes of a dark leaden hue.

It is oblong with eight longitudinal keels, starting near the base and running up the side over the crown. They resemble fluted frosted glass. The spaces between the keels are concave and transversely ribbed.

THE CATERPILLAR

When first hatched it is of a very light ochreous green, almost whitish green. After the *fourth* moult, before pupating, the ground-colour is a

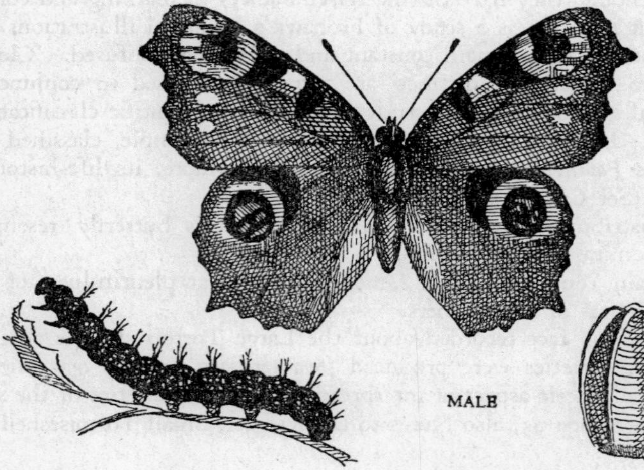

MALE

rich velvety-black with six longitudinal rows of black shining spines. After becoming full-fed, two days elapse before pupating. Before each moult they congregate in a dense mass on a thick carpet of silk spun over the eaten part of the food-plant.

THE CHRYSALIS

The normal ground-colour is a light yellow-green washed with gold. Some are speckled with blackish olive. Before emergence the pupa becomes a dusky brown, the wing markings showing distinctly.

The head is sharply pointed with two sharply pointed horns, the base of the wing-cases bi-angular, and the waist contracted. It is attached by the cremastral hooks to a pad of silk.

THE BUTTERFLY

The fore-wings are of a rich dark brownish red, having on their front margins two black triangular marks which are partially eclipsed by a large 'eye,' the ground-colour of which is yellowish buff and within whose orbit are marks of black and purple red with a border of blue spots. The outer margins of the wings are brown with streaks of dark yellow and black.

The hind-wings are also reddish brown, the base being studded with specks of yellow dust. Near the outer corner is a very large 'eye' surrounded with white. The eye itself is black with five blue specks in it.

Underside: Blackish brown, resembling a piece of charred wood.

This butterfly varies very greatly in size from two to three inches, but little in colour and markings, though the tendency to variation increases among specimens bred in captivity.

Though it hibernates in barns and sheds, the most usual resorts are holes in tree-trunks where, it is said, it has been heard to emit a faint hissing noise.

Distribution

Widely distributed and common throughout England and Wales, becoming rarer northwards. In Scotland it is rare, but it has been seen as far north as Moray. In Southern Ireland it is common. (See Notes.)

Notes

The most noticeable feature about this butterfly, apart from its rare beauty, is its regular plentifulness, thereby differing from other species which hibernate as butterflies or migrate. This is undoubtedly due to its extreme hardiness, seen as it is in the winter on the wing with snow on the ground, when the sun is shining warmly.

SMALL TORTOISESHELL

Vanessa urticae

(State of Hibernation—Butterfly)

Egg

Size—?
Incubation period—10 to 14 days
No. of Broods—2
Food-plant—Stinging nettle

Chrysalis

Size—22 mm.
Pupation period—12 days

Caterpillar

Size—1·25 to 22·2 mm.
Larval period—28 days
No. of Moults—4

Butterfly

Wing-span—$1\frac{3}{4}$ to $2\frac{1}{4}$ in.
On the wing—June–September

THE EGG

Laid in heaps of as much as 1,000 on the undersides of the leaf of the food-plant.

The colour is a clear green, changing to paler ochreous, zoned at the middle with translucent green.

It is of oblong shape, fullest near the base, which is rounded and smooth. There are nine prominent longitudinal keels, fluted and very elevated where they commence round the micropyle. The spaces near the keels are strongly ribbed transversely.

The Caterpillar

On hatching, the body is a translucent green with ten longitudinal series of small tubercles bearing a fine black hair slightly curved. After the fourth moult, before pupating, the body is thickly speckled with white and yellow warts, each bearing a spinous hair and all varying in length. The caterpillars vary greatly in colour, some being almost wholly black while others are variegated with a preponderance of yellow. (See Notes.)

Up to the fourth moult they are gregarious, and when moulting they rest in a heap one upon another. After the fourth moult they separate, enfolding themselves in a nettle leaf stitched together with silk. Here they finish feeding and then wander before pupating.

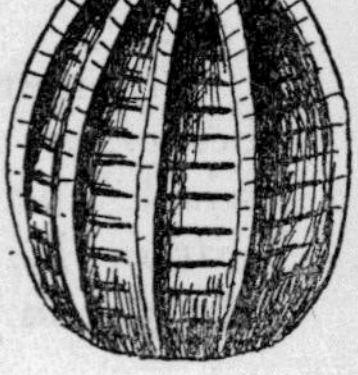

FEMALE

The Chrysalis

The colouring is very varied, even in the same brood, all reared together and pupated side by side under precisely similar conditions. Some are of a beautifully gilded form, others smoky brown, and some intermediate between these two colours (see Notes).

The head is sharply pointed in front, the thorax rising to a central triangular point, and the abdomen swelling and curving to the anal segment.

In the last stage of casting the larval skin the pupa, by curving the apex of the abdomen, contrives to reach the pad of silk with its cremastral hooks while still adhering to the shrivelled skin. Immediately the hooks touch the silk the pupa vigorously twists to and fro, and becomes anchored, after which the skin usually becomes detached and falls. (See Chapters II and XII.)

The Butterfly

The fore-wings are of a rich red orange colour, dark at the base. On the front edge there are three black patches, and between these the ground-colour is paler. Beyond the outer one is a white triangular-shaped mark. Near the base of the middle part is a large irregular spot, and above this two smaller ones. The outer edge is dark buff, followed by a black indented stripe in which is a series of small blue crescents. The hind-wing colouring is very similar but the black spots are replaced by a uniformly dusky base.

Underside: the markings are the same but the orange is changed to stone colour. The margins also are the same, but darker, and the blue crescents are replaced by crescent-shaped blackish green spots.

This butterfly varies greatly in colour and markings, one wing sometimes differing from the opposite one. The sexes are the same except that the female is the larger. They generally hibernate in buildings and often in churches. One such was observed to hibernate for nine months—July to April. (See Notes.)

Distribution

Common throughout the British Isles except in the Shetlands, where it does not occur.

Notes

In every stage, except that of the egg, these butterflies of the *same* brood vary greatly, notwithstanding the exclusiveness of the food-plant. The variations are thus due to the interbreeding of varieties in a state of nature (see experiments with *Drosophila melanogaster*, Chapter XI). The original varieties are likely to have arisen through the varying action of temperature on two separate broods bred at the same spot. (See Comma.)

It is interesting to compare the similarity in appearance of the Large and Small Tortoiseshells and the complete dissimilarity of the eggs. (See Notes to Large Tortoiseshell.) The frequent finding of this butterfly in a state of hibernation *in the summer* in churches seems to show that they need strong sunlight to keep their machinery working. Once in a church, quite *warm* in summer though continually dim, the insect is unlikely to be touched by sunlight until a beam strikes it through a window or door.

RED ADMIRAL

Pyrameis atalanta

(State of Hibernation—Butterfly)

Egg

Size—0·8 mm.
Incubation period—9 days
No. of Broods—3
Food-plant—Stinging nettle

Chrysalis

Size—22·2 to 23·8 mm.
Pupation period—17 days

Caterpillar

Size—1·6 to 35 mm.
Larval period—23 days
No. of Moults—4

Butterfly

Wing span—2½ to 3 in.
On the wing—May–October
(hibernates in the winter)

The Egg

Laid singly on the terminal leaves of separate nettles.

When first laid it is light green, gradually changing to a more yellowish green and becoming pearl grey before hatching.

In form it is oblong, the surface is flattened, and the base rounded. There are from eight to ten longitudinal keels which run the entire length and elevated on the crown. They are delicately fluted, white and glassy; the spaces between the keels are concave with slight transverse ridges.

The Caterpillar

On hatching the colour is light ochreous yellow tinged with green. After the *fourth* moult, before pupating, the whole colour varies greatly.

FEMALE

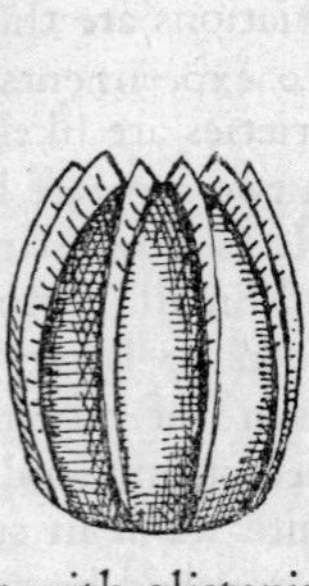

The most common form is velvety black in ground-colour with glistening black spines surrounded by red-brown. The legs are black, the claspers brown, and the feet buff.

The Chrysalis

The ground-colour is usually buff brown and adorned with gilded metallic markings which vary in size. The pupae vary considerably in colour.

The head is blunt, the thorax rises to a point, and the abdomen forms a continuous curve terminating in a long cremastral point.

The pupa is suspended by the cremastral hooks to a pad of silk spun on the under-surface of a leaf, the edges of which are spun together to form a tent.

The Butterfly

The ground-colour of the forewings is velvety blue-black on the outside half, and copper brown on the inner. A bar of bright red runs across them.

Between this bar and the wing-tips is a short bar of white, formed of three patches, a fourth spot lying beyond it. The hind-wings are velvet brown-black with a broad margin to all the middle part of red, in which are four black dots.

Underside: the fore-wings are mottled brown at the tip, and near it are two small white dots. The red bar and the white spots show through from above. The hind-wings are beautifully variegated, with a triangular yellowish white mark in the middle of their front margins. Little variation occurs in this species.

This butterfly, like the Painted Lady, is often seen on the wing at night (see Notes). It is also constantly observed to return to a particular spot, after feeding, or after being chased.

Distribution

General throughout the British Isles but very erratic in its plentifulness. Some years it is very scarce.

Widely distributed throughout the Continent.

Notes

The Red Admiral, one of the loveliest of our native butterflies, is generally treated as a near 'ally' of the Painted Lady. Frohawk classes it with the Clouded Yellow and the Painted Lady as a migrant, whose home, he says, "is the southern part of Europe where cold weather does not occur, whence it migrates annually to Central and Northern Europe." This statement is completely at variance with the facts which he himself records. The Red Admiral, so far from being non-hardy like the Painted Lady and the Clouded Yellows, is exceptionally hardy. Hibernated specimens have frequently been recorded in Britain; Frohawk himself records cases in which specimens that had endured the bitterest of winters, with a temperature at zero, were seen flying strongly and in perfect condition in February. So far from being natives of Southern Europe, our British specimens are two- and three-brooded in the British Isles, their whole life-cycle being about fifty days, except in the case of the imagines of the last brood which mate in the following spring.

As in the case of Clouded Yellows and Painted Ladies, the plentifulness or scarcity of Red Admirals in any year is conditioned by the weather conditions the previous autumn. The Red Admiral might be classed as a hardy native passage migrant, like the Bramblings and Fieldfares in the bird world. Survivors of the last brood all over Europe, as well as here, will tend to drift southwards, and will remain on the wing as *vagrants* until they are overtaken, wherever they are, with a temperature that causes torpidity. At that place they will hibernate, returning north to their breeding spots when the spring and southerly winds arrive. Thus hibernated specimens are generally if not always vagrants from home, and vagrants that have yet to mate. The Red Admiral's 'migratory' habit is therefore in harmony with that of another hardy vagrant—the Camberwell Beauty, with the vital distinction that whereas the former is very much a native, the latter is a foreigner.

It is interesting again to note that the Red Admirals on the wing in the spring have frequently been recorded as clinging, like the Painted Ladies, to a particular spot—the home where they were born and where they will breed and die. (For an example of plentifulness as well as of wholesale drift to leeward of Red Admirals, see Chapter XI, pages 81-2, and Chapters IX, X, XI, generally.)

The fact that this butterfly is often seen flying after sunset, like the Painted Lady, and indeed like all butterflies upon which long-range vagrancy has been enforced, is to be attributed to its urge for recovering its home from which it has been drifted. When at home it roosts at night at a particular spot to which, when not feeding or being chased, it returns permanently. Red Admirals seen on the wing at night are thus on the way home to their birthplace.

NON-HARDY NATIVE MIGRANTS

Pale Clouded Yellow . . .	*Colias hyale*
Clouded Yellow . . .	*Colias edusa*
Painted Lady . . .	*Pyrameis cardui*

PALE CLOUDED YELLOW

Colias hyale

(State of Hibernation—None [see Notes])

Egg

Size—1·1 mm.
Incubation period—6 to 10 days
No. of Broods—2 or 3
Food-plant—Clover

Chrysalis

Size—20·5 to 22·2 mm.
Pupation period—17 days

Caterpillar

Size—1·6 to 31·8 mm.
Larval period—31 days (see Notes)
No. of Moults—5

Butterfly

Wing-span—2 to $2\frac{1}{4}$ in.
On the wing—May–October

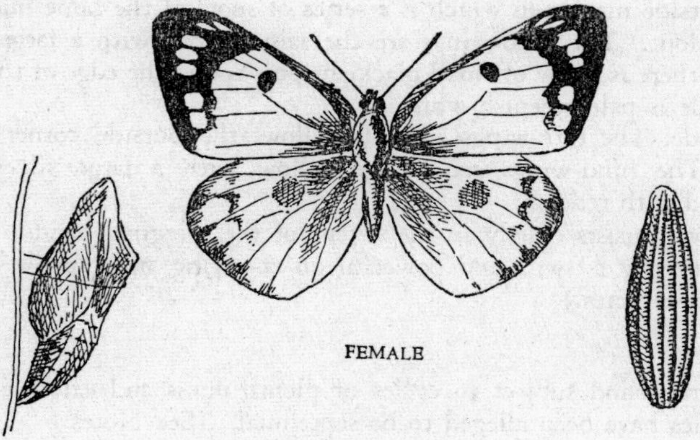

FEMALE

THE EGG

Laid singly, standing erect, on leaves of the food-plant.

At first it is a pearly yellowish white, gradually deepening in hue. When three days old its summit is transparent, white and glassy, shading into yellow for one-fifth down the side where it turns to rosy orange. Before hatching it turns to a purplish leaden. The shell is exceedingly delicate and has a glittering silvery appearance.

Its greatest diameter is about one-third its height and in form it is an elongated oval attenuated at both ends, which are rounded. There are from nineteen to twenty-two longitudinal keels, mostly running the entire length. The spaces between the keels have a flattened surface and are most delicately crossed transversely with about forty-six ribs.

Eggs have been laid as late as September 20th.

THE CATERPILLAR

On hatching, the ground-colour is pale ochreous yellow. After the *fifth* moult, before pupating, the ground-colour is clear light green. It is sprinkled with black warts, each emitting a black bristle. The head, claspers and legs are also green, with black bristles.

THE CHRYSALIS

Green, with an ochreous border to the wing-cases and an ochreous stripe down the side.

The head terminates in a short straight beak, the thorax is humped dorsally, the abdomen rounded and tapering to the anal point.

The pupa is suspended by a silken band round the waist and attached by the cremastral hooks to a silken pad spun on the stem of the food-plant.

THE BUTTERFLY

The ground-colour of the male is primrose yellow, varying in intensity, with a black central spot and an irregular broad band edged with light pink on the outside margin in which is a series of spots of the same hue as the ground-colour. The hind-wings are the same colour with a large orange spot, and there is a row of small blackish spots round the edge of the wing. The female is pale greenish white.

Underside: The fore-wings are pale yellow, the outside corner orange yellow. The hind-wings are orange yellow with a large silvery spot surrounded with reddish.

Variation consists chiefly in the extent of the marginal bands.

This butterfly is swift and powerful on the wing and capable of long flights. (See Notes.)

Distribution

Very erratic and subject to cycles of plentifulness and extreme rarity. These cycles have been alleged to be septennial. (See Notes.)

Notes

This butterfly, like the Clouded Yellow, has perplexed lepidopterists since the study of the life-history of butterflies was first undertaken. But assuming that Frohawk's facts are correct, and that this species cannot in the larval stage endure a temperature below 40°, then it clearly cannot hibernate in the British Isles, and its life-history must be the same as that of the Clouded Yellow, which is considered in detail as a *non-hardy migrant* in Chapter IX. That Frohawk gives details of the hibernation of the caterpillar (240 days) in spite of his definite assertion that it does not hibernate, is presumably to be attributed to captivity, under conditions similar to a non-hardy plant under glass in the winter. The circumstances under which there was a phenomenal plentifulness of Painted Ladies in the famous year 1903 have a bearing upon the Pale Clouded Yellow, though the precise effect of weather conditions may be different in the latter case owing to differences in life-habit during the breeding season. Hence the years of plentifulness and scarceness would differ according to the weather conditions of the preceding season.

This butterfly, like the Clouded Yellow, is common on the Continent, and in the event of unusual and strong east winds in the summer large numbers of *foreign* vagrants would appear in England. These, however, are quite distinct from the British natives, which breed here. They will return to their foreign homes as soon as weather conditions permit.

CLOUDED YELLOW

Colias edusa

(State of Hibernation—None)

Egg

Size—1·1 mm.
Incubation period—6 to 10 days
No. of Broods—2 or 3
Food-plant—Clover

Chrysalis

Size—22·2 mm.
Pupation period—18 days

Caterpillar

Size—1·5 to 33·4 mm.
Larval period—31 days
No. of Moults—?

Butterfly

Wing-span—2 to 2½ in.
On the wing—May–October

The Egg

Laid similarly to that of *hyale* which it closely resembles; the spaces between the keels are concave instead of flat, the ribs fewer, and the colour a little paler.

The Caterpillar

Almost identical with that of *hyale* but a little paler.

The Chrysalis

Almost identical with that of *hyale*.

The Butterfly

A dark edition of *hyale*. The male only is figured and may be distinguished from the female by the latter having a series of pale yellow spots inside the black border.

Distribution

Similar to *hyale*, but years of plentifulness do not coincide.

Notes

There seem to be grounds for thinking that *edusa* and *hyale* may be variations of the same species, their migratory and life-habit, and periodical appearances, being identical, and their eggs nearly so.

MALE

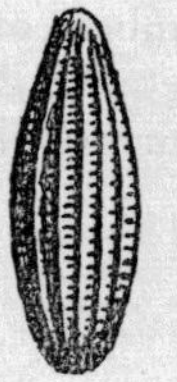

Emphasis is frequently laid on the effect of temperature on the appearance of imagines of the same species. Bearing this in mind it seems reasonable to suppose that *edusa* may be the progeny of the second brood (summer brood) of eggs, and *hyale* of the third brood when such a brood occurs, and if the weather permits of this brood coming to fruition. If this is so, the years of plentifulness would not coincide. This will be seen to be the case when the respective years of plentifulness of the two are compared.

Both Clouded Yellows should be compared with the extremely hardy Brimstone which spends all but a fraction of its life at home as an imagine. It is noteworthy that the Brimstone drifts far from its birthplace as a vagrant, just as do hardy British birds, but being very hardy it is not liable to extinction by adverse weather. Instead of being killed, like the caterpillars of Clouded Yellows, the Brimstone comes to fruition and hibernates in cold latitudes. It is also interesting to note the great similarity between the shape of the eggs of these three species and, indeed, of all the Whites, with the notable exception of the Swallow-tail. None, however, are identical, except the *hyale* and *edusa*, which are nearly so.

PAINTED LADY

Pyrameis cardui

(State of Hibernation—None)

Egg

Size—0·65 mm.
Incubation period—7 days
No. of Broods—3
Food-plant—Thistle, sometimes stinging nettle

Chrysalis

Size—24 mm.
Pupation period—25 days

Caterpillar

Size—1·6 to 28·6 mm.
Larval period—30 days
No. of Moults—4

Butterfly

Wing-span—$2\frac{1}{4}$ to $2\frac{3}{4}$ in.
On the wing—May–October

FEMALE

The Egg

Laid singly on the upper surface of the food-plant. When first laid it is light green soon developing to smoky grey green.

In form it is oval, indent just below the middle; the micropyle is granular and surrounded by the elevated apices of sixteen longitudinal glassy white fluted keels which run to the base. They are uniform in structure, all rising regularly round the micropyle, where they are highest, gradually becoming less and finally disappearing at the base: the spaces between the keels are slightly ribbed transversely.

The Caterpillar

The ground colour on hatching is pale olive ochreous and is thickly covered with black points. After the *fourth* moult, before pupating, the body is velvety black and is densely sprinkled with white dots each having a fine white hair. A yellow longitudinal stripe starts on the fourth segment and ends on the eleventh. The ventral surface is coppery brown and the claspers and legs tawny.

The Chrysalis

The colouring varies, but the ground-colour of normal specimens is pinkish peanut grey, slightly tinged with copper and gold with a pale longitudinal dorsal line running the entire length.

The head is conical, rising from the apex in almost a straight line to the centre. The abdomen is swollen at the middle and curves to the extremity of the cremaster which is furnished with hooks. The pupa is suspended by the cremastral hooks to a small but dense pad spun on a stem of the food-plant.

The Butterfly

The fore-wings are brown at the base, the tips blackish with five white spots, the largest of which adjoins the front edge and the other four form a curved line. The rest of these wings are fulvous orange with a suffusion of pink and with three indented black united spots. The hind-wings have the base and inner margin brown, the remainder fulvous with many black spots arranged in three rows.

Underside: the fore-wings are marked much as above; the dark spots are smaller and the tip of the wing is dark stone colour. The hind-wings are mottled with pale olive brown, yellowish-buff and white, the veins being white.

This species varies in the markings and in the ground-colour, but striking aberrations are rare.

Distribution

Throughout Britain, but very erratic in its appearances. Sometimes very plentiful and sometimes very scarce. The Painted Lady occurs in almost every known part of the world.

Notes

The Painted Ladies that occur in the British Isles are, like the Clouded Yellows but unlike the Camberwell Beauties, non-hardy natives because they breed here, though foreign vagrants will from time to time drift across to us from the Continent. Indeed, a case is on record of an American 'type'—*Cynthia huntera* or *Vanessa huntera*—being taken in England (see Chapter X, page 72). This reproduces the phenomenon of the occasional appearance of the Black-veined Brown in these islands and in reverse of the occurrence of a British Brown-tailed Moth in America as revealed in Chapter X, page 69.

The migratory phenomenon of our native Painted Lady is identical with that of the Clouded Yellows which is examined in detail in Chapter IX. (See also Chapter X, where the periodical 'invasions' of Painted Ladies are considered.) Here again it is the surviving imagines of the late autumnal brood which are drifted, like the swallows, to the south, and some of which return in the spring to mate. As in the case of the Clouded Yellows, the weather of the preceding autumn is the determining factor in the plentifulness or otherwise of Painted Ladies in the succeeding season. (See years 1879 and 1903 as recorded in Chapter XI.)

Frohawk again emphasises that the early immigrants cling to a particular spot and habitually return to it if chased away. This confirms the inviolability of the homing instinct for purposes of mating, an instinct which alone can bring order out of what would otherwise be the chaos of butterfly drift.

Frohawk also stresses that this migrant butterfly is frequently to be seen on the wing at night. This phenomenon is common to all migrant, or very vagrant, butterflies (of which the Red Admiral is an example), which are overtaken by darkness far from their homes for which they are making. Many examples of this night flying are given by Williams in *The Migration of Butterflies*.

FOREIGN VAGRANTS

Camberwell Beauty . . .	*Euvanessa antiopa*
Bath White	*Pontia daplidice*
Queen of Spain Fritillary . .	*Argynnis lathonia*
Black-Veined Brown . . .	*Anosia plexippus*
Long-Tailed Blue . . .	*Lampides boeticus*
Short-Tailed Blue . . .	*Cupido argiades*

CAMBERWELL BEAUTY

Euvanessa antiopa

(State of Hibernation—Butterfly)

Egg

Size—0·91 mm.
Incubation period—19 days
No. of Broods—? 1
Food-plants—Willow, sallow, birch and elm

Caterpillar

Size—1·8 to 54 mm.
Larval period—6 weeks
No. of Moults—4

Chrysalis

Size—25·4 to 31·8 mm.
Pupation period—4 to 6 weeks

Butterfly

Wing-span—3 to 3½ in.
On the wing—Autumn

The Egg

The colour, when first laid, is deep ochreous yellow gradually deepening to olive brown. It has a finely mottled appearance resembling crocodile skin, the ground-colour being amber brown. After fourteen days one batch of eggs changed to deep lilac-red. Such a deep red colour is unusual, red-brown being the normal.

In form it is oblong, with eight to nine longitudinal keels commencing below the summit and rising prominently; they then decrease and disappear before reaching the base. The spaces between the keels are slightly concave and finely fluted transversely. The micropyle is slightly raised in the centre and is finely granulated.

The Caterpillar

On hatching, the colouring of the body is olive-brown, head shining black, and a few black bristles scattered over the surface.

After the *fourth* moult, before pupating, the head is dull black, covered with black warts each emitting a white hair. The ground-colour is velvety black and covered with pearl white warts each emitting a fine white hair. Down the centre of the back is a series of conspicuous red markings. (See Notes.)

THE CHRYSALIS

The ground-colour is pale buff, covered with fine fuscous reticulations. The surface is covered with a whitish powdery substance, giving a pale lilac or pinkish bloom to the pupa. If this powder is brushed off it assumes a brownish hue. (See Notes.)

THE BUTTERFLY

The fore-wings are of a fine rich claret colour, margined with yellow, sometimes white (see Notes). Inside the margin is a row of blue spots on a velvet black ground. The hind-wings are similar.

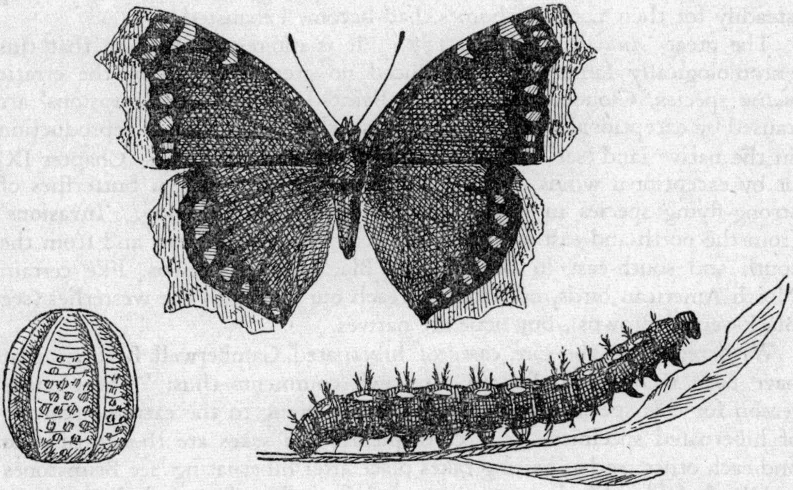

Underside: the wings are ash-brown with many slender transverse black lines; the margin and spots show through, as do the bar and the blue spots, but very faintly. Variation is chiefly in the intensity of the colouring of the yellow margin and spots.

Distribution

Generally rare over the British Isles, but occasionally to be taken in large numbers. It is widely distributed over the Northern Hemisphere, and is particularly common in Norway.

Notes

Few butterflies have caused more interest or speculation than this beautiful foreign insect, for foreign it certainly is. Though a few specimens are recorded as having hibernated in England, no record of the finding of the egg, caterpillar or chrysalis in a natural state in this country exists. As all authorities agree, so large and distinctive a caterpillar could not be overlooked indefinitely. The Camberwell Beauty is therefore a foreign vagrant and not a native.

Frohawk and other authorities class it as a rare *migrant*, just as they class the Clouded Yellows, but the distinction is clear. The *home* of the Camberwell Beauty that visits us is Northern Europe, and particularly Norway, and it is carried here in the autumn by exceptional northerly and north-easterly winds just as, in the bird-world, Bramblings, Fieldfares, Snowy-owls, and other northern species are carried to Britain in the winter. These birds never breed here, however, and return to their northern homes when the weather that brought them moderates.

In 1819 vast numbers of Camberwell Beauties were seen floating dead off the Durham coast. These had been drifted south and, while flying steadily for their northern homes, had become exhausted.

The great '*Antiopa* year' was 1872. It is interesting to note that this entomologically famous year produced no great invasion of the erratic *native* species, Clouded Yellows and Painted Ladies. All 'invasions' are caused by exceptional weather conditions either at the time of reproduction in the native land (see Clouded Yellows and Painted Ladies, Chapter IX) or by exceptional winds at any time during the period that butterflies of strong-flying species in unsheltered places are on the wing. 'Invasions' from the north and east are liable to occur later in the year, and from the south and south-east in the spring. Black-veined Browns, like certain North American birds, occasionally reach our shores in the westerlies (see Black-veined Browns), but none are natives.

With regard to the rare cases of hibernated Camberwell Beauties that have been recorded in Britain, Frohawk comments thus: "The obvious reason for this species not breeding here is owing to the extreme scarcity of hibernated specimens . . . consequently the sexes are then unable to find each other, and as pairing takes place after hibernating (see Brimstones and Red Admirals) they are prevented from breeding and die without depositing."

Elsewhere the author has shown that in the case of other butterflies there must be something that draws them together for mating, as otherwise the sexes would rarely meet. This, undoubtedly, is the common home for which all survivors of a brood strive. These *hardy* hibernated Camberwell Beauties, on 'coming to' in the spring, would fly north and 'home' to mate, just as do survivors of the last brood of *non-hardy* Clouded Yellows fly north from the south (where they wintered) to their homes in England.

Because Camberwell Beauties hibernate as butterflies in Norway and elsewhere in Northern Europe, and are thus hardy, they are foreign counterparts of our native Brimstones and Red Admirals which, it will be remembered, are notorious for vagrancy because on the wing during the late autumn.

One other carefully recorded observation of Frohawk's deserves mention. The colour of the pupa changes from a purplish or lilac hue to a brown one *if the fine powder is brushed off*. This has a bearing on the respective colouring of the upper and lower membranes of a butterfly's wing. If the infinitely fine 'powder' on the upper membrane acts as a light-filter for the colouring of the lower membrane, by analogy the brown underside of a Purple Emperor's wing should appear purplish on the upper side with the powder intact and brownish if the powder is displaced. According to Frohawk's illustrations of the Purple Emperor this is the case. Furthermore, the fading of the yellow band to dullest white and the variations between brown and purplish brown in variously worn specimens taken in this country, seems still further to indicate that the colours of the upper wings of a butterfly are the filtered products, or illusions, of the undersides. This same fading tendency in old Brimstones is frequently remarked. (See page 212, and Notes to Purple Emperor, etc.)

BATH WHITE

Pontia daplidice

(State of Hibernation—Chrysalis on the Continent)

Egg

Size—0·86 mm.
Incubation period—10 days
No. of Broods—2 to 3
Food-plant—Various kinds of mignonette

Chrysalis

Size—19 mm.
Pupation period—3 weeks

Caterpillar

Size—1 to 25·4 mm.
Larval period—20 days
No. of Moults—4

Butterfly

Wing-span—$1\frac{3}{4}$ to 2 in.
On the wing—May and June, August and September

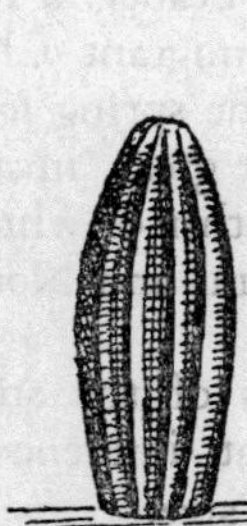

MALE

THE EGG

Laid singly on the underside of leaves and on blossoms of the food-plant. When first laid it is light yellowish green, gradually turning to orange. Its form is that of an elongated cone; the summit is flat. There are thirteen or fourteen longitudinal keels running the entire length, and about thirty transverse ribs. The egg closely resembles that of the Orange Tip and other Whites, and notably the Green-veined White.

THE CATERPILLAR

On hatching, the body is of a rich sienna. After the *fourth* moult, before pupating, the ground-colour is a clear lilac with four yellow longitudinal bands. The surface is sprinkled with black warts, each bearing a fine spine.

THE CHRYSALIS

The colour is pale lilac-grey and in shape exactly resembles that of the Green-veined White.

THE BUTTERFLY

The ground-colour of all the wings is white. The fore-wings are black at the base with a large black spot in the centre of the wing. The hind-wings are white, the markings of the underside showing faintly through.

Underside: The marks on the fore-wings are greenish with a spot on the inner edge. The hind-wings are yellowish green mottled with white markings.

The butterflies of the spring broods are smaller than those of the summer broods. (See Notes.)

Distribution

Extremely rare, and only taken near the south and south coasts of England. It is native and very common in Central and Southern Europe.

Notes

This butterfly is a foreign vagrant because in the course of 200 years there is no record of it having bred in this country in a state of nature, though one case of a chrysalis developing into an imagine, *in captivity*, is recorded by Frohawk.

It is noteworthy that the sighting or taking of the Bath White in England is always late in the year, like the Camberwell Beauty, a foreign vagrant from farther north, and unlike the non-hardy migrant Clouded Yellows and Painted Ladies which reach our shores in the spring *to breed*. It is interesting to note that the year 1872 is famous for great 'invasions' of both the Bath White and the Camberwell Beauty, neither of which are native to Britain, but both of which are native to Central and Northern Europe.

Frohawk emphasises the larger size of the imagines of the summer broods, thus giving yet another example of the great influence that temperature exercises over variation, both in colour and size.

For an analogy of Bath White invasions see Camberwell Beauty, and for contrasts between the 'immigration' or 'invasion' of native migrants and foreign vagrants see Painted Ladies and Clouded Yellows in various parts of this book.

The egg, caterpillar, chrysalis, imagine and life-habit of the Bath White all closely resemble those of the Green-veined White.

QUEEN OF SPAIN FRITILLARY

Argynnis lathonia

(State of Hibernation—Caterpillar on the Continent)

Egg

Size—6 mm.
Incubation period—7 to 10 days
No. of Broods—2 to 3
Food-plant—Wild heartsease

Chrysalis

Size—17 to 19 mm.
Pupation period—?

Caterpillar

Size—1·6 to 31·8 mm.
Larval period—15 days
No. of Moults—4

Butterfly

Wing-span—2 to $2\frac{1}{4}$ in.
On the wing—August–September

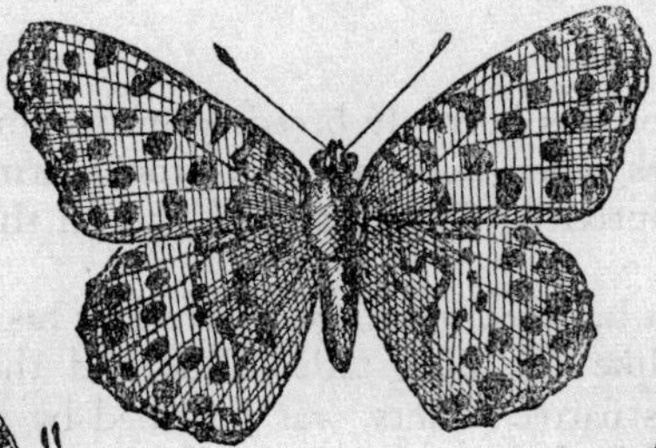

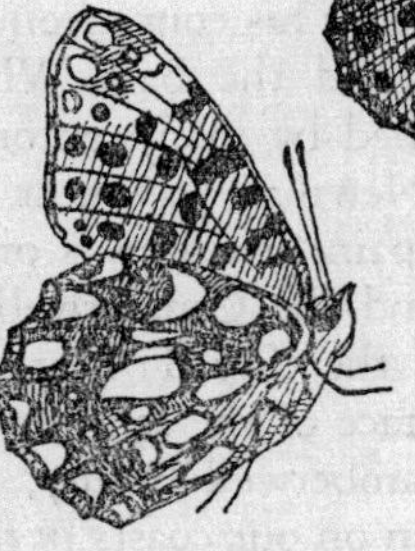

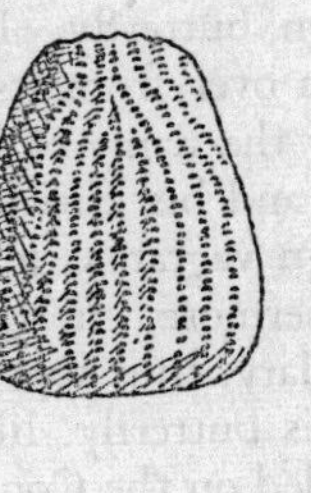

FEMALE

The Egg

Laid in clutches on the food-plant. When first laid it is pale lemon gradually deepening in colour.

In form it is a straight-sided cone, widest at the base. There are about forty longitudinal keels of differing lengths. The spaces between the keels are finely ribbed transversely.

The Caterpillar

On hatching it is of a pale olive yellow colour. After the *fourth* moult, before pupating, the ground-colour is mainly black with a broken greyish white medio-dorsal line.

The Chrysalis

The head, thorax and wing-cases are shining olive brown.

In form it closely resembles the pupa of the Small Pearl-bordered Fritillary.

THE BUTTERFLY

The fore-wings are fulvous with many distinct spots, those at the tip uniting with the dark margin. The hind-wings are very similar, their base also being dusky.

Undersides: the fore-wings have much the same markings as the upper side, but at the tip is a ferruginous patch, at the base of which is a silvery spot. The hind-wings are buff, varied with reddish brown, with several silver patches of varying size and shape. In general appearance it normally closely resembles the Small Pearl-bordered Fritillary. (See Notes.)

Distribution

Common in Central and Southern Europe where it is native. Occasionally, but rarely, taken in late summer and autumn, and then almost invariably near the coasts of Kent and Sussex opposite the French coast.

Notes

No record exists of this butterfly breeding in Britain, except in one case recorded by Frohawk when a female sent from Zermatt on 2nd August 1903 laid eggs in captivity. These hatched, but all the larvae died during the winter.

Newman, nearly a hundred years ago, wrote that his conviction that this foreign butterfly, like the Long-tailed Blue and the Bath White, was blown over from its native haunts, was ridiculed by many entomologists under the name of 'the blown-over theory'. Newman was most certainly right and his critics wrong. The Queen of Spain Fritillary is one of our foreign vagrants, just as is the Bath White and the Camberwell Beauty. Furthermore, it resembles in all respects the Small Pearl-bordered Fritillary, thus suggesting it is a geographical race of the same species.

This butterfly, like the Bath White and Camberwell Beauty, is multi-brooded on the Continent, and like both is seen on our coasts *in the autumn* and for the same reason. Frohawk records that in the year 1872 there was a great 'invasion' of these three very different species of foreign vagrants, *and all in the autumn*. The cause common to them all was an exceptional easterly wind after the maturing of the autumn broods. (See Bath White and Camberwell Beauty, and contrast these with the non-hardy migrant *native* Clouded Yellow or Painted Lady, and with the *hardy* native vagrant Red Admiral.)

BLACK-VEINED BROWN

Anosia plexippus

(State of Hibernation—Butterfly)

Egg

Size—1·3 mm.
Incubation period—3 days
No. of Broods—? 3
Food-plant—various milkweeds

Chrysalis

Size—25·4 mm.
Pupation period—15 days

Caterpillar

Size—56 mm.
Larval period—16 days
No. of Moults—4

Butterfly

Wing-span—4 to 4½ in,
On the wing—9–12 months

MALE

THE EGG

Laid singly on the upper side of leaves of the food-plant. When first laid the colour is pale primrose turning to pearl white and mottled with yellow.

In shape it is conical, resembling an acorn. There are twenty to twenty-two longitudinal keels, fourteen of which run the entire length; the remainder commence one-quarter from the apex and run to the base. It is ribbed transversely with about thirty-four ribs.

THE CATERPILLAR

On hatching, the colour is pearly grey. After the *fourth* moult, before pupating, the ground-colour is pale yellow and white, the white forming a median band round each segment. The segments are striped and banded with steel black.

THE CHRYSALIS

The ground-colour is pale green, and the pupa is very firmly attached to a dense pad of silk by the cremastral hooks.

THE BUTTERFLY

The ground-colour is deep amber, the nervation black, and the margins of both wings are banded with black. The outer marginal bands enclose two rows of white dots.

Underside: the undersides of both wings are very similar to the upper sides. Variation is slight.

Distribution

The distribution and migration of this remarkable butterfly are examined in detail in Chapter IX. The specimens seen or taken in Britain occur almost invariably in the autumn. (See Notes.)

Notes

We are indebted to Frohawk for the life-history of this species which he derived from female specimens received from Dr. Skinner of Philadelphia in May 1910. These laid eggs, and perfect imagines were reared from them in captivity.

Frohawk asserts that "this great butterfly is only endemic in the southern portions of the United States and Central America where, owing to the absence of cold weather, a continuity of broods is produced." He then correctly likens this butterfly to the Clouded Yellow which, it will be remembered, he treats as a *native* of Southern Europe and North Africa. In fact it is a non-hardy migrant native of North America, just as our Clouded Yellows are of Britain.

The specimens occurring in the Malay Archipelago and in Britain are equally vagrants carried east and west, respectively, by the N.E. trade-winds and the westerlies from the outer fringes of the vast flocks of the North to South American 'migrations.' (See page 70.)

This foreign butterfly, like the other foreign vagrants, has never established itself here, and, it may confidently be predicted, never will.

Note once again that it is in the autumn that it appears, just as do the Camberwell Beauties, Bath Whites and Queen of Spain Fritillaries—and for the same reason.

LONG-TAILED BLUE

Lampides boeticus

(State of Hibernation—? None)

Egg

Size—0·5 mm.
Incubation period—7 days
No. of Broods—? 3
Food-plant—Common pea

Chrysalis

Size—10·5 to 12·7 mm.
Pupation period—10 days

Caterpillar

Size—0·80 to 19 mm.
Larval period—25 days
No. of Moults—3

Butterfly

Wing-span—$1\frac{1}{4}$ to $1\frac{1}{2}$ in.
On the wing—?

MALE

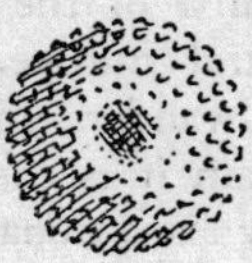

FEMALE

The Egg

Laid singly on the base of flowers of the food-plant. When laid the colour is bluish green-white, fading to whitish.

In form it is a compressed sphere, the centre rather concave and the micropyle sunken. The whole surface is covered with fine reticulations forming a pattern over the crown which, turning over the brim, turn into a fine network composed of knobs. Each knob radiates six ribs, forming a hexagon.

The Caterpillar

On hatching, it is pale yellow. After the *third* moult, before pupating, the colour varies from ochreous to grass green. A pale yellow lateral stripe extends down the side and round both extremities.

The Chrysalis

The ground-colour is pale creamy ochreous, some being sparsely and others thickly speckled and spotted.

The Butterfly

The ground-colour is light purple with a narrow black border to the fore- and hind-wings, which are clothed with light silvery blue scales. The

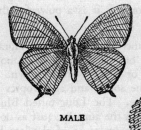

hind-wings are elongated into a slender white-tipped tail, measuring 2·6 mm.

Underside: pale brownish-buff with numerous pale transverse streaks. The hind-wings have a white transverse band beyond the middle; the two black spots at the anal angle have each an orange blotch above and are edged light silver green.

Variation is considerable, especially in the depth and brilliancy of the purple, blue and black *which are affected by the density of the scaling or powdering of the upper surface of the wings.* (See Notes on the colouring of the Purple Emperor.)

Distribution

Native to, and widely distributed throughout, Central and Southern Europe, and very occasionally taken in the *autumn* in the southern coastal areas of England. It never breeds here. Like all the other 'migrant' or 'vagrant' butterflies, whether British or foreign, it is a powerful flier.

Notes

To deal in detail with the rare appearances of this foreign vagrant, or 'visitor,' would be to repeat most of what has already been said about the Bath White, Queen of Spain Fritillary, or Black-veined Brown. Once again Frohawk classes it as a *native* of the south and sub-tropics which 'wanders' in the spring to Central Europe. The Long-tailed Blue is a native of Central Europe, which 'wanders' in the autumn, just as do other multi-brooded natives. Here again it is the imagines of the late broods which are drifted to our shores by exceptional winds. This Blue should be compared with British Blues, notably the Common and Holly Blues, and particularly the egg. Such a comparison immediately suggests that it is a geographical race and not a distinct species. This butterfly, like the Holly Blue, is multi-brooded, and appears in all four stages simultaneously, and has no definite hibernating stage.

SHORT-TAILED BLUE

Cupido argiades

(State of Hibernation—Caterpillar)

Egg

Size—0·4 mm.
Incubation period—6 days
No. of Broods—2 to 3
Food-plant—Furze and bird's-foot trefoil

Chrysalis

Size—8·5 mm.
Pupation period—10 ro 14 days

Caterpillar

Size—0·6 to 9·5 mm.
Larval period—25 days to 6 months
No. of Moults—4

Butterfly

Wing-span—1¼ in.
On the wing—June–September

The Egg

Laid singly at the base of a leaf of the food-plant. In colour it is pale greenish blue but variable.

In shape it so closely resembles those of the Common and Small Blues that no special description is needed.

The Caterpillar

When hatched it is pale ochreous yellow. After the *fourth* moult, before pupating, or in the last brood hibernating, it is pale green with a darker medio-dorsal stripe and tinged with pinkish-brown. (See caterpillars of the Small and Common Blues.)

The Chrysalis

See Small and Common Blues.

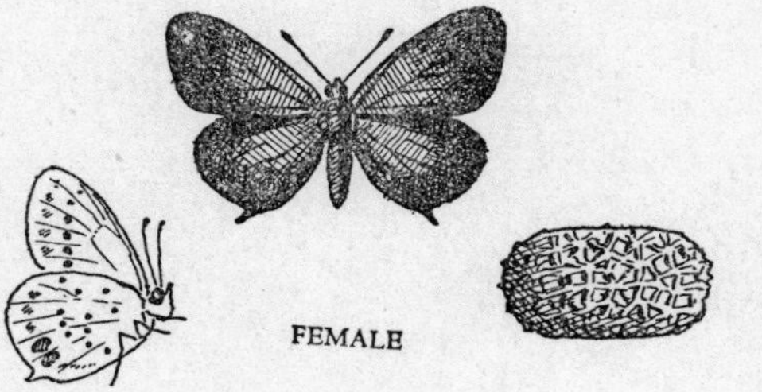

FEMALE

The Butterfly

The ground-colour is light violet and the outer margin narrowly imbued with black. The female is dusky brown with a suffusion of violet scales over the base of the fore- and hind-wings, the latter having two orange spots near the anal angle.

Underside: Closely resembling those of the Holly Blue. (See Notes to Purple Emperor, etc., on question of colouring.)

Distribution

Two examples of this butterfly were taken in 1874 near a quay at Frome, Somerset, and three more on Bloxworth Heath in 1885, from which specimens this Blue obtained its alternative name of the Bloxworth Blue. Apart from these five specimens, and one other taken in 1885 near Bournemouth, no others apparently have been reported in England. This, Frohawk says, may be due to confusion with the Silver-studded and Common Blues which it closely resembles and which are common on Bloxworth Heath. (See Notes.)

Notes

This caterpillar is, like that of the Large Blue, the Orange Tip and the Hairstreaks, 'cannibalistic' (see Notes to these butterflies). The Short-tailed Blue is common on the Continent and particularly in Brittany. The fact that it continues to abound in Brittany, from which it is a very rare vagrant after disappearing from its few restricted haunts in England, is another example of the tenacity with which butterflies cling to their place of origin, and of why they fail to re-establish themselves in a locality from which circumstances have, in any particular year, extirpated them. This curiosity is noticeable in the Western Isles and the Hebrides where particular species occur only in particular islands, except on rare occasions as vagrants. Vagrancy in most of the small species is very rare because their habitats are sheltered, and when the autumnal winds commence they are normally hibernating as eggs, caterpillars or chrysalids.

EXTINCT NATIVE RESIDENTS

Large Copper	. . . .	*Chrysophanus dispar*
Mazarine Blue	. . . .	*Zizera semiargus*

LARGE COPPER

Chrysophanus dispar

(State of Hibernation—Caterpillar)

Egg
Size—0·65 mm.
Incubation period—16 days
No. of Broods—? 1 (British and French), 2 (Hungary)
Food-plant—Great Water dock

Chrysalis
Size—11 to 12·7 mm.
Pupation period—12 days

Caterpillar
Size—1·2 to 21 mm.
Larval period—21 days to 7 months
No. of Moults—3

Butterfly
Wing-span—$1\frac{1}{2}$ to 2 in.
On the wing—July–August

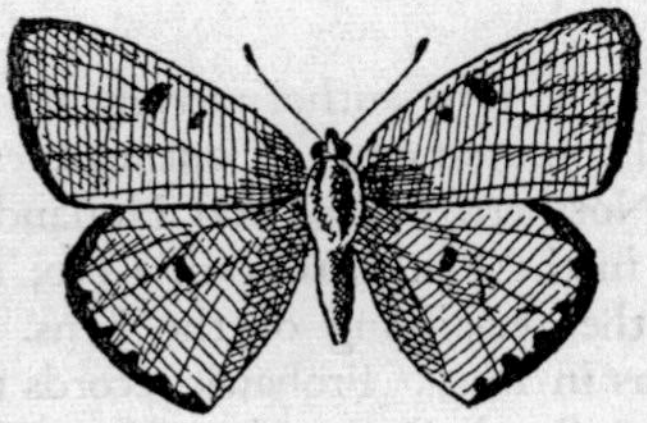

MALE

FEMALE

THE EGG

Laid singly and scattered over the surface of the leaves of the food-plant. Before hatching it is of an opaque creamy white colour.

In shape it resembles a coronet with a bold cellular pattern on the crown. The micropyle is sunken and surrounded by six or seven crescent cells. The walls of these cells stand in high relief, forming a flower-like pattern.

THE CATERPILLAR

On hatching it is citrine yellow. After the *third* moult, before pupating, it is brilliant green with darker markings showing in certain lights. (The British species is said to have been bright green with white dots.)

THE CHRYSALIS

Head, thorax and wing-cases pale ochreous; abdomen brown spotted with white, and the remainder olive brown.

The head is rounded, the thorax swollen, and the anal extremity bluntly attenuated.

THE BUTTERFLY (extinct British race)

The fore-wings were of a splendid copper colour with a black edging to the outside of the wings. There was a black spot in the centre of the wing. The hind-wings were very similar in the male, but in the female they were mainly black with a copper band along the border.

Underside: the fore-wings were pale orange, the outside edge being blue-grey. Near the base were two large spots and a small one, their edges bordered with pale orange. The hind-wings were silvery blue with an orange bar edged with black spots.

The existing Dutch 'race' is hardly distinguishable from the extinct British race.

Distribution

This beautiful butterfly is now authoritatively designated as extinct in Britain, though it is still common on the Continent, especially in Germany and Hungary, and in Northern France and Holland. The species seems to have been abundant in the Fen district in 1830; in the 'forties it was becoming scarce with the reclaiming of the Fens. The last authentic capture of this insect was in 1847. Frohawk records the finding of a dead specimen at Slapton Lea, South Devon, in 1865. The food-plant of the caterpillar, the great water-dock, still grows abundantly in this and other localities. (See Notes.)

Notes

The particulars of this butterfly in its egg, larval and pupal stages, as given here, were obtained by Frohawk from specimens reared in captivity, the progeny of living females received from Hungary and Colmar, in Alsace-Lorraine. These foreign specimens were reared successfully on the normal British food-plant—the great water-dock—which still abounds, as previously shown, in South Devon and elsewhere.

In Hungary, where the Large Copper is still common, it is said to be disappearing with drainage.

The Continental varieties of this butterfly become progressively similar to the extinct British race as the location of the place of nativity approaches our shores. In the marshes of the Somme Valley it is hardly distinguishable from the extinct British race. The French race is single-brooded, as was the British.

The foregoing facts about the Large Copper, in Britain and on the Continent, confirm the conclusions reached in Chapter XI on the causes of the confinement of species and varieties to particular localities, and of *extinction*.

It will be noted that the food-plant of the Large Copper is still with us, though in different localities to those where this butterfly used to abound. The climate has not changed, and there is therefore no environmental obstacle to the continuation of the species in Britain.

It will also be noted that in Hungary it becomes extinct in the localities where drainage has taken place.

It therefore seems clear that the inveterate habit of breeding at the original birthplace, instead of indiscriminately wherever the food-plant abounds, is the correct explanation of the confinement of species, or 'races,' to particular localities, and their extinction in certain circumstances.

It is also noteworthy that this butterfly, though common in Northern France, is seldom if ever seen in England as a *vagrant*. The dead specimen found at Slapton Lea was certainly a rare exception. Here again the reason seems clear. This butterfly is single-brooded in France, and spends the autumn and winter in the larval state. It is a very strong flier, and is only on the wing for a short period in the summer. There is therefore no combination of habit and environment which tends to impose vagrancy on this species as there is in the case of other hardy species such as the native Red Admiral and Brimstone, or, in the case of a foreign species, the Camberwell Beauty which is multi-brooded and therefore liable to be on the wing in late autumn.

For a further account of the Large Copper, its extinction, and *artificial* re-establishment, see Chapter XI.

MAZARINE BLUE

Zizera semiargus

(State of Hibernation—Caterpillar)

Egg

Size—0·6 mm.
Incubation period—10 days
No. of Broods—1 (? 2)
Food-plant—Clover and Kidney vetch

Chrysalis

Size—10·5 mm.
Pupation period—17 days

Caterpillar

Size—0·8 to 11·8 mm.
Larval period—275 days
No. of Moults—5 (see Notes)

Butterfly

Wing-span—1 to 1¼ in.
On the wing—?

THE EGG

Very similar to that of the Large Blue, but the micropyle is smaller.

THE CATERPILLAR

On emergence from the egg it is exactly similar to that of the Large Blue. So is it after the fifth moult, before pupating.

THE CHRYSALIS

Almost identical with that of the Large Blue.

THE BUTTERFLY

The fore-wings of the male are dark purplish blue, the front fringe edged with white; near the centre there is a dark spot. The outer edge is dark

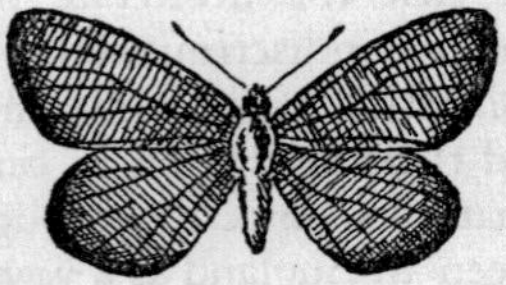

MALE

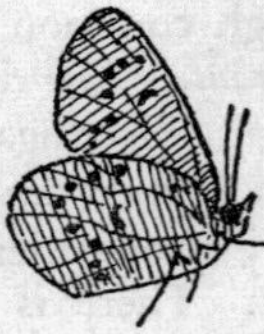

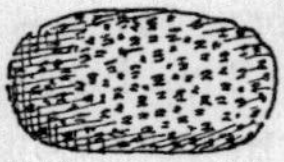

brown. The hind-wings are very similar. The female is rich brown with a bronze sheen and has no trace of the blue of the male.

Underside: the fore-wings are of a uniform bronzed-grey, the base bluish grey; the spot shows through, edged with white: beyond it is a waved row of seven spots, ringed with white.

The female differs from the male in being basically brown rather than purplish blue on the upper sides. The undersides are very similar. (See Purple Emperor and Purple Hairstreak.)

Distribution

A hundred years ago this butterfly was common but very local, its usual habitats being meadows, hayfields and uncultivated ground. To-day, it is doubtfully recorded as *extinct*, though it is considered that it may still be found in remote and unworked localities. (See Notes.)

Notes

Here again we have an example of the extinction of a butterfly (if it is extinct in Britain) which was once common though always very local. The significant fact to notice is this. On the Continent this butterfly still abounds in hayfields, laying its eggs on clover as it used to do in England. In this connection Frohawk speaks of the consequent "mystery surrounding the supposed extinction of this species in Britain, as their habitats remain unchanged." It must certainly remain a mystery under all circumstances apart from the explanation given in Chapter XI, and in the particular case of the Large Copper. Hayfields abound near previous hayfields which were once its 'home.' Its life-habit, and notably its long caterpillar state of existence, explains its complete lack of recorded *vagrancy*, either in this country before its extinction or from the Continent where it still abounds.

It should be also noted that, like other members of the 'Blues', its food-plant can be varied in captivity, and that on the Continent the food-plant of the larvae varies in a state of nature. All of which facts seem to show, as suggested elsewhere, that some of the 'Blues' are geographical races or varieties of the same species, the variations depending upon climate, soil and food in the particular habitats where they have been taken. In this connection it is interesting to note that Frohawk emphasises the close resemblance between the egg, caterpillar, chrysalis and life-habit of the Large and Mazarine Blues.

LATEST CLASSIFICATION OF BRITISH BUTTERFLIES

RHOPALOCERA—BUTTERFLIES

DANAIDAE

Danaus plexippus.
Black-Veined Brown.

SATYRIDAE

Melanargia galathea.
Marbled White.

Eumenis semele.
Grayling.

Parage megera.
Wall Brown.

Pararge aegeria.
Speckled Wood.

Coenonympha pamphilus.
Small Heath.

Coenonympha tullia.
Large Heath.

Aphantopus hyperanthus.
Ringlet.

Maniola tithonus.
Hedge Brown.

Maniola iurtina.
Meadow Brown.

Erebia aethiops.
Scotch Argus.

Erebia epiphron.
Mountain Ringlet.

Aglais urticae.
Small Tortoiseshell.

Polygonia c-album.
Comma.

Apatura iris.
Purple Emperor.

Limenitis camilla.
White Admiral.

Argynnis paphia.
Silver Washed Fritillary.

Argynnis aglaia.
Dark Green Fritillary.

Argynnis cydippe.
High Brown Fritillary.

Argynnis lathonia.
Queen of Spain Fritillary.

Argynnis euphrosyne.
Pearl Bordered Fritillary.

Argynnis selene.
Small Pearl Bordered Fritillary.

Euphydryas aurinia.
Marsh Fritillary.

Melitaea cinxia.
Glanville Fritillary.

Melitaea athalia.
Heath Fritillary.

NYMPHALIDAE

Vanessa atalanta.
Red Admiral.

Vanessa cardui.
Painted Lady.

Nymphalis io.
Peacock.

Nymphalis polychloros.
Large Tortoiseshell.

Nymphalis antiopa.
Camberwell Beauty.

LYCAENIDAE

Lampides boeticus.
Long-tailed Blue.

Cupido minimus.
Small Blue.

Everes argiades.
Short-tailed Blue.

Plebeius argus.
Silver-studded Blue.

Aricia agestis.
Brown Argus.

Polyommatus icarus.
Common Blue.

Lysandra coridon.
Chalk-hill Blue.

Lysandra bellargus.
Adonis Blue.

Cyaniris semiargus.
Mazarine Blue.

Celastrina argiolus.
Holly Blue.

Maculinea arion.
Large Blue.

Lycaena dispar.
Large Copper.

Lycaena phlaeas.
Small Copper.

Thecla betulae.
Brown Hairstreak.

Thecla quercus.
Purple Hairstreak.

Callophrys rubi.
Green Hairstreak.

Strymon pruni.
Black Hairstreak.

Strymon W-album.
White Letter Hairstreak.

RIODINIDAE

Hamearis lucina.
Duke of Burgundy Fritillary.

PIERIDAE

Aporia crataegi.
Black-veined White.

Pieris brassicae.
Large White.

Pieris rapae.
Small White.

Pieris napi.
Green-veined White.

Pontia daplidice.
Bath White.

Leptidea sinapis.
Wood White.

Euchloe cardamines.
Orange Tip.

Gonepteryx rhamni.
Brimstone.

Colias croceus.
Clouded Yellow.

Colias hyale.
Pale Clouded Yellow.

PAPILIONIDAE

Papilio machaon.
Swallow-tail.

HESPERIDAE

Erynnis tages.
Dingy Skipper.

Pyrgus malvae.
Grizzled Skipper.

Carterocephalus palaemon.
Checkered Skipper.

Adopaea sylvestris.
Small Skipper.

Adopaea lineola.
Essex Skipper.

Adopaea acteon.
Lulworth Skipper.

Ochlodes venata.
Large Skipper.

Hesperia comma.
Silver Spotted Skipper.

STATES OF HIBERNATION

EGG

Blue, Chalk Hill
Blue, Silver Studded
Fritillary, High Brown
Hairstreak, Black
Hairstreak, Brown
Hairstreak, Purple
Hairstreak, White Letter
Skipper, Essex
Skipper, Silver-spotted

CATERPILLAR

Admiral, White
Argus, Brown
Argus, Scotch
Blue, Adonis
Blue, Common
Blue, Large [IN ANTS' NEST]
Blue, Mazarine
Blue, Short-tailed
Blue, Small
Brown, Hedge
Brown, Meadow (Large) [PARTIAL]
Copper, Large
Copper, Small [PARTIAL]
Fritillary, Glanville
Fritillary, Heath
Fritillary, Marsh
Fritillary, Pearl-bordered
Fritillary, Small Pearl-bordered
Fritillary, Queen of Spain [ON THE CONT.]
Fritillary, Silver-washed
Grayling
Heath, Large
Heath, Small [PARTIAL]
Purple Emperor
Ringlet [PARTIAL]
Ringlet, Small Mountain
Skipper, Checkered
Skipper, Dingy
Skipper, Large
Skipper, Lulworth
Skipper, Small
Wall [PARTIAL]
White, Black-veined
White, Marbled
Wood, Speckled [PARTIAL]

CHRYSALIS

Fritillary, Dark Green
Fritillary, Duke of Burgundy
Hairstreak, Green
Orange-tip
Skipper, Grizzled
Swallow-tail
White, Bath [ON THE CONT.]
White, Green-veined
White, Large
White, Small
White, Wood

BUTTERFLY

Admiral, Red
Brimstone (Sulphur)
Brown, Black-veined
Camberwell Beauty
Comma
Peacock
Tortoiseshell, Large
Tortoiseshell, Small

UNCERTAIN

Blue, Holly [VARIOUS]
Blue, Long-tailed
Painted Lady
Yellow, Clouded
Yellow, Pale Clouded

BIBLIOGRAPHY

1. *Natural History of British Butterflies:* F. W. Frohawk, M.B.O.U., F.R.E.S., etc.

2. *Introduction to Entomology* (4 volumes): the Rev. William Kirby, M.A., F.R. and L.S., Rector of Barham; William Spence, F.R.S., F.L.S.

3. *Migration of Butterflies:* C. D. Williams, M.A. (Entomologist to the East African Agricultural Research Association).

4. *Butterfly Lore:* H. Eltringham, M.A., D.Sc. (Oxon.), F.R.E.S., F.Z.S.

5. *The Natural History of British Butterflies and Moths:* Edward Newman, F.L.S., F.Z.S.

6. *British Butterflies:* the Rev. F. O. Morris, B.A. (Member of the Ashmolean Society and Life Member of the British Association).

7. *Butterfly Hunting in Many Lands:* G. B. Longstaff, M.A., M.D., F.R.C.P., F.G.S.

8. *British Butterflies:* A. M. Stewart, F.R.E.S.

9. *Migrant Lepidoptera in Canna:* J. Lorne Campbell.

10. *The Study of Plants:* — Woodhead.

11. *Trees and Shrubs:* W. H. Rowe.

INDEX